I Will Not Kill Myself, Olivia

By Danny Baker

D0068162

This book is dedicated to my parents, for always believing in me when there were so many reasons not to.

CONTENTS

Prologue

~ ~ ~

I picked up the sharpest piece of glass I could find on the side of the road and put it to my throat.

'No!' someone screamed, running towards me.

'Stay back!' I yelled, holding out the glass.

The man froze, raising his hands in the surrender sign.

'Pl-please . . .' he stuttered. 'Please don't do this. Whatever happened . . . it can be fixed.'

'What the fuck do you know?' I yelled. 'You don't know what it's like to be me! You're not crazy! You don't want to kill yourself one week and chase hallucinations the next! What the fuck do you know? What the *fuck* do you know?'

'OK, OK,' he motioned, patting the air. 'I'm sorry. Just please don't do this. *Please.*'

The crowd all tried to talk me into dropping the glass, but once again I brought it to my neck. I pierced the skin, felt hot blood dripping onto my hand.

Death. I craved it, craved it.

It was like a maddening hunger that I wanted to feed so badly. Everything was just so fucked up. Everything had been fucked up for so long and I was sure that this was the only way out. There was nothing I wanted to do but satisfy that craving. Nothing I wanted to do but die. Running that piece of glass over my throat made me feel better, thinking that the craving's about to be fed, thinking that the pain's about to end. So close to the apathy of death. Nothingness! The end! An escape at last!

Plunge it through your throat! Through your fucking throat! Now! Now!

My hand trembled wildly. My whole body shook.

Do it! Kill yourself! End it now!

My hand kept trembling and trembling before finally, the glass slipped through my fingers and fell to the ground. I couldn't do it. I exploded into tears, cried loudly as all my emotions ruptured inside me – in large part because I knew I'd have to keep living and fighting in this crazy fucked up world – but regardless, I knew I couldn't do it. I'm just not a quitter. When it really comes down to it I'm just not a quitter.

A couple of people helped me to my feet, moved me away from the wreckage. I sat hugging my shins on the sidewalk, crying with my head buried in my knees as the crowd watched on silently.

'You're not a quitter,' I kept sobbing to myself. 'You're not a quitter.'

The police arrived. They asked me what happened.

'You're not a quitter,' I kept repeating.

'So fix this.'

Taking a deep breath, I did my best to gather myself before looking up at the officers. And then I told them what happened.

'I'll plead guilty to whatever offence you see fit to charge me with,' I said when I had finished. 'But first, I need to be admitted to a psych ward.'

Part I

IT ALL STARTED WITH MARK OCCHILUPO

The best way of getting to Manly from Sydney City is by ferry. It boards at Circular Quay, glides over the glittering sea as tourists giddily snap that classic picture of Sydney Harbour – the one of the Opera House on the royal blue water, the Harbour Bridge overlooking it, and the skyscrapers and Centre Point Tower standing tall to the left. After passing the big-toothed, grinning face at Luna Park and Kirribilli House where the Prime Minister's invited to live, it's a smooth cruise through the emerald-green, mansion-freckled headlands of the North Shore and the Eastern Suburbs. Other vessels pass by from time to time, and the passengers always seem to wave to each other, strangers becoming friends in the splendour of the moment, surrendering to their natural impulse to share all that's beautiful. And why wouldn't you? The sky's clear and bright, the sun's warm against your skin, there's a cool breeze in your hair and you're travelling in one of the most pleasant ways known to man.

Your first clear glimpse of Manly is of its famous tall Norfolk Pines that line the golden sand. Next come the high-rise apartments with the million-dollar views, and the dozens of boats moored to the right of the wharf. When it's only a few hundred metres out, the ferry begins to slow. The chatter reduces to next to nothing. Everyone's just watching those Norfolk Pines grow taller and taller, the shore coming to life as people bask in the sun, throw Frisbees to each other, paddle within the shark net, kayak or paraglide. The white "Manly Wharf" sign then comes into focus, the ferry eases into the dock and there you are – Manly – *"seven miles from Sydney and a thousand miles from care,"* as the old saying goes.

Talk excitedly picks up again as the crewmen secure the boat to the wharf and everybody disembarks. Some join the diners at Hugo's Pizzeria, the Bavarian Bier Café or Phoenix's Chinese Restaurant; sit down for a leisurely coffee at Gloria Jeans; are lured by the ethereal aroma of chocolate into Max Brenner; or in true Aussie spirit, get some fish 'n' chips or an ice-cream and eat it outside on the blue and white benches in the shape of surf boards. Others visit Manly's Art Museum; race down the winding slides at Waterworks; go diving with tropical fish, turtles, stingrays and sharks at Oceanworld; or follow the crowd and cross the road to The Corso, Manly's long pedestrian plaza that takes you from the harbour to the ocean. Named after the famous street in Rome, The Corso is filled with people shopping for board shorts, t-shirts and thongs at surf stores, and buying "I Love Australia" towels, boxing kangaroos, stuffed koalas and boomerangs from souvenir shops. Families and friends dine at the plethora of Asian, European, Middle Eastern and seafood restaurants; sit outside eating burgers from Hungry Jacks or meat pies from Hamlet's; or sip beers at the Steyne or on the balcony at the New Brighton Hotel. Depending on the time of year there may be the Manly Art-, Jazz- or Food and Wine Festival or free salsa lessons on Thursday nights, and even if there's no official entertainment, there'll always be buskers playing music or acting out a skit.

Then across the road from The Corso lies the grand attraction – the birthplace of Australian surfing: the first beach where Aussies bodysurfed, legally surf-bathed and rode a board; the home of the country's first surf lifesaving club; the setting of the first ever World Surfing Championships; and as of March 10, 2012, one of four Dedicated World Surfing Reserves on the planet – none other than the famous, breathtaking, Manly Beach. It's a carefree paradise with line upon line of crisp, pure blue waves that surfers queue to glide upon. When it comes to their turn they plunge into the rip, paddle furiously in front of a wave, rise steadily as it carries them forwards and stand flexed at the knees as they fly on its thick white-tipped crest before it breaks and charges towards the shore as a ridge of turbulence and foam. The sea's full of those strong tanned dancers, twisting along the waves, floating on top of them, sliding through the barrels with strength and power and impeccable grace. For some of those born and raised here, this is their first memory of the world – those smooth, curling waves, their undulation magnificent as they rise and fall, rise and fall with the sublime rhythm of poetry and those gleeful surfers sailing on top, doing the most inspiring, sensational thing they've ever seen.

I was lucky enough to grow up in this vibrant town, a few blocks from the wharf in a two storey house overlooking the harbour. Mum and Dad were both hardworking, career-driven folk who worked long hours as a lawyer and an investment banker, respectively, but like everyone else in the area they had a love for the sea, so all our weekends were spent down by the beach. When I was little I used to like building tall sandcastles, and then filling up a bucket of water and making a moat around them. I'd chase seagulls all over the sand, and when I'd get tired I'd feed them some of my chips. Dad, Mum and I used to play catch with a blow-up beach ball, and if there weren't many people around to get in harm's way, we'd kick around a footy. Thanks to me, there were also a lot less shells scattered along the sand. I used to like putting them to my ear when I was home and listening to the waves pound against the shore. In my third summer I built up quite a collection of them, and lined my bedroom shelf with snail shells and others with smooth pale tusks, and also some mussels, different coloured starfish and a couple of crabs. Once I even found a slightly chipped shark tooth. Dad drilled a tiny hole in it and threaded through some string to make a necklace, and I wore it proudly everywhere I went.

Like a lot of local kids, I learned to swim within the shark net in the calm sea by the wharf, paddling between my parents with yellow inflatables around my arms. But as soon as I was comfortable in the water and could swim unassisted, we headed straight over to the beach. I fell in love with the waves right away. I'd get a huge kick out of waiting for one to come and then ducking below it, feeling it roar through my hair before I'd bob back up again and watch it dissipate towards the shore in a white rush of froth. I quickly learned how to bodysurf, and would catch wave after wave with my parents and race them to see who could reach the shore first. Other times, I'd find myself standing in waist-deep water just watching groups of bleached-haired blokes get on their boards and disappear inside the break, skate through the tunnel and jump out the other side. My eyes would be glued to them as they'd hoot and holler and swoop across the sea, doing what seemed like the most enjoyable thing anyone could possibly do. I pleaded and pleaded with my parents to take me to surf school, but they said I was too young, so instead I had to settle for Little Nippers.

That's where I met my best friends to this day – Corey, Brent, Sean, Chris and Steve. Every Saturday we'd meet at Manly Surf Life Saving Club and learn about surf safety and the marine environment, and then team up to win all the water relays. After Nippers we'd stay back and play tag amongst the waves, or dive underneath them and see who could stay down the longest without bursting back up and gasping for air. Other times one of us would throw a tennis ball as far as he could and we'd all swim like mad to try and be the one to grab it, or we'd play Marco Polo or catch waves and race each other to the shore. A few months after Nippers started we all began school together at Manly Village Public just off The Corso, and often their mums and my babysitter Amanda would meet us at the gates in the afternoon and take us down to the beach for a swim. We were mates because we all loved the water. None of us could get enough of it.

But the one thing we all really wanted to do was learn how to surf. We'd all been individually pestering our parents to take us to surf school for months, and once they'd all gotten to know each other and we started having barbeques at each other's houses and going for picnics down by the beach, the six of us began nagging them together.

'No surfing, boys,' they'd all say. 'It's too dangerous – wait until you're a little bit older.'

We'd all be disappointed, but our enthusiasm would revive by the next time we met up, and brimming with hope, we'd ask them again. They must've said no at least 20 times, but then the week after we finished our first season of Nippers and had passed our surf education assessment, they took us down to the beach where we found six brand new surf boards lying in the sand. When we were told they were for us, we all jumped up and down and screamed for joy as our parents watched on beaming. We spent the rest of the day trying to stand on our boards, and even though we fell off every time, we felt so good and had so much fun that no one seemed to care.

From then on, that's all we did. We took surfing lessons on weekends, and after school their mums and Amanda would pick us up with our boards and take us down to the beach. In that year when we were six we surfed so much that our lips were sun-split and our nipples were chafed, and our mums would have to rub Sorbelene over our chests at night. Improvement didn't come easily, but as the weeks passed we all gradually found our feet, and then on one glorious day in the heart of Sydney summer, I caught my first wave.

Quiksilver was having a big sale that day, so I went shopping with my parents and they bought me a new wetsuit. It was a real snazzy one, jet black with these killer yellow lightning bolts straight down the side. I thought it was the coolest thing I'd ever seen, and as soon as I put it on I was filled with a newfound confidence – as if all of a sudden I was a better surfer just by wearing such a ripper wetsuit.

'I'm going to do it today!' I told the boys when we were down by the beach. 'I'm going to catch my first wave!'

At that point, catching *my* first wave would've meant catching *our* first wave. They were all stunned.

'How do you know?' Corey said.

'With this new wetsuit I'm going to do it. It's my lucky charm!'

'Do you really think you will?' Brent asked.

'Yep! Today's the day!'

He studied me for a few seconds. When he realised how serious I was, he started nodding his head eagerly.

'OK if you're going to do it, then I'm going to do it with you!' he said.

Then all the other boys avidly jumped on board.

'I'm going to do it too!' said Sean.

'Me too!' announced Corey.

'And me!' exclaimed Chris.

'And me, and me, and me!' cried Steve.

'All right then! Let's all do it! Let's all go get our first wave!'

We were all jumping up and down, arms around each other and excitedly squealing as one. We'd made a pact now and we were all in it together.

'Come on! Let's go!' we all screamed as we charged for the sea.

For the first half an hour no one caught one, although on multiple occasions we all came close, getting to our feet for a few seconds before falling off as the wave was breaking. But then Brent – probably the most naturally athletic of us all – rose to his feet and zipped across a wave, holding his balance all the way and riding it to the shore as the rest of us clapped and screamed and jumped up and down.

'I did it! I did it!' he yelled when he was done. 'I caught my first wave!'

We all swarmed him and continued carrying on ecstatically, hugging Brent gleefully and whooping and whistling. There was no envy, no jealousy – just a group of six year olds all revelling in their good mate's triumph. I was thrilled for Brent, and seeing him catch his first wave made me all the more determined to get one myself.

An hour later, my moment finally came. I arrived at the line up just when a set of evenly peeling beauties rolled right in. I paddled as hard as I could, felt the push, rose on a foot and a knee, stabilised myself and then leapt to my feet. The wind flew through my hair and plumes of spray spattered my face and for the first time, everything felt right, everything came together as I found myself soaring across the face of the wave.

'Yes!' I screamed. 'Yes! Yes!'

I was so hyped, so puffed up with confidence, so utterly untouchable. I felt like a rock star, like the king of the world as I howled with joy and rode the wave all the way in, and even though it was 15 crazy years ago, I still think of it as one of the best moments of my life.

Now that Brent and I had caught our first waves, everyone else was even more keen to get one. I was feeling incredible, like I could do no wrong, and in the next half hour managed to snag another two. After that, Corey really did start believing that my wetsuit was lucky, and asked me if he could borrow it.

'Yeah! Go for it!' I said as we swapped wetsuits. I just wanted all of us to get one, especially Corey because he was my best friend.

We surfed for the rest of the afternoon. For a while Brent and I were the only ones who'd scored, but then just before the sun whispered 'goodnight' and we were forced to paddle in, Corey caught a stunner and rode it all the way to the shore. It was the perfect way to end the day, and I gave him the biggest hug in the world. We both dumped our boards with our parents and then skipped with great big smiles from the beach to the other end of The Corso, holding hands the entire way. Our mums took at least ten pictures each, and still talk about it as one of the cutest things they've ever seen.

The following week, Chris, Sean and Steve joined the club too, and our parents took us all out to Pizza Hut to celebrate. We stuffed our faces with slices of pepperoni-, Hawaiian- and margarita pizza, and topped it off with chocolate sundaes, all the while basking in each other's glory, talking excitedly about how gnarly we'd all surfed. And I remember thinking about how sweet it was that we'd done it together. All for one and one for all, as the old adage goes.

In the beginning, it was purely out of love. We surfed because it was our favourite thing to do in the world. And even though that was still true for the next decade to come, after a few years, something changed for me. The way I looked at surfing. The way I approached life in general. To paraphrase Rita Dove, I had one of those moments where I came alive for the first time, one that I often go back to and think, *this is when I became myself.*

It all started when Mark Occhilupo began making a run for the world title in 1999. A teen superstar on the professional circuit in the mid-eighties, Occy seemed destined to rule the surfing kingdom before a downward spiral into drug abuse shattered his world and led him to quit the tour when he was only 22. He spent his prime in a debilitating depression, sitting on the couch watching TV, gaining over 30 kilos, and isolating himself from everyone before going all Rocky-like and making a dramatic comeback seven years later.

Occy had the juice, I tell you. Anyone who's ever seen him surf will rave about how naturally brilliant he was, how jaw-droppingly spectacular he looked carving up the waves. He probably had the best backside bottom turn the sport's ever seen, and in 1999 he was on top of his game. After winning the Fiji tournament he was ranked first in the world, and on track to complete arguably the greatest comeback in the history of professional sport. There was a buzz going around the country, particularly in Sydney where he was born and raised. Every surfer was talking about him, devotedly cheering him on to win the world title and bring it back to Australia's shore. Like everyone else, my friends and I got swept up in it, and before long we'd all fallen in love with him. Our bedroom walls were covered with posters of Occy owning the waves, and we watched his surfing films so many times that we knew them back to front, particularly *Bunyip Dreaming, The Green Iguana* and *The Billabong Challenge*. We nagged our parents to buy us whatever wetsuit, board shorts or t-shirt we happened to see him wearing, and if they ever did, we'd wear whatever it was day after day after day until we were forced to take it off and put it in the wash. Whenever we were surfing we'd all attempt to copy his moves, and that year we even grew our hair long to try and *look* more like Occy. He was our idol. He was the guy we all wanted to be.

We followed his world title quest as closely as we could, and it was an emotional rollercoaster all the way to the finish. After winning in Fiji and being at the top of the rankings, Occy only got a 17th at Jeffrey's Bay, and followed it up with a dreaded 33rd at Huntington. With Taj Burrow, Victor Ribas and Mick Campbell snapping at his heels, the pressure was definitely on, but then in true Occy fashion he rose to the occasion in Lacanau and scored a second. Everything appeared to be back on track, but then in Hossegor he suffered another 17th, and the fellas and I were back to anxiously biting our nails.

The wait until the next competition in Spain was a long and nerve-racking one, but after Occy won it, it really looked like he was going to go all the way. The world title was his to lose, and there were even reports circling that he was ahead enough in the rankings to clinch it in the next tournament in Brazil. We excitedly counted down the days until the start of the contest, and when it finally arrived we were all giddy as anything. Occy won his first heat against a local, and as they walked back up the beach, the local raised Occy's hand in the air. The cameras swarmed.

'Occy,' a reporter began, 'did you know that if Mick Campbell loses his next heat, you'll be the world champion?'

The look on Occy's face was priceless. He couldn't believe it.

All eyes were then on Mick's heat. He was losing. Time was running out. The crowd gathered around Occy, counting down the final seconds, and when the horn sounded, everybody went nuts. He'd done it! A few years earlier Occy weighed 111 kilos and was too depressed to get off the couch, and now he'd won the world title. Everyone was stoked for him. At school the boys and I were cheering and carrying on and slapping each other fives. Corey and Brent even got detentions for being too loud and disruptive during class. But neither of them cared. Occy was the world champion and we were all over the moon.

And like thousands of other grommets around the world, we were inspired by our hero.

'I want to become a pro surfer like Occy and win the world title!' I announced.

'Me too!' Corey exclaimed. 'I want to win on my 18th birthday and then drink beer at the pub, just like all the other pro surfers do!'

'I want to win in Brazil! Just like Occy did!'

'I want to win and have you guys carry me down the beach!'

'I want to win and have *Occy* carry me down the beach! And if Occy's retired, I want Kelly Slater to do it!'

'No one's going to be carrying me! When I win I'll be somersaulting down the beach. I'll be way too hyped to let anyone carry me!'

We continued yapping excitedly and getting caught up in the dream, imagining how amazing it would be to be crowned the world champion. I was completely lost in the fantasy, vividly picturing myself standing on the podium, being presented with that huge golden trophy and raising it high into the air with the whole world watching on and cheering. I had goose bumps just thinking about it. My body was tingling. I felt the overwhelming pull of desire, a wanting so strong that it made me ache. It was a feeling I'd never felt before, and a feeling so powerful that I knew it was there to stay.

At the beach that afternoon, everything was different. Instead of surfing happy-go-luckily, I was focused on improving. I was paying attention to detail. I was practising with a purpose. That image of me hoisting the world champion's trophy was at the front of my mind, and I knew that if I wanted it to become a reality, my approach had to change. I had to work harder. I had to train my ass off. I had to throw everything into it, just like Occy did when he was making his comeback.

At half-past-six, the rest of the fellas left to go home for dinner. I was supposed to go with them, but instead I decided to stay back and continue practising. At seven-thirty my mum arrived at the beach, seething with fury.

'Jimmy!' she yelled from the shore. 'Jimmy!'

'Hey, Mum!' I called back. 'Hey check it out! I'm practising to become the – '

'Jimmy come here this minute!' she screamed.

I paddled in. As soon as I got there she started blasting me.

'Jimmy what on earth are you doing? Why didn't you come home on time? I've been worried sick! I thought you might've drowned! I thought you might've been killed by a shark!'

She paused, wiping a tear from her eye.

'I didn't . . . I didn't know what to think . . .'

I apologised, telling her that I didn't mean to upset her and that I was only trying to train really hard to become the world champion. She made me promise never to do anything like it again before we started walking home in silence.

Once she'd cooled off a block or two away, she asked me about it.

'So you want to be the world champion, huh?'

'I sure do!'

'Just like Occy, right?' she smiled.

'Yep! Just like Occy!'

She kept smiling at me, and ruffled my hair before she looked away without saying anything.

I don't think she took me too seriously then. I'm sure she thought it was just a phase, soon to be replaced by another and then another. And I guess that's how it was with my mates. Despite also saying they wanted to become the world champion, they just continued on with their lives as if nothing had changed, coasting through it as most ten year olds do. But for me, the gears in my mind had switched for good. I was no longer Jimmy Wharton: "Casual Surfer;" I was now Jimmy Wharton: "Serious Athlete Dedicated To Going Pro." Whether alone or with the boys, I surfed every day after school until dusk, and all day on the weekends too. Just like some of the pro surfers did, I put together a table of moves to work on each day that would keep me focused. Monday was cutbacks, Tuesday was tail-slides, Wednesday was snaps, Thursday was airs, Friday was big turns, and Saturday and Sunday was a combination of everything. When I wasn't surfing, I was watching film, pausing and rewinding, pausing and rewinding, learning from the best before going out and trying to imitate them. Being the world champion was all I could think about, and I wanted it more than anything. And as I rapidly kept improving, I really started to believe I could do it. I was convinced that if I kept training fanatically then I could make it happen.

Just work hard, I'd keep telling myself. *If you work hard and never slack off, you're going to achieve your dream.*

Every night before I went to sleep, I'd pray to God that it would happen, as I did every Sunday at church as well. *Please, God. Please.*

Six weeks after Occy won the world title, it was time for the fellas and our families' annual camping trip to Kangaroo Valley. We always had a great time, kayaking and canoeing and staying up late and mucking around. It would've been fun, but there was no way I was going to spend a whole week away from the beach.

'I can't go,' I told my parents. 'I need to train so that I can become the world champion.'

'Come on, Jimmy. You can take a week off.'

'No I can't. I've got to train every day.'

'Jimmy even professional surfers take time off sometimes.'

'I already waste enough time going to school. In my free time I just want to surf.'

'Jimmy . . . you're becoming obsessed.'

'So? That's what it takes to be the best.'

'But it's tradition to go to Kangaroo Valley.'

'I know, but there's no surf there. I don't want to go anywhere where there isn't any surf.'

They kept trying to talk me into it, but there was nothing they could say to change my mind. I had tunnel vision on my goal, and I wouldn't let anything stand in the way of it. Eventually, they agreed to let me stay with my grandparents in Dee Why, which is a few suburbs from Manly and home to a pristine beach of its own.

When I told the boys I wasn't coming next time we were at the beach together, they were openly disappointed.

'Come on, Jimmy! Remember how much fun we had last year? You've got to come!'

'I know. It was sick. But I've got to stay here and practise.'

'But you've got the whole year to practise! One week won't make a difference.'

'Yeah it will. It all adds up.'

'But you're going to miss out on so much, man! Remember last year, when we capsized the canoe and we all got soaked?'

'Or when we threw water bombs at that guy's tent while he was sleeping?'

'Or when Brent took a shit on that dude's doorstep?'

'I remember,' I sighed. 'It was awesome. But I've got to stay here and surf.'

Later that afternoon, they all went to Corey's place to watch *The Simpsons*. I stayed at the beach to work on my cutbacks until it was dark.

As you can see, it all started off so harmlessly. I was just obsessively pouring myself into achieving my goal. I never thought it would lead to me running that piece of glass back and forth across my throat, but as I'd find out time and again, sometimes the most fucked up disasters are the ones that start with the purest innocence.

WHAT MIGHT HAVE BEEN

Over the next few years, I trained like a maniac. Whenever I wasn't at school I was in the water surfing, or breaking down film, honing my competition strategy or working on my strength and conditioning. I did sit-ups, squats, lunges and jumping exercises to build my lower core and improve my balance; flies, dips, chin-ups, push-ups, shoulder presses and bicep curls to strengthen my upper body; yoga and stretching exercises to enhance my flexibility; and I went on a five kilometre run three times a week to improve my fitness. I also arranged for my coach to put me on a special high protein, high carb, low fat diet that I never wavered from. 'Whatever it takes' became my mantra, and I threw everything I had into achieving my dream.

And over time, I gobbled up the fruits of my labour. I started entering local surf competitions at age 11, and found myself winning most of them comfortably. Pretty soon I attracted the eye of Manly Surf Academy's head coach named Mark, who loved my work ethic and began investing a lot of time in me. Under his tutelage my surfing really improved, and before long he was taking me travelling with the squad to tournaments around the state. About 20 of us would usually go, all crammed on the team bus with Mark and a couple of other coaches. Some of the guys were as old as 18, so a lot of the trips got pretty wild. Most nights there'd be parties, often with other surf schools joining in as well. A lot of the older guys would get drunk and wrench bongs, and since we'd all usually be sharing a clubhouse it was hard to get away from it. During the state championships in my twelfth year, one bloke was always having sex in the room next to mine, so I had to get some ear plugs to fall asleep. For a lot of the guys, the parties were the main reason they came on tour – but for me, it was all about winning the event. At the state championships I could've gotten wasted and probably hooked up, but I was disciplined and focused and didn't get caught up in any of the extracurricular stuff. Fresh as can be I cruised through my heats, had a great final and won my age division.

You're doing well! I told myself elatedly. *Just keep training really hard and next you'll be the national champion, and then if you keep training really hard after that you'll become a professional surfer, and then you can work your way up the ranks and become the world champion!*

One day when I was 13 and had another state title under my belt, I was approached by a bleached-haired bloke on Manly Beach.

'Jimmy Wharton, right?' he asked, sticking out his hand.

'Ah, yeah,' I said, shaking it. I was thinking, *who on earth is this guy?*

'My name's Russ,' he said. 'I work at Quiksilver.'

I just nodded, genuinely having no idea where the conversation was heading.

'I've been watching you surf,' he continued. 'You're the real deal, man. And your coach Mark says you've been the state champ two years running. That's pretty impressive.'

'Thanks,' I said.

'You're a real star,' he continued. 'So we want to sponsor you.'

He said it so casually that it was a while before it registered.

'W . . . w-what?' I finally stuttered.

'We want to sponsor you.'

I couldn't believe it. I thought it must've been some sort of joke.

'You . . . *Quiksilver* . . . want to sponsor *me*?'

'Yeah!'

I was too swept away to process it. Only when Russ gave me a huge box of free stuff did it start to sink in. There were shirts, board shorts, wetsuits, a leather wallet, two pairs of sunglasses and a ton of stickers. I was so stoked. I mean, I was sponsored by *Quiksilver*! The same company that sponsored Kelly Slater! What more could a grommet ask for?

To celebrate, my parents made a special point of coming home early from work that night to take me go-karting with Corey, Brent and the rest of the boys. When I told my friends I was sponsored, they couldn't believe it either.

'No way, man! Really?'

'Yeah!'

'Shit, dude! That's sick!'

'That's awesome, bro. That's really, really cool!'

'About time they sponsored you, man! You've been killing it for ages!'

They were really psyched for me, and I gave them all a t-shirt before my parents drove us to the go-karting track and we howled and hollered and raced around like crazy.

After Quiksilver started sponsoring me I really got on a roll, winning a heap of local tournaments in a row, another state title the following year, and a couple of months after that, the Under 14 National Title. By then, JS Industry Surfboards had jumped on as sponsors, and Quiksilver was bankrolling my training expenses and travelling costs, as well as continuing to give me heaps of free clothes. The *Manly Daily* was frequently running articles on me, calling me a *"surfing prodigy"* and the town's *"next world title hope,"* so people on the streets started recognising me. I'd often get stopped in The Corso or along the beach by someone who'd tell me they were right behind me, hoping I'd follow in the footsteps of Barton Lynch and return the world title back to Manly Beach. Manly's a big surfing town, and it meant a lot to them that I was doing well, representing them with pride as part of the next generation. It was all so surreal. I was on my way to living the life I'd always dreamed of, and the success only made me push myself harder and harder. The more I improved, the more I wanted to improve. The more I won, the more I wanted to win. I loved it too much not to chase it with all the energy bundled inside of me. The rush I'd get when I'd surf the highest score, the pride that comes with being the best, the satisfaction in knowing that my hard work had paid off – I just couldn't get enough of it. Winning a competition made me feel invincible, and once I'd tasted it, it was all I wanted.

When I wasn't training, I was hanging out with the boys, listening to surfing music and watching surfing videos. We liked Jack Johnson, The Atlantics and Planet Seven, and also a lot of the old school stuff by Dick Dale and The Beach Boys. When it came to movies, we were all convinced that *The Green Iguana* with Occy was the best film ever made, but we also loved *Endless Summer*, *Thicker than Water* and *The September Sessions*. The fellas still loved to surf too, of course, and most mornings they'd join me amongst the waves. But I was the only one of us who was training to go pro. They were all "soul surfers" – they did it purely out of love. Plus as we'd all gotten older, they started developing other interests. Corey liked to make surfing videos, Brent wrote songs, Chris and Sean were both lifeguards, and Steve played guitar in a band. They were also starting to get drunk at parties, but even at that point in time I wasn't interested in getting on the piss. The only thing I cared about was becoming the world champion.

We all went to Manly High together, and spent most of our time there talking about surfing or flirting with the girls, and if we thought we could get away with it, we'd nick off to the beach. Over the years we must've wagged at least 20 or 30 times, and we only got caught twice. The first time was when we cut a double period of English in Year 8. The teacher never marked the roll, so we skipped out during lunch and never came back, thinking we'd be in the clear. But unfortunately, a substitute took the class that day, and after our absence was reported we were hit with detentions. The second time, we were caught red-handed by a middle-aged teacher who was having a lunchtime sunbake. We'd spent the whole day surfing, and had just gotten changed for fifth period when he noticed us across the beach.

'Hey! What are you doing here?' he yelled.

'Run!' we panicked.

We grabbed our stuff and bolted. He chased us screaming but we were able to turn a corner and lose him in some backstreets.

'You reckon he made us?' Sean panted as we came to a stop.

'Nah,' Chris said. 'I think he only saw our uniform from a distance.'

'You sure?'

'Yeah. We were too quick for the old fart. No way he got a good look at us.'

But as soon as we turned up to class we were all called into the principal's office and given two hour detentions.

Back outside, Brent burst into hysterics.

'What are you laughing at?' Corey demanded. 'We've got to spend our Friday afternoon at *school* now!'

'Who cares?' he kept on laughing. 'We went for a four hour surf and only got a two hour detention! We killed it!'

We all started laughing then. Thinking about it like that, it was pretty funny.

By now, I guess it's pretty obvious that I did hardly any schoolwork. Throughout primary school I'd always been a top student, but in high school it was much harder to coast on pure intellect, and surfing took up all my free time. In Year 7 my marks dropped significantly. In Year 8 they were well below average. In Year 9, I was scraping the bottom of the grade in the majority of my subjects. Of course, dicking around during class didn't help, but since I was pushing myself to the limits in my so-called "leisure time," I thought of my time at school as my chance to relax. Not to mention that schoolwork in general was just uninspiring. I wanted to be the best surfer on the planet – how could I get motivated to study when my thoughts were dominated by being presented with the champion's trophy and holding it up in front of the world? My parents were always supportive of my surfing career, but at the same time, they were concerned about how little I studied and my indifference towards my appalling grades.

'You need to focus more on school!' Dad used to stress.

'But I want to be the best surfer in the world! It's my dream!'

'But you're putting all your eggs in one basket!' he'd exclaim. 'What if you don't become a professional surfer? What are you going to do for a career?'

'That's not going to happen, Dad! You've seen how hard I train! I *will* be a professional surfer!'

Mum would frequently burst into tears.

'What if you get injured?'

'I'm not going to get injured! I'm going to keep training really hard, and one day, I'm going to be the best surfer in the world!'

'But Jimmy, your grades used to be so good! You could be anything! A doctor. A lawyer. A veterinarian. Anything! Absolutely anything!'

'But I don't care about school! I want to be the world champion!'

I finished Year 9 ranked 142nd out of 152 students. My parents were furious, but I didn't care. I was about to surf in the Under 15 World Junior Championships in Hossegor, France and I really didn't care.

In the few months leading up to the world championships, I hardly thought about anything else. I didn't watch TV, barely attended any social outings, and I sure as hell didn't do any homework; all I did was surf my ass off, and when I wasn't in the water, I was analysing film, studying competition strategy, lifting weights, improving my flexibility and going for runs – even more so than I usually did. I knew this was it – this was my chance to burst onto the international scene, to make a name for myself in front of the whole surfing world. It meant everything – previous winners had picked up new sponsorship deals, been cast in surfing movies, and joined the pro circuit the following year. I was so amped up – and so was Manly. The local paper was talking me up, and the whole town really got behind me. Strangers would stop me in the street and wish me luck. Crowds would sometimes form while I'd be practising and everyone watching would cheer me on. They'd congratulate me when I came out of the water, tell me that I was the favourite to win in Hossegor and that they couldn't wait for me to bring home the title. There appeared to be girls everywhere, and often I'd get their numbers without even asking for them. It was all so flattering, but I didn't let anything distract me. I was surfing for everything I'd ever wanted, and I wouldn't let anything stand in my way.

After weeks of preparation, the championships finally came. I had a farewell surf with the fellas in the morning and then arrived in Hossegor a day-and-a-half later with Coach Mark, and also my parents – who'd luckily been able to get the week off work. It was a beautiful place to host the World Junior Championships, Hossegor was – tucked right down in the corner of south-west France, it's the epitome of paradise with its trankil pine trees, its emerald-green forest, its saltwater lagoon, the Pyrenees on the horizon, and of course, its long and luscious sandy beach, home to some of the most magnificent waves in the world. After unpacking I headed straight for the sea, eager to get some practice in and acclimatise to the conditions. I'd been told that the tides at Hossegor fluctuated a lot, so I wanted some time to get used to everything before the championships were due to start in a few days' time.

On the morning of my first heat, I woke up at dawn, had a shower, got some breakfast into me and went straight to the beach. It was packed – full of all the contestants from each age group, their families and coaches, and all the locals who'd come down to watch. I found a little space of my own and started going through my pre-heat ritual – doing my stretches and jogging on the spot to get warm, all the while listening to fire-up songs like Nelly's "Heart of a Champion" and Survivor's "Eye of the Tiger" on my MP3 player. Just before my heat was due to start, Mark and my parents came over to me.

'Good luck,' Mum and Dad said, giving me a hug.

Mark patted me on the back.

'Let yourself be great.'

I nodded seriously. The announcer called my name and in I went.

Twenty minutes later, I came back victorious.

'Good start, Jimmy,' Mark said. 'One round down, five more to go.'

'That's right.'

I started gathering my things to leave when a girl charged up to me.

'Jimmy!' she exclaimed.

'Ah, yeah,' I said, slightly taken aback.

'Hi! My name's Vanessa! It's so incredible to finally meet you!'

Mark and my parents left to give us some privacy, so I found myself standing there alone with Vanessa. She was about my age, with flaming red hair, narrow green eyes and fair skin covered with freckles. She stared at me for a few seconds before handing me a permanent marker.

'Could you please sign my t-shirt?' she asked.

I shrugged.

'Sure. If you want me to.'

'Oh yes! Thank-you!'

I took the pen and signed it, feeling her stare burning into me the whole time.

'Could you also sign my hand, please?' she asked once I was done.

'Your hand?'

'Yes.'

'Ah, yeah. I guess so.'

So I signed the back of her hand too, having to hold it with my spare one for balance. She squeezed it tightly, so much so that I could feel her nails digging into my flesh. Feeling creeped out, I let go as soon as I was finished.

'I'd better go,' I said quickly. 'Got to eat something before my next heat.'

'You shouldn't eat at the restaurant you ate at yesterday,' she said. 'There are much nicer places closer to your hotel.'

'What? How do you know where I – '

'There's a good seafood restaurant right around the corner. You walked past it on your way here this morning.'

I was speechless.

'Have you been . . . have you been following me?' I eventually managed to ask.

'I wanted to see if you'd changed at all.'

'Changed? From . . . from when?'

But at that moment, a woman stormed up to her.

'Vanessa!'

'Mum!'

'I'm so sorry, Jimmy!' Vanessa's mum uttered frantically. 'I told her to stay away from you.'

'But, Mum! I have to tell him how – '

'Enough, Vanessa! We're leaving!'

And at that, she yanked Vanessa by the arm and started pulling her away.

'Why are you doing this to me?' Vanessa screamed. 'Why are you doing this to me?'

'I'm so sorry, Jimmy,' her mother stressed over her shoulder. 'I'm really, really sorry . . .'

I just stood there, flabbergasted, having no idea what I'd just witnessed. But I pushed it from my mind as I walked back to the hotel to meet Mark and my parents for lunch. Hell, I was trying to win the Under 15 World Title – I didn't have time to think about anything else.

That afternoon, I won my second heat, scoring a nine and a 9.5 to my opponent's sixes.

'You're killing it, Jimmy,' my mate Rick said, another bloke sponsored by Quiksilver who was surfing in the Under 16s.

'Yeah, man,' continued Brad, his younger brother from the 14s. 'I reckon you're the favourite to go all the way.'

'I think it's going to come down to you and Stan,' said Will, another Quiksilver boy who'd just been knocked out.

'Who's Stan?' I asked.

'Stan Connors – from Hawaii. Haven't you heard of him?'

'Nah, bro. How good is he?'

'He's their golden boy, dude. They reckon he's going to be the next Andy Irons.'

I nodded.

'When's he surfing next?'

'He's on after this heat. Want to watch?'

'Definitely.'

So we stuck around and witnessed him shred his second round opponent. His turns were so precise, his airs so in control, his barrels long and smooth and graceful. He was better than any surfer I'd ever been up against.

'Reckon you can take him?' Rick asked.

'I'd better be able to.'

'Well, we'll be here to cheer you on,' Brad encouraged, clapping me on the back.

'Cheers, mate.'

'All right, all right, enough of this soppy shit,' Rick said. 'Let's get out of here and get something to eat.'

We all laughed.

'Sounds good,' I said.

We grabbed our stuff and started walking to the shops. I was talking to Brad and Will on the way, and Rick was dawdling behind us. Then all of a sudden he started laughing his head off. We all turned around to see him reading something on a purple polka-dotted piece of paper.

'What's that?' we asked.

But he couldn't talk for laughter.

'What is it?' we repeated.

He couldn't stop cackling.

'W-why don't *you* t-tell them, Jimmy!' he finally managed to get out.

'Me? How would I know what it is?'

'What? You actually don't know?'

'No. How could I?'

He fell to the ground in hysterics. Overcome with curiosity, Will then snatched the note out of his hand and began reading it. Within seconds he'd joined Rick howling with glee.

'Let me see this!' I said, making a play to grab it. But Brad got there before me and started reading it out loud.

Dear Jimmy,

When we were talking today I felt all squooshy inside,

I felt like my heart was racing down a slippery slide.
There you stood, all sexy and wet,
All I wanted to do was catch you in my net.

My dearest Jimmy, you're the most wonderful bloke,
You make me feel more alive than I would drinking a gallon of Coke.
I love you more than my favourite movie, "Lost at Sea,"
Being with you, one plus one would make three.

What I'd love to do with you Jimmy is go on a date,
Where we can kiss under the stars and share food from the same plate.
So meet me at seven tonight, my baby, my dude,
At the restaurant by your hotel, where we'll eat some seafood.

ALL my love,
Vanessa.

P.S. Sorry about my mum today. She can get REALLY crazy sometimes.'

The boys cracked up like mad.

'Stalk-*er*! Stalk-*er*! Stalk-*er*! Stalk-*er*!' they chanted.

'First she follows you! Then she slips a love note into your bag when you're not looking!'

'Stalk-*er*! Stalk-*er*! Stalk-*er*! Stalk-*er*!'

'Hey Jimmy with this freak after you, I bet you wish *you* were *"Lost at Sea!"* '

At that, the fellas went nuts, laughing like hyenas, jumping up and down and slapping me around.

'This isn't funny,' I said, fending them off. 'This chick is scary. Trust me on this one.'

But they kept on laughing about it the whole way to the shops, and no matter what I said, I couldn't shut them up.

The next morning was the third round, and boy did it give me a scare. The South African I was facing opened up with an 8.5, and with five minutes to go, my highest score was a seven. As I sat up on my board scanning the sea for oncoming waves, I found myself momentarily crippled with fear.

What if I lose? I fretted. *What if I get knocked out right now and have to go home early? That would be such a disaster. That would be such a failure. Seriously, having the goal of winning the tournament but getting knocked out in the* third *round? That would be so fucking embarrassing. That would be so fucking hopeless. That would make me such a pathetic fucking loser. I'd never be able to show my face in Manly ever again.*

You probably think I'm being far too hard on myself, but that's the way my mind worked, that's the kind of pressure I put on myself to succeed. A few years later that mentality would be my undoing, but in that moment, my overwhelming fear of failure snapped me back into focus. I dipped my hand in the cool ocean water, splashed a little on my face to clear my mind, heighten my senses. As I licked the salt on my lips, I resumed the search for a wave, and within 30 seconds, saw one building in the distance. As it approached I fought back my nerves, and at just the right moment, I threw myself into the rip, paddling like my life depended on it before leaping to my feet and pulling off a series of backside bottom turns that Occy himself would've been proud of and then ending with a backside floater to the cheers of the crowd. The judges awarded me a 9.5.

'Yes!' I screamed, thumping my chest. 'Yes! Yes!'

On his next wave, my opponent was only able to score a seven, which resulted in me squeaking out a one point win.

'*Man* that was close!' Mark exclaimed when I'd returned to the shore.

I shook my head.

'Too close.'

'Well, at least you're through,' Dad said. 'That's all that matters.'

At that moment, the Quiksilver boys came over and congratulated me. Mark and my parents then left to get some lunch, saying that they'd see me back at the hotel in a couple of hours.

'So Jimmy,' Rick began. 'Did you end up meeting your stalker for seafood last night?'

'Did you both "kiss under the stars?" '

'Did you get "lost at sea" together?'

'Get fucked,' I said.

'Hey, do you reckon she left you another note today?'

'Ooohhh! She might've, Jimmy – I did see a redhead hovering around where Mark and your parents and all your stuff was!'

'Check your bag, mate!'

I tried to change the subject.

'Come on, boys. Let's forget about Vanessa and go get some food.'

But they wouldn't let it go until I'd searched through my bag. To shut them all up, I quickly looked through it.

'Nah, nothing there, fellas,' I said with relief. 'I think she got the message after I didn't show up last night.'

'Wait, you didn't check your front pocket,' noticed Will. He unzipped it, and rummaged around a bit before ecstatically pulling out another purple polka-dotted piece of paper.

'Another letter!' he exclaimed.

'Fucking hell . . .' I muttered.

'Read it out loud!' Brad and Rick chorused.

Will unfolded it and started reading.

> '*Dear Jimmy,*
>
> *I was so disappointed when you didn't meet me for dinner yesterday, but as I sit here writing this to you this morning, I think I know why.*
>
> *It's because you think I'm like all the other girls who probably fall for you, isn't it? You think that yesterday was the first time I've ever seen you surf and that I hardly know you from a hole in the road, don't you?*
>
> *But the truth is Jimmy, I've been following you FOREVER.*
>
> *I first saw you in Australia when you were 12 years old, surfing in the state championships. My brother's heat had finished, and then you were up. When you were in the water, it was as if the sun was shining only on you. I remember thinking you were the best surfer I'd ever seen. And the HOTTEST surfer I'd ever seen. And when you came out of the water, I looked at your hands and your feet and they were so small and cute! You were so perfect. Like a little Ken doll but with longer hair! I fell in love with you straight away.*
>
> *My brother went to Manly Surf Academy too, so I watched you surf all the time. I'd never take my eyes off you – from the moment you'd arrive at the beach until the moment you left. Sometimes I'd even walk behind you on your way home and wait around your street, hoping to catch a glimpse of you if you took the garbage bins out or checked the mail. I'd try to work up the courage to talk to*

you, but I'd always chicken out. And then the next thing I knew, me and my family were moving to California.

I was so upset when we left Sydney, Jimmy. I cried for days and days, thinking I'd never get the chance to see you again, that I'd never get the opportunity to tell you how much I love you so that YOU could fall in love with ME and we could live happily ever after. But I did my best to keep track of you, in the hope our paths would cross again. I'd check the Manly Daily *online every day, hoping to find a story on you. If a few months went by without one, I'd email the paper asking for an update (did you ever wonder why you'd get called up out of the blue all the time? It was never really "out of the blue" – it was because I'd emailed them! I was trying to help your career!). Then they wrote that you'd be heading to the world championships in Hossegor and I was the happiest I'd been since I'd moved to California! I knew that my waiting hadn't been for nothing! I knew that fate had brought us together again! I promised myself that I wouldn't chicken out this time. I promised myself that I'd tell you exactly how I feel and not take no for an answer!*

Because you're perfect, Jimmy.

Because WE would be perfect TOGETHER.

Do you know how much you and I have in common, Jimmy?

Like you, my favourite singer is Jack Johnson.

Like you, my favourite surfer is Occy.

Like you, my favourite surfing movie is The Green Iguana.

Like you, my favourite food is fish (why do you think I wanted to eat SEAFOOD with you last night?).

AND, my brother is sponsored by Quiksilver, too!

Don't you see how perfect we are for each other, Jimmy? Can't you see that we're soul mates? Can't you just see us one day living in a big blue house, listening to Jack Johnson and eating fish in our Quiksilver clothes before switching on the TV and watching some old Occy films? I can see it so clearly, Jimmy, because it's all I've been picturing for the last three years. And I know that after reading this letter, and after we have dinner together at that seafood restaurant tonight (meet me there at seven – we'll eat FISH!), that you'll be able to picture it just as clearly as me.

ALL my love,

Vanessa.'

'OK, so this is starting to get really weird,' Rick said.

'Fuck, man . . . this chick is *obsessed* with you.'

'She's *actually* been stalking you.'

'For *three* years!'

Once again Vanessa had left me speechless. All I could do was shake my head.

'What am I . . . what am I supposed to do about this?' I eventually asked.

'I don't know. Ignore it?'

'I can't. This is fucking weird, man. It's creepy as hell. I'm completely freaked out.'

'Maybe tell your parents about it.'

'I don't want *them* to know.'

'Tell Mark, then. See what he says.'

'Well . . . yeah. I guess I could do that.'

So after eating with the boys I went back to the hotel to talk to Mark, but he wanted to study film in preparation for the quarterfinals, and my parents were keen to watch too so I never got the chance. It was the same story at dinner as well – I didn't get a moment alone with Mark, and I didn't feel comfortable bringing it up in front of my folks. Eventually I decided to just try to forget about it, and deal with it after the quarters the next day.

But when I got back to my hotel room at 9:30 after dinner, I checked my phone and realised I had 44 missed calls from an unknown number. As I stood there staring at the screen in disbelief, it rang again.

'Ah . . . hello?' I answered nervously.

'Jimmy! Are you OK? Where have you been all night?'

'What?'

'It's Vanessa! Why aren't you at the restaurant? I've been waiting here for you since seven o'clock!'

I was flabbergasted.

'How did you . . . how did you get my number?'

'It was on your flight confirmation receipt.'

'Huh? I threw that out yesterday.'

'I know. I got it out of the bin.'

I shook my head, exasperated.

'Vanessa, this *has* to stop. *Now.*'

'What? But Jimmy – '

'Enough already! Just stop following me, stop leaving notes in my bag, stop going through my rubbish, and stop calling me. Just stop everything. Just leave me alone.'

'But Jimmy we're soul mates!'

'No we're not! We're nothing! We're less than nothing! Now just go away and leave me alone!'

I hung up the phone and switched it off. I felt bad for being so blunt with her, but she just wasn't taking the hint.

In the quarter-finals the next day, I was up against a fellow Australian called Drew who I'd been friends with for years. It wasn't easy surfing against a mate with so much on the line, and once while I was waiting for a wave, my mind flashed back to some of the memories we'd shared together – being the only two people at Manly Beach surfing in the pouring rain when he was down in Sydney one time for a tournament; seeing a five metre long great white shark in the water at his hometown beach in Coolangatta and swimming like madmen to try and make it to the shore; and another time when we were lying on the beach together talking about how sweet it would be to represent Australia on the pro circuit, and how stoked we'd be if we could both win the world title one day for our awesome country. But there's no place for sentimentality in the heat of competition. In that moment, Drew was the enemy, and I desperately wanted to beat him and advance to the semis. Consequently, I narrowed my focus to the task at hand, and towards the end managed to surf an eight and an 8.5. With a few minutes left, Drew was behind with a nine and a six. He waited for a good wave to come but it never did, and with a huge sigh of relief and a subtle clench of my fist I was able to escape with the win. Even though Drewy was obviously disappointed, he was a good sport about it, congratulating me afterwards as we walked up the beach.

'Good luck in the rest of the tournament,' he said, clapping me on the back. 'Go win it for Australia.'

'Cheers, dude. I'll try my best.'

'It'll probably come down to you and that prick Stan Connors in the final. I hope you kill him. The guy's a shit-talker – never stops running his mouth while you're trying to surf.'

I would've liked to have kept talking to Drewy, but he saw his coach and started veering towards him, wishing me luck again and saying that he'd see me later.

After having a relaxing, Vanessa-free day (*At last!* I remember thinking, *she's finally gotten the message!*), I went out to dinner with my parents. Halfway through the meal, Mark arrived and pulled up a chair.

'All right, I've got the scoop on your next opponent,' he said. 'His name's Pierre Leblanc – he's a local boy, from right here in Hossegor. The whole town's behind him.'

'So the crowd's all going to be on his side,' I acknowledged. 'All two or so thousand of them.'

'If not more. So you've got to try and use that against him. Make his advantage your own.'

I frowned.

'How do I do that?'

'You've got to surf from ahead. He's going to come out blazing with energy, feeding off the fans – but if you get an early lead, then everyone will get restless. They'll all get tense. And he'll sense that. If you come out and surf two nines, then every wave he surfs that scores less than that will be met with nervous silence. Or worse – disappointed groans. Instead of revving him up, the crowd will just be adding to the pressure. And that can psych a lot of guys out.'

I couldn't help but laugh.

'Isn't the plan always to come out and surf two nines?'

'Yes,' Mark said seriously. 'But this time, it's more important than ever.'

Just as we'd expected, the next day the beach was packed with locals, French flags in hand and ready to cheer on their man. I ran through the gauntlet of fans to a few lone claps, but when Pierre came out they roared to life, chanting his name and waving their flags in a frenzy. Mark was right – I realised that if I didn't do something about them, then they might just give him the extra push he'd need to get over the line. When the competition's as fierce as it is at the World Junior Championships, an edge like that can sometimes be the difference between winning and losing.

Fortunately, I rose to the occasion early on, floating an eight and barrelling a nine. Just like Mark predicted, the crowd got antsy, gasping and groaning when I surfed my high scores. I think it rattled Pierre a bit – for a long time he couldn't get any better than a six or a seven. But then with a few minutes to go, he barrelled one of the waves of the tournament and scored a 9.5. Everyone went crazy, yelling and screaming and jumping up and down. With all the cheering from the fans it was difficult to concentrate, not to mention that the wind was severely thickening, filling my ears and forcing me to squint to see the approaching waves. But when the next one came I was able to gather myself, landing one of my best cutbacks of the championships by holding the turn from the top of the wave right to the bottom and then all the way around to smash the lip behind me, Taylor Knox style. The judges scored me an 8.5 for it, which gave me a one point lead over Pierre and meant that he'd need an 8.5 himself to beat me. He took his time, waiting patiently for the right wave before he took off. I stopped breathing momentarily as I sat frozen on my board, watching him climb atop the crest, zigzag across it. But then he fell off the lip to the shriek of the crowd. He was wiped out, and there was no time to recover. Overcome with relief, I fell back off my board and into the water. I'd made it to the final.

Afterwards, I stuck around to watch the other semi with Mark and the Quiksilver boys. Stan Connors was up against another Hawaiian bloke, and after going back and forth a couple of times, he managed to beat him with two nines. As he sauntered up the beach, our eyes met. I nodded my head respectfully. He gave me the finger and kept on walking.

It caught me off guard.

'What the . . . ?'

Mark shook his head.

'Don't worry about it. He's just trying to mess with you.'

'Drewy did say he was a prick,' I recalled.

'Forget about him,' Rick said. 'I'm starving – let's get something to eat.'

'OK. Just let me shower and change first.'

So the boys and I walked back to the hotel together, while Mark stayed to chat with a couple of other coaches he knew.

When we arrived, the concierge called me over.

'Delivery for you, Jimmy,' he said.

'Delivery? From who?'

'Not sure,' he replied, handing me a video tape. 'It was dropped off before I got here.'

I studied it carefully. There was no indication of who it was from.

'All right,' I shrugged. 'Thanks.'

In my room, my curiosity got the better of me. I put the video in the VCR and started watching it with the boys.

'What. The. *Fuck*.' Brad spat once it was finished.

'That was the most disgusting thing I've ever seen . . . but I couldn't look away.'

'Jimmy . . . what the hell are you going to do?'

Everyone was staring at me. I was too stunned to speak.

At that moment, Mark walked in the room. He looked at the screen.

'So instead of getting lunch you guys decided to stay in and watch porn, did you?' he laughed.

I shook my head.

'You don't understand.'

'What?'

I shook my head again, still dismayed as to how things had escalated to this point.

'Promise you won't tell my parents?' I sighed.

He shrugged.

'Yeah, sure.'

I rewound the video and played it again. It began with Vanessa sitting on a bed in her hotel room, wearing nothing but a purple polka-dotted bathrobe.

'Don't worry, Jimmy,' she spoke into the camera. 'I know you didn't mean what you said on the phone. You're just really stressed out trying to win the world title.'

She paused, moistening her lips.

'But you've got to loosen up a bit, babe. You need to let off some steam. You need to unwind.'

She pulled off her robe, threw it over her shoulder.

'This is for you, Jimmy,' she winked. 'Something you can pleasure yourself to until you experience the real thing.'

At that moment, two guys appeared on camera. After they took off their clothes, she started rubbing them off – one with each hand – up and down, up and down, up and down in an out-of-sync rhythm. A couple of minutes later, a third guy appeared in the corner of the screen and started masturbating, and a few minutes after that, a fourth guy entered the picture. He lay on his back underneath Vanessa like a naked car mechanic, and she knelt down to suck his dick to the chorus of moans, staring at the camera – staring at me – the entire time.

I looked at Mark. His face was ashen with horror.

'What the . . . what the hell is this?' he managed to say.

I shook my head.

'It gets worse.'

Right on cue, a beefy, 20-something year old bloke appeared. He undressed himself quickly, splashed on some lube, and then with loud thrusts started fucking her in the ass.

That made five of them in total: the two guys getting wristies, the bloke wanking in the corner, the car mechanic getting head, and Beefboy doing her in the tradesman's entrance.

'Oh . . . ! Oh . . . ! Oh . . . ! Oh . . . !' the screaming continued.

'Yes . . . ! That's it . . . ! Yes . . . !'

'Fuck . . . ! Fuck . . . ! Oh *fuck*!'

Vanessa pulled Car Mechanic's cock out of her mouth.

'Look how turned on everyone is, Jimmy!' she shrieked above the guys. 'This is what I can do for you! This is how good I can make you feel!'

Never breaking eye-contact, she returned to sucking Car Mechanic's dick, who after another couple of minutes blew his load in her mouth. Shortly afterwards, the other guys finished too. They picked up their clothes and walked out of view, leaving Vanessa all by herself. She sat on the bed, legs spread wide into the camera.

'Notice how I didn't let anyone touch my pussy?' she murmured, rubbing her clit. 'I'm still a virgin, Jimmy. I've been saving myself for you. I've been saving myself for you since I was 12 years old.'

She then told me where she was staying, and said that she'd be waiting in bed for me until I came for her. After she blew me a kiss, the screen went blank.

'That's just . . .' Mark trailed off, speechless.

I then filled him in about everything else she'd been doing. He said he'd go straight to the police with my parents to put a restraining order in place, and that after he'd done that, she wouldn't bother me ever again. I didn't want to get my parents – least of all the police – involved, but it was worth it if it was guaranteed to get Vanessa out of my life. Hell, I was surfing for the Under 15 World Title the next day, and I couldn't afford to let anything distract me.

The day of the finals was one of the most memorable of my life. It started off at six when I woke up and went for a light surf before breakfast. As I was coming out of the water, I saw Stan heading down with his board. We were walking straight at each other, staring one another down.

'What the fuck are you looking at?' he growled.

'You,' I said. 'What are you going to do about it?'

He stopped walking.

'I can't believe you actually made the final,' he spat. 'You should've lost to that South African in the third round. Those biased judges saved your ass – no way your shitty moves on that last wave deserved a 9.5.'

'Fuck off,' I muttered and continued walking.

'You can't fluke your way to a victory this time, Wharton!' he called out after me. 'I'm going to fucking kill you today!'

'Piss off!' I snarled back over my shoulder. 'Go fuck yourself!' Hell, Drewy had been right – Stan was a prick and I wanted to destroy him.

Back at the hotel, I had some breakfast before taking a shower. I found myself feeling a little tense, a little nervous about the final, so I decided to try and calm down a bit by taking a wank over Britney Spears. For the next 15 minutes, the world was blocked out – I was in my own private fantasy land, imagining myself doing the wild thing for the very first time. I started tugging harder as my orgasm approached, moaning with pleasure as the sensation flooded my cock. But then mid-ejaculation, the bathroom door flew open, and she was charging towards me like a bull out of a gate.

'They'll never keep us apart, Jimmy!' she screamed, throwing her arms around me.

'What the – '

'They'll never keep us apart! They'll never keep us apart!'

'What the fuck!' I yelled. 'What the fuck are you doing!'

'They'll never break us up, Jimmy!'

At that moment, two security guards burst in and tried to pull Vanessa off me.

'I'll always love you! I'll always love you!'

They dragged her away kicking and screaming.

'I'll love you forever, Jimmy!' she cried. 'No matter what happens I'll never stop loving you!'

I managed to pull a towel over myself before Mark appeared out of nowhere.

'What the hell just happened?' he demanded.

I was hugging my knees on the bathroom floor, shaking from head to toe. I tried to speak but no sound came out.

'Jimmy?' he stressed, crouching down beside me. 'What happened?'

Several moments passed where I couldn't speak. Then in a trembling voice I managed to tell him.

'It's just so freaky,' I concluded by saying. 'I mean . . . she's *everywhere*. I can't get away from her. No matter what I do I can't get away from her . . .'

'Jimmy listen to me,' Mark said sternly, grabbing me by the shoulders and looking me straight in the eye. 'Vanessa's on her way to the police station right now, and she's not going anywhere until you're on a plane back to Sydney. Forget about her. She will never bother you ever again. Never, ever again.'

He paused for a moment, gripping me tightly.

'Now Jimmy, I want you to listen to me very carefully. In less than two hours, you're going to be versing Stan Connors for the Under 15 World Title. And you're going to go out there and surf the best you've ever surfed, and you're going to beat him. Because this is *your* title, Jimmy. In my 12 years as a professional surfer and my ten years of coaching, I have never, ever, *ever* met anybody who works harder than you do. You've put your blood into this, and you *are* the best 15 year old surfer on the planet. I know it, you know it, and now it's time for the world to know it.'

He shook me by the shoulders.

'You're going to do this!' he yelled in my face. 'You're going to win the Under 15 World Title!'

'Yeah,' I nodded.

'Say it!'

'I'm going to win the Under 15 World Title.'

'Louder!'

'I'm going to win the Under 15 World Title.'

'Louder!'

'I'm going to win the Under 15 World Title!' I roared, jumping to my feet.

'Yeah you are!'

'Yeah I am!'

I was fired up now. *Mark's right*, I thought. *This is my moment, and I'm going to go out there and own it. Nothing's going to stop me. No one's going to stand in my way — not Vanessa, not Stan, not anybody else. I'm going to win and go home a champion.*

I spent the next hour getting ready before heading to the beach to start stretching and warming up. As they'd been doing throughout the tournament, my parents came over to wish me luck and hug me just before I was about to get called in. And then for the first time ever, Mark hugged me, too.

'Remember what I said,' he whispered in my ear. 'Forget about everything and just surf your ass off. You are the best. You've got this.'

He pulled away, and I nodded earnestly before the announcer called my name and in I went.

It was a beautiful day. The sun was bright and there was a crisp wind out, heightening the waves to an even six feet. We both had good starts, Stan scoring an eight and me an 8.5 in the first few minutes. But then neither of us caught anything special for a while — just a bunch of sixes and sevens. I had a slight lead, and towards the end, I started thinking that it might be enough to win. But then with a couple of minutes left, Stan scored a nine.

'Suck it, Wharton!' he yelled over the breaking waves. 'Suck my fat fucking cock!'

Now the pressure was really on. I took a few deep breaths, did my damnedest to compose myself as I scanned the sea while Stan kept trying to break me.

'I told you you were shit!' he screamed. 'I told you you fluked your way into the final! The judges saved you against that Saffa in the third round! You barely beat your piece-of-shit Australian friend in the quarters! And you only won the semis because that French faggot choked and fell off his board! You don't deserve to be here! You can't beat me! I am better than you! I am just *better* that you!'

But what Stan didn't know was that my close calls throughout the tournament had strengthened my resolve, and given me the confidence I needed to be able to perform under pressure.

Don't panic, I said to myself. *If you get a nine, then you'll win. You can do this – just like you did when you were losing with only a few minutes to go in the third round. Do what you did then – just pick the right wave and own it.*

I waited patiently for it to come. Second by second the time ticked away, but I held my nerve, analysing the sea, working out when it would be best to seize my chance.

Then, with just under a minute left, God sent me the wave of the day – a six-and-a-half foot masterpiece breaking in near-perfect formation. After paddling as hard as I could I got to my feet and entered the pipe, sticking my weight on the front of the board, grabbing the rail and throwing it down. The tunnel hid me from the shore as I skated through with a primal thrill, a huge rush of bliss, stoned on the smell of brine and the raucous noise and the whipping wind whooshing through my hair. This was my promised land, my sweet nirvana, deep in a celestial barrel where I felt free and complete and at peace with the world. I dug the board in even further, hung on tight amidst the wisps of spray before I shot out the other side to the roar of the crowd. They screamed and hollered, clapped with vigour, and even though it wasn't official yet, I knew I'd won. My lips were a permanent grin, my fists clenched in triumph. A couple of seconds later, the judges held up tens.

'Come on!' I screamed, Lleyton Hewitt style. 'Come on!'

I punched the air. I'd done it! I'd fucking done it! The cheering continued as I rode the wave all the way back to the shore where Mark and my parents ecstatically jumped up and down. When I reached the sand I fell into their arms, and tears of joy started streaming down my cheeks. I'd worked so hard, and to be crowned the Under 15 World Champion was the best thing that could've happened to me at that point in my life. I was so happy. So purely and utterly happy. And seeing Stan crying on his coach's shoulder was the icing on the cake.

The next month was like a dream. When I arrived home, Quiksilver organised a promotional campaign outside their shop in The Corso, where they unveiled a huge poster on the front window of me barrelling a wave. The following week, Red Bull and FCS Fins signed me to lucrative sponsorship deals, and Oakley wanted me to model their sunglasses, saying how much they liked my look and that they could envision me as surfing's next pin-up boy. Justin Gane, the bloke who made *Pulse* and *Unleashed* featuring guys like Joel Parkinson, Taj Burrow, Dean Morrison and Occy himself wanted to cast me as one of the stars in his next surfing movie. Internationally read *Surfer* magazine wanted to do an article on me and put me on the cover of their next issue. Rip Curl offered me $50,000 to sign with them and go pro the following year, and Quiksilver was in the process of trying to match the offer. Aside from Vanessa continuing to send me love letters, my life was perfect. I was so excited. So overjoyed. Every day I woke up and thanked the Lord for blessing me with the opportunity to live my dream. I just felt so incredible. All I had to do was complete Year 10 and then I could join the pro tour at age 16. There was no need to finish school. While the rest of my grade would be sitting their final year exams, I'd be in Hawaii riding waves at the Pipeline Masters, taking on all my surfing heroes like Kelly Slater, Mick Fanning and even Occy for a shot at the world title.

Maybe I wouldn't have gone on to win. Maybe I would have. I'll never know. As I'd realise time and time again, things have a habit of turning out differently from the way we plan.

Like so many accidents, mine was the sum of one part stupidity and one part bad luck. It happened in Western Australia while I was on holidays for the Queen's Birthday long weekend with my parents and the boys and their families, about two months after the World Junior Championships. The surfing conditions were deadly, made so by a thunderous storm, gale force winds and vicious swells leading to murderous rips and currents. And it was on this day that I decided to try and surf "The Box" near Margaret River. Recommended for only the best surfers, The Box was hurling 15 foot waves over hard flat rocks.

'There's no way I'm surfing that,' Corey said. 'It's bloody suicide out there.'

The rest of the fellas agreed.

'How about you, Jimmy?'

Corey was right. The waves were huge and merciless, breaking ferociously with a violent crash. I'd never attempted anything like it before. I stood there watching them in the pouring rain, tittering on the edge of heading in or suggesting we leave.

'Those waves really are insane,' Brent marvelled. 'You'd have to be a bloody pro to surf those.'

It was that remark that pushed me over the cliff.

I practically am a bloody pro, I thought to myself. *I'm the Under 15 World Champion. I can surf this. I'm not a pussy. There's no way I'm backing down from this.*

'I'm going in,' I said, and in a moment I've wished I could take back a million times, I ran for the sea. I plunged into a rip as the boys, eager to see me tackle the impossible, hooted out encouragement from the safety of the sand.

'Yeah, Jimmy!'

'Kill that shit!'

'Earn your sponsorship money, mate!'

I tried to ease into it, first carving a few waves. Then I did a floater or two. By then, I thought I was ready for a tube ride. I waited and waited before an 18 foot mammoth came roaring forwards. I felt that pulsing rush, the endorphins kicking in as I slid inside the barrel. But I'd underestimated how fast it was breaking. Before I could make it to the other side it crashed against me, sweeping me up and hurling me to the hard ocean floor. I slammed against the rocks. Pain engulfed my head, neck and back. I was dazed. I couldn't feel my legs.

I slowly floated to the surface. When I finally got there I spluttered up water, moaned 'help!' to the boys back on the sand. But they couldn't hear me above the storm. Another huge wave came charging towards me, and it was only by God's own intervention that it broke late and didn't catapult me right back down to the rocks again.

By then, I was shitting myself.

I can hardly move, and there are 15 foot waves breaking around me. I'm helpless, and there's nothing but hard solid rock beneath me.

I realised that I could die. My survival instincts kicked in as I desperately kept screaming and yelling for help. Eventually the boys heard me, and as a group were able to drag me back in.

They laid me carefully on the sand. By then I was hardly with it, but I remember gritting my teeth in the most intense physical pain I've ever felt, and Steve saying he'd run and find someone who could call an ambulance. I remember lightning attacking the sky, and trembling violently in the freezing cold before Corey laid a jacket across my chest for warmth. And I remember clutching the cross around my neck. *Please God,* I begged in my head. *Whatever's happened to me, please help me recover as soon as possible so that I can continue to train really hard and one day become the world champion.*

Steve finally came back and said that an ambulance was on its way. When it came, I told the paramedics what had happened. They wanted to take me by stretcher to hospital, but that would have involved carrying me a considerable distance to the ambulance which, because I'd in all likelihood suffered a spinal injury, they weren't comfortable doing. So they organised a helicopter evacuation. I was air-lifted to hospital.

My parents were called and given the shock of their lives. They rushed right over, arriving while the doctor was performing a series of tests as I lay on my back. They held each other a few feet away, doing their best to fight back tears.

The doctor eventually diagnosed me with a spinal concussion.

'You're very lucky, Jimmy,' he said. 'You could've been paralysed. You could've been killed. You're very lucky.'

I stayed there overnight. The next day I could feel my legs, and I could even walk, but my head and neck and back still hurt. Nevertheless, the doctor said I was right to leave. I asked him if I could surf. I was in considerable pain, but I was only six months away from turning pro, and I needed to be training harder than ever so that I'd be ready to compete. But the doctor said I couldn't.

'You've injured your spine, Jimmy. Until we know the extent of the damage, any surfing you do puts you at serious risk of paralysis.'

I was crushed. My whole world had been shaken.

'How . . . how long will it take . . . for you to know?'

'I can't say,' he replied. 'But until we work it out, you absolutely cannot surf.'

I left the hospital feeling devastated. *How am I supposed to compete with the best surfers in the world if I can't even train?* Injured or not, not training, not working my ass off went against everything I believed in. My philosophy was that if I could stand, I could surf. How could I just sit idly by waiting for the doctors to determine the severity of my injury when I would be going pro in six months' time? The mere idea made me sick. But then again, I tried to be logical: *the doctor's right – it's not worth getting paralysed over.* So with the heaviest of hearts I accepted my fate, vowing to train even harder once I'd been medically cleared to make up for lost time and give myself the best chance of succeeding on the tour.

When I got back to Sydney, I immediately booked an appointment to see a specialist. He looked at my X-rays, ran some more tests, but none of it proved conclusive so I still couldn't surf. Instead, I spent my time breaking down film, trying to learn techniques from the best – but there's only so much of that you can do. I needed to be in the water, honing my skills. I couldn't stop stressing as the weeks dragged on. Even though the pain gradually went away, the specialist still couldn't work out exactly what was wrong with me.

'It takes time, Jimmy,' he kept repeating. 'The spine's a very complex part of the body, and until we know the extent of the damage, you unfortunately just can't surf. If you were to hurt yourself again, there's a huge risk that you'd be paralysed from the neck down. You'd have to spend the rest of your life in a wheelchair. It's just not worth the risk, Jimmy.'

But not being able to surf was maddening. I was always so fractious. So tense. The days seemed to stretch on forever – agonising hour after agonising hour. Without surfing I had nothing to do. I was bored as fuck. And that old sporting adage would continuously torture me:

"Whenever you're not training, somebody else is, and when the two of you meet, they are going to beat you . . ."

I couldn't take it. Sometimes I'd scream into a pillow. Other times I'd just break down and cry. But as distraught as I was, I still remained positive.

When you get the go-ahead from the specialist you'll get back into training. You'll work your ass off and go pro next year, and then you'll keep working your ass off until you're the best surfer in the world. This is just a temporary setback. You'll get past it and still achieve your dream.

But it didn't turn out like that. I was blinded by love – the fact that I'd never become the world champion hadn't sunk in yet, not even by the day I was told by the specialist, two months after the accident itself.

When he called me into his office, I sat down in a chair beside the window. It was a beautiful Manly day – clear blue sky, sun out, wind a little crisp. I remember thinking what a great day it was for a surf.

'As you know, Jimmy,' the specialist began, 'I've been assessing your injury and trying to determine the severity of it.'

He paused, looking at me solemnly.

'Your injury has left serious and permanent damage to your neck and your spine. You'll be able to run and do most normal activities, but you'll always have a degree of weakness in your limbs, and be highly vulnerable to paralysis should you injure your spine again.'

'But I'll still be able to surf, right?' I stressed. 'I'll be able to train really hard and one day become the world champion, won't I?'

He shook his head sympathetically.

'I'm sorry, Jimmy. It's too dangerous. The risk of paralysis is too great.'

'No!' I cried. 'There's got to be something you can do!'

'I'm sorry, Jimmy. The damage is permanent. There's nothing I can do.'

I begged him and begged him to try something, to try anything, but he just kept reiterating that it was beyond his control. Eventually, I was convinced. My head fell to my hands. I cried loudly, bawled my eyes out for a long, long time as it finally started to hit home.

My surfing career is over.

Done.

Finished.

Kaput.

I will never turn pro.

I will never surf against all of my heroes.

I will never win the world title.

And perhaps what hurt the most was the realisation that I'd been robbed of the chance to even try. I felt like my dream was ending before I'd even opened my eyes. And as the hours turned to days and then bled into weeks, I continued crying for what I'd lost, but also for what might have been.

VINDICATION IS THE SWEETEST JOY NEXT TO BEING WITH A WOMAN

I was shattered that my surfing career was over. It felt like the end of my world. Dad was right – I'd put all my eggs in one basket, and now, I had nothing. I was in mourning for weeks. Apart from to go to school, I barely left the house. I couldn't handle walking through The Corso and having people stare at me with all that pity in their eyes. I thought I'd cry if I went to the beach. I took all my gear and every trophy, plaque, medal and poster I had and put it in the basement. It was all too painful to look at. I'd lost everything. There'd be no surfing movie or magazine cover, Quiksilver had taken my poster down from their shop window, and all my sponsorship deals had been withdrawn (hell, even *Vanessa* had stopped writing to me). Everything I'd worked so hard for was gone. I felt like the life had been sucked out of me. I was barely a shell of a boy. I didn't eat much. Didn't sleep much. Hardly spoke to anyone. It was devastating. I was living my worst nightmare.

But after a couple of months, I started to pull myself together. The way I saw it, it did me no good to ruminate on my injury or wish that it hadn't happened. I started blocking those thoughts out, and doing my best to look towards the future.

I need to get on with my life, I figured. *I need to adjust to a world without surfing, and make the most of what I have. If I don't, I'll be miserable forever.*

I began by making an effort to get out of the house and be more social. I was 15 – my mates were going to parties, getting drunk and starting to have sex, but in favour of surfing I'd never gotten into it (I'd pashed a grand total of three girls, and never even gotten past first base before). So when a guy in our grade had a party a couple of months after my injury, I went with the boys and we brought a case of beer.

'No excuses this time, bro,' Corey said. 'Now that you're no longer surfing, you've got to get on the piss.'

By ten o'clock I was wasted, and found myself in a bedroom with a caramel-haired, hazel-eyed girl called Tina.

'Kiss me, Jimmy,' she slurred.

I pressed my lips against hers, pushed my tongue inside her mouth as we started hooking up on the bed. I gradually got a boner, which Tina fumbled around with before the last beer I'd drunk really started to hit me. I felt a queasiness in my gut, a sick feeling in my throat, and then before I could stop myself, I puked on her face.

'What the fuck!' she shrieked.

'Sorry . . .' I murmured.

She stormed out of the room. I went to go after her, but I fell on my first step and threw up again.

The boys then burst in.

'Dude, what the fuck just happened?'

All I could do was groan. They all started cheering.

'About fucking time, mate! About fucking time!'

I puked again. They dragged me into the bathroom where I kept throwing up before eventually passing out with my head in the toilet.

Despite being messy, I loved my first drinking experience. I loved how the booze made me forget about my problems, loved how serene it made me feel. Ever since I'd gotten injured, I'd been desperate for a way to unwind, yearning for a way to relax. And I suppose by default, alcohol became my release. From then on, every weekend I'd binge like mad, and despite my late start, I quickly developed a reputation as being one of the loosest drinkers in the year.

There was also a second reputation that I quickly developed – that of being nothing more than a washed up surfer. I'd been envied for so long, but after my injury, everyone in the year – except for the fellas – seized the opportunity to pounce. Now that I was down, everyone revelled in kicking the shit out of me.

'Your best days are behind you,' they all said.

'You've got nothing going for you now.'

'You're a nobody.'

I became known as "Washed Up Wharton," implying that I used to have it all but that I'd peaked too early, and in the end had amounted to nothing. It was all a bit of a joke to them, but it really, really annoyed me. I'd laugh it off, but seriously, every time someone called me that, I wanted to punch them in the fucking head. I was pregnant with rage, and then one afternoon, I finally exploded.

Sometime in October of Year 10, my school ran what it called a "University Seminar," where representatives from all the local unis came to talk about the courses they offered and the requirements for getting in. I had no idea what I wanted to do after school, but given that I was trying to rediscover myself and learn about my options, the University Seminar seemed like a sensible event to attend. It was due to start in fifth period, but I had a check-up appointment for my spine beforehand which ran a little overtime. When I arrived at the hall the talk had already started, so I figured I'd just quietly enter and quickly sit down. But when I opened the door and exposed myself to the 100-odd students, everyone started laughing at me.

'Washed Up Wharton! What the hell are you doing here? This is for people who want to go to *university!*'

'Wharton! This isn't the physio, mate! You've hobbled into the wrong room!'

I tried to laugh it off, but inside, I was fucking furious.

You all think that just because my surfing career ended that you're better than me? You all think that I'm just a washed up athlete whose life is over? That I'm stupid because my grades were shit for the last few years because I was so focused on surfing that I never bothered studying? Well fuck you. Fuck you all. You stupid fucking cunts. You don't know me. You have no right to judge me.

It was probably only a few seconds but it felt like far longer as they kept pointing and laughing, yelling out abuse. It was such a disturbance that the bloke speaking actually stopped in the middle of his talk and started staring at me too.

'Waaashed up! Waaashed up! Waaashed up!' some of them jokingly drawled.

'You're not even going to pass Year 10! How the hell are you going to get into uni?'

'Waaashed up! Waaashed up! Waaashed up!'

'Be quiet!' a teacher finally yelled. 'Jimmy, sit down!'

The crowd eventually fell silent as I stormed to the back of the room and sat down seething. I was fuming with rage. Frothing with white-hot anger.

Those fucking cunts! I kept thinking. *Those stupid motherfucking cunts! Who the fuck are they to judge me? Who the fuck are they? They don't know me. I'm not an idiot. The only reason my marks were shit was because I spent all my time surfing. I could do really well in school if I wanted to. I could outwork all those cunts and get better grades than all of them. If I wanted to.*

And over the course of the seminar, the idea gradually started to evolve in my mind.

Trying hard in school? Well, it would make sense, given that I can no longer surf. I could go to uni, get a degree, get a good job and have a successful career. Plus it would feel really good to get a great mark and prove all these cunts wrong. That would feel really fucking good. Then I'd be the king again. No one could fucking look down on me then. The way I was feeling resonated with the point made by John Updike in his novel *Rabbit, Run*:

"*. . . after you've been first-rate at something, no matter what, it kind of takes the kick out of being second-rate.*"

It couldn't be truer. *Being called "Washed Up Wharton" after I've been crowned the best 15 year old surfer in the world? No way. There's no way I'm going out like this. There's no way this is the end for me. There's no way those cunts are right.*

I kept stewing with fury.

I'll show them, I kept repeating to myself. *I'll show them . . .*

And by the end of the seminar, I'd made a vow that would dominate my focus for the next two-and-a-half years.

I'm going to finish school first in the year. I'm going to score a UAI (University Admissions Index – equal to the percentile in which one is ranked in the state) *of 100.00. I'll prove everybody wrong in the most emphatic way possible. I'll outwork everyone, just like I did with surfing, and kick all their asses. Let's see them call me a washed up surfer then.*

So for the remaining few months of the year I worked my ass off. In class I took notes and paid attention. After school I did my homework, and meticulously studied all the seventh-, eighth-, ninth- and tenth grade material that I hadn't learned because I'd been too busy surfing. I threw myself into it with the same discipline and determination I'd applied to surfing. I worked so hard, driven by my quest to prove everybody wrong. Whenever I felt like slacking off or I wasn't in the mood to study, I'd think about everyone laughing at me at the University Seminar and then push on.

Do you want them to be right? I'd ask myself. *Do you want to end up a washed up surfer? No? Then fucking study!*

No one but my parents knew about my goal. The closest I came to telling anyone else was mentioning to the fellas while I was wasted one Saturday night of many that I'd started studying and taking school seriously. Despite working hard, I was still drinking like a fish on weekends. As far as I was concerned, there was nothing better than getting piss-blind drunk with your mates after a week of gruelling study.

I continued pushing myself throughout Year 10, and ended up finishing 119th out of 156 students — an improvement on the previous year when I finished 142nd out of 152, but a ranking still heavily influenced by my terrible first semester. Nonetheless I was encouraged, and in the summer holidays of 2005 that led up to the start of Year 11, I bought the textbooks and worked my way through a good chunk of the eleventh grade material. I started learning some economics, and found that I really enjoyed it. Same with business studies. I did some reading for my other subjects too — maths, physics and beginner's Spanish — although not for English, which was a subject I hated and saw absolutely no point in studying (*seriously, why would anyone waste their time analysing Shakespeare once school is finished?* I thought). So by the time Year 11 started I was ahead of the game, focused and ready for the two years ahead. And it is now time, fine readers, for you to meet Olivia. Olivia. O-li-vi-a. Love of my life Olivia. And so this fucked up love story really starts, with a girl, as all fucked up love stories inevitably do.

It was in an advanced maths class where I first laid eyes on her. I was sitting up the back of the room, and when the teacher called my name on the roll, everyone turned around and started laughing at me — just like they did at the University Seminar.

'Washed Up Wharton! What are you doing here?'

'This is an *advanced* maths class, you idiot!'

Once again I tried to laugh it off, but inside it was burning me up. *Laugh it up now, you fucking assholes. In two years' time I'll have kicked all your asses and I'll be the one laughing at you for ever doubting me,* I remember thinking. I looked around at all the faces in the room and felt fury surge through my veins until my eyes fell upon a girl sitting by herself in the front row.

For all our bravado, I think almost every young guy has a vision of his ideal woman that's treasured very dearly in the core of his heart. There's a girl who takes our breath away, who dances through our dreams, who walks down the aisle when we picture ourselves getting married. In our eyes, she is the most beautiful woman on the face of the earth, and from the time we're old enough to fall in love, we're filled with a white-hot longing to meet her in person. If we're ever so blessed as to do so, we find ourselves feeling almost . . . lightheaded, just gazing into her eyes. We find ourselves feeling nervous, and excited, and alive, all at the same time. We feel something tugging at our heart . . . a desire to open ourselves up . . . to leap into her soul. We lose ourselves in the moment, we're mesmerised, and at least for those few seconds, we believe in the notion of love at first sight.

That's how I felt when I first saw Olivia. Mahogany-brown hair cascaded down her shoulders, shimmered against her clear olive skin. Her lips were full and luscious; eyes soft, warm and spectacularly blue. And unlike all the others, she wasn't laughing at me. Instead, she looked at me with her head slightly tilted, and there was something about her expression – although I can't quite pinpoint what, exactly – that exuded compassion. Awash with her empathy, my anger and frustration just melted away. I wouldn't have thought it possible, but right then and there, I found myself feeling at peace with the world and everything in it, because I was face-to-face with the girl of my dreams.

The laughter eventually ceased and the teacher went on with the lesson. When it was over, the class stood up and made their way to the playground for lunch. I saw Olivia leave, and, desperate to talk to her, I pushed my way past everyone clogging the exit of the hall to reach her.

'Jimmy, what the fuck are you doing here?' someone asked, but I ignored them as I looked around before spotting her in the canteen line. I lined up beside her. She noticed me looking at her, and smiled a warm, vivacious smile.

'H-hey,' I said nervously. 'My name's Jimmy.'

'I know,' she said. 'You're the surfer who got injured.'

I nodded.

'My name's Olivia. I only came to Manly High at the start of the year.'

'Where were you before that?'

'Melbourne.'

'Why did you move to Sydney?'

'Dad got transferred for work.'

'Cool,' I nodded lamely.

We reached the front of the line and Olivia was asked what she wanted to order. She got a ham, cheese and tomato sandwich and a chocolate milk, and I decided to get the same. We paid for our food and moved aside for the people behind us to reach the counter. I was so nervous. My body was moist with sweat as we stood together awkwardly beside the line. Eventually, I sucked up the courage and asked her:

'Want to . . . ah . . . eat together?'

'Sure,' she smiled.

We walked outside and sat on the grass under a big shady tree. I was too nervous to look at her, so I clumsily studied my ham, cheese and tomato sandwich before finally saying something.

'So . . . ah . . . how are you liking Manly High so far?'

'I like it a lot,' she said perkily. 'It's nice and casual – a lot more laid-back than my old school.'

'Yeah? How so?'

'Just everything, really. I used to go to a private school, so it was really strict. Particularly with uniform and stuff.'

'Yeah, you can pretty much wear whatever you want here. The only thing that's compulsory is the school shirt.'

'I know! I can't believe you guys don't have to wear long pants! Or a tie!' She smiled.

'I can even see your chest hair, Jimmy.'

I laughed, feeling myself loosen up a little.

'You know, Olivia, you're actually dressed pretty conservatively for Manly High standards. I mean, your skirt almost comes down to your *knees*.'

She giggled.

'I know, right? And my shirt's actually done up. You can't even see my cleavage.'

I couldn't help but check. She caught me and broke into a grin.

'Look aaallll you want. There's nothing to see!'

We both laughed, and she playfully slapped my thigh with the back of her hand.

'So tell me, Jimmy,' she started again. 'What's a jock like you doing having lunch with a new girl like me? Shouldn't you be off hanging out with all the cool kids?'

I couldn't help but chuckle.

'I'm not a jock, Liv.'

'You were going to be a professional surfer though, weren't you? And didn't you also model sunglasses for Oakley? Before you got injured?'

'Yeah. Before I got injured.'

'What happened?'

I told her how I hurt my spine surfing "The Box."

'I'm really sorry to hear that, Jimmy,' she said sympathetically. 'I really, really am.'

'It's OK,' I said. 'It happened nearly a year ago.'

She nodded softly.

'What do you want to do now?' she asked. 'Like for a career and stuff?'

I hesitated. The only people I'd ever talked to about my goals for the future were my parents. I studied her carefully, taking note of her slightly raised eyebrows and her delicate, gentle features. She looked . . . warm . . . genuinely interested instead of judgmental like the others. It instilled within me a sense of comfort.

'I think I want to become a . . . a lawyer . . . or an investment banker . . . just like my parents.'

'That'd be awesome, Jimmy . . . having a job like that.'

'For sure,' I said. 'I could make a lot of money, and be able to give my future family a really good life.'

'You sure could!'

I paused for a few seconds, reflecting on how no one believed in me and how everybody thought of me as just a washed up surfer. Then all of a sudden, that dormant volcano erupted, and some of my accumulated exasperation poured out.

'No one thinks I can do it, but I'm going to prove them wrong. I've been studying hard all holidays, and I'm going to keep studying hard so that I come first in the year and get a UAI of 100. Let's see everyone call me a washed up surfer then.'

'Oh I hope you do it, Jimmy,' she said. 'I really hope you shut everyone up.'

My jaw dropped. *Did she really just say what I thought she said?* Once again I studied her carefully, staring into her deep blue eyes.

'Do you . . . do you really think I can?' I asked. 'Everyone else would say it was nuts.'

She was staring right back at me.

'Yes, Jimmy, I do. You seem like a very determined person . . . and you really want this. You're going to do it.'

At that moment, I became filled with an unprecedented lust, a desirous sort of feeling that bordered on yearning. *This girl is special,* I thought. *She's different from everyone else. She actually* gets *me.* My heart was pounding in my chest. I remember thinking, *is this what it feels like to fall in love?*

We talked effortlessly for the rest of the lunch hour, and I relished the chance to discover as much about her as I could. She told me that she wanted to become a psychologist, that the human mind and why people do things and react to the same things in different ways had always fascinated her.

'And the best part is,' she said, 'that I'll be able to help people. I think psychologists have the chance to really make a difference. I mean, imagine helping a girl conquer anorexia, or helping someone with depression or bipolar disorder get their life back on track. How amazing would that be?' Her compassion stirred me, drew me to her like waves to a shore. She also told me that she loved playing the harp, and had done so for seven years.

'I'll bring it to school and play for you tomorrow,' she joked.

I had lunch with her every day for the rest of the week. We talked about so much – our hobbies and interests, the things that had happened in our past, and all about our hopes and dreams for the future. I found her so easy to talk to, and unlike with anyone else apart from Corey and Brent and the rest of the fellas, I felt like I could really be myself around her – that I could speak openly and honestly and not be ridiculed or laughed at or judged. And when I wasn't with her, I thought about her all the time. I'd find myself daydreaming about kissing her forehead, eyelids, nose and lips before working slowly down her neck, between her collarbone, to her cleavage, breasts that were soft and supple and then descending with anticipation down to her navel and with a trembling excitement towards her waiting vagina. I'd circle it slowly, feel her quiver as I'd rub her outer thighs, push them into my ears before gradually climbing back up her body and entering her for the melting of our innocence. In my fantasy, we'd then spend the rest of the night together wrapped up in the sheets, holding one another, exploring each other's souls until the birth of a new day.

My mates were starting to tease me about it.

'Jimmy, what's up with you and the new chick?' Corey asked. 'You done anything with her yet?'

'Nah.'

'What? You've been blowing us off all week and you haven't even hooked up with her?' said Sean.

'Yeah, what's up with that?' chimed Chris.

'I don't want to rush it,' I said. 'I really like this girl.'

'Ooohh! Jim-my's in lo-ove, Jim-my's in lo-ove,' they crooned.

'Fuck off.'

'Tell you what,' said Brent. 'Bring her to my party next weekend. You're not going to do anything with her at school, but at a party where everyone's getting loose? Guaranteed to get to first.'

'Guaranteed,' said Steve.

'I'll see if she wants to come.'

'You reckon she's done it before?'

'Done what?'

'Fucked, you idiot.'

I thought about it.

'Don't think so.'

'How well do you know her? She could be loose, man. You could score a homer in Brent's bed!'

'Fuck off, man. She's not like that.'

'Could be! Jimmy's going to get laid!'

They broke out into a *"Jimmy's going to get laid!"* chant and I told them to shut up but they wouldn't listen.

After another week of having lunch with her, I asked her if she'd like to come to Brent's party and she said she'd love to. I was there early with the rest of the guys having a chat over a few beers, but when I saw her arrive with a couple of girls she'd met in class, I became so filled with desire that I stopped talking to Corey mid-sentence. Mascara lengthened her lashes, accentuated her luscious, deep blue eyes. A light coating of blush covered her cheeks, and sparkling gloss made her lips look deliciously irresistible.

She wore a figure hugging, white strapless dress that succeeded in making her look voluptuous yet not at all promiscuous, and paired the ensemble with red high heels. In my infatuated mind she looked like a goddess, and often when I picture her, it's how she looked that night, wearing that white strapless dress and those hot red heels.

I approached her with a smile, and we hugged each other the way you do when you really like someone and never want to let them go. She gently rubbed my back, and I savoured the smell of her peach-blossom hair before we eventually pulled away.

'Wow . . .' I said. 'You look ah . . . I mean you look really . . .' I trailed off. She started giggling.

'Feel free to finish your sentence, Jimmy. Every girl loves a compliment!'

I laughed.

'You look gorgeous, OK? You look really gorgeous! Is that better?'

She was still giggling.

'Thanks, Jimmy. You look gorgeous too!'

I introduced her to my friends, and we sat and talked in a group for a while. I was drinking Toohey's Extra Dry, and she a Smirnoff Double Black. I wanted to drink to calm my nerves so that I could try to kiss her, but I didn't want to get so drunk that I was puking and unable to control myself – which is what had happened the last couple of weekends. I was studying so hard throughout the week that on Saturday nights I just craved relief.

After we'd relaxed with a few drinks, I asked her if she wanted to take a walk down to the beach. She said yes. We strolled through the lively Corso before kicking off our shoes and walking along the sand to a more secluded area. We sat down within range of a streetlight, and listened to the waves break in the distance before washing up upon the shore. The sides of our bodies were touching – thighs, hips and shoulders – yet anticipation was rendering us mute. *Baby steps,* I kept telling myself. *Just look at her and take it from there.* Another few moments passed in nervous silence. *Look at her! Just look at her!* Finally, I did. She turned her head too, and all of a sudden I found myself staring into her soft blue eyes, watching them apprehensively as they didn't turn away. She broke into her beautiful smile, and I knew then that everything was going to be OK. I started smiling too as our heads naturally moved closer and closer together, as our lips came to within inches of touching. My heart beat as hard as a thousand drums as they slowly melted into one.

I think I always knew it would happen, although I never really knew what the kiss would be like. It was short, maybe 20 seconds long, maybe even less. My tongue swam slowly around her mouth, circled hers gently before I softly pulled away. We gazed at each other, both flushed with emotion before our lips met again. We caressed each other's tongues, leapt into each other's mouths. We grew so comfortable together, the motion slowing, growing more and more passionate with the gradual erosion of nerves. Nothing could have sullied something so blissful. Everything had been blocked out – we were in our own ardent bubble, floating in a sublime nirvana. When we finally pulled away, we remained one, cuddled up together gazing up at the stars. And as I lay there holding her with a smitten look spread across my face, I remember thinking that I was the happiest I'd been since I'd won the Under 15 World Title.

We jumped straight into a relationship. We spent so much time together, talking, laughing, kissing, leaping into each other's souls as our love continued to bloom. At school we'd hold hands as we'd walk to class, and I'd sit with my fingers resting on the inside of her thigh. She'd write love notes in the margins of my exercise books, and during lunch we'd make out by the pines behind the football field. After school we'd always study together at my house since my parents would be working late, and pash on my living room couch whenever we'd take a break. On weekends we'd go to parties together, or have long, relaxing dinners in The Corso. Afterwards we'd walk along the sand, stop at the spot of our very first kiss and melt back into it as if no time had passed. We'd hold each other's faces, gaze into each other's eyes that were only centimetres apart.

'You make me so happy,' I'd tell her. 'I thought only winning the world title could make me feel this way, but when I'm with you . . . I didn't know this was possible. You make me feel complete. I don't even miss surfing any more . . .'

'You're the best thing to ever happen to me,' she'd say. 'I never thought I could care about someone this much. I love how passionate you are. I love your drive, love how you follow your heart no matter what everyone else says. You're so inspiring. So different from anyone else I've ever met. You fascinate me. I can't stop thinking about you.'

On our three month anniversary, at the ripe old age of 16, we exchanged our virginities. Liv's parents were away so I went over to her place, and within five minutes we were making out on her living room couch. She nibbled my ear. I breathed hotly on her neck, pressing my lips against her flesh, running my teeth over her soft smooth skin. Her breathing deepened. I went to finger her clit. I rubbed it a few times before she took my hand.

'Jimmy . . .' she panted.

'Yes?'

She gazed at me fervently.

'What is it, baby?' I asked.

'Jimmy . . . will you . . . will you make love to me?'

I was surprised.

'Are you serious?'

She nodded.

'Yes.'

I looked deeply into her eyes, ran my fingers through her thin brown hair.

'Are you sure you're ready?'

She leaned in and kissed me.

'I'd always wanted to be madly in love with the guy I gave my virginity to. And Jimmy . . . Jimmy . . .'

My heart was thumping. I was speechless. All I could do was nod my head, kiss her lips before picking her up and carrying her into the bedroom without ever breaking our gaze.

I laid her gently on the bed, panting with excitement. I couldn't believe what was about to happen.

'Undress me, Jimmy,' she whispered.

I undid the buttons of her dress, slipped it off her slender body. I fingered her red laced panties before sliding them down her legs and flinging them across the room. I stood there mesmerised by her splendid nakedness as my prick shot out from beneath my shorts. My clothes disappeared. I found myself on top of her. Both our hearts were going crazy as I reached for my pants on the floor and retrieved a condom from my wallet. I slipped it on, held my throbbing cock, gazed back at Olivia. She was breathing excitedly – short, quick, shallow breaths. She smiled slightly. I knew it was time. With a trembling hand I traced my finger around the lips of her vagina, used my other hand to gently guide myself in. She gasped slightly.

'Did I hurt you?' I asked.

'Only for a second. Keep going . . .'

I gently moved back and forth inside her. It was so delicate. I was so careful not to hurt her.

'Are you . . . OK?' I kept panting.

'Yes . . . I love it . . . don't stop . . .'

I gradually penetrated deeper. We moaned in harmony; thrusting together in soft, tender ecstasy; holding each other tightly; clinging with passion. I'd never been so physically aware of my body, never been so emotionally in tune with my feelings.

'I love . . . you Olivia,' I kept panting. 'I love you so, so much . . .'

'I love . . . you too, Jimmy . . . keep going . . . don't stop . . .'

As it always does when you're blissfully in love, it ended far too soon. I moaned loudly, mouth wide open before the most intense pleasure I'd ever felt flooded my prick, and in that moment, I felt so close to Olivia – as close as any two people could possibly be – almost as if our bodies, minds and hearts were one before the sensation finally faded and I collapsed on top of her in delirious capitulation.

'That was . . . that was . . .' Liv eventually murmured.

I lifted myself onto my elbows, gazed at her dreamily.

'That was . . .' Tears filled her eyes. I held her tightly as they ran down her cheeks. Then I started crying too. We were both that emotional.

We lay there for hours, just holding each other, filled with joy and wonder and most of all love. Eventually, we drifted off to sleep, and as soon as we woke up, we did it again.

I was as happy as I'd ever been. I had Olivia, I had the boys, and I had a goal in mind that I was striving for relentlessly. Even though I'd fallen in love, my focus never wavered. I always paid diligent attention during class, and always studied after school with Olivia for an hour-and-a-half or two at my house. After taking a break to walk her home, I'd then have some dinner and by eight-thirty be hitting the books again, studying determinedly for another couple of hours before exhaustedly calling it a day and going to sleep. On the weekend, I'd study for another six hours a day. I was so disciplined, so locked in. I wanted to succeed so badly.

You must get a UAI of 100 to shut all those fuckers up and prove to them that you're more than a washed up surfer, I'd tell myself. *You have to study your ass off, do whatever it takes to make it happen. Don't let anything stop you. You must do this. You must!*

The first real test of my progress came in June: the Year 11 mid-year exams. I'd been looking forward to them ever since I'd started learning the eleventh grade material way back in the holidays before the year had even started. I was pumped. I knew this was my chance to prove myself to everyone, to come first in the year and tell everybody to go fuck themselves. In the weeks leading up to the exams I amped up my study regime, squeezing in an extra hour a day after dinner each weeknight and an extra two hours a day on Saturday and Sunday. I was excited, I was energised, and I felt that I sat the exams prepared and ready. But when I got my report card, I was thoroughly disappointed:

Subject	Mark	Rank
English	73%	83/152
Spanish	79%	19/50
Physics	76%	25/65
Economics	89%	7/72
Business Studies	83%	19/75
Maths	88%	20/142

Overall Rank: 42/156

Fucking hell, I swore when I saw it. *Fuck-ing hell. What the fuck happened? You thought you nailed it, but you did shithouse. Those marks are terrible. They're a disgrace. You need to be getting at least 95 in every subject to get a UAI of 100, and the highest mark you got was only eighty-fucking-nine! You fucked up. This was your first chance to prove yourself to everybody and you failed it miserably.*

I was devastated. I spent the next hour ruminating on my disappointment, beating myself up for failing so badly before Liv gave me a call.

'Hey, baby. Did you get your report card today?'

I sighed.

'Yeah.'

She sensed my dejection.

'What happened?'

I told her my marks.

'Wow! Sweetie that's great!' she exclaimed.

'What do you mean it's great? It's fucking terrible. It's nowhere near good enough to get a UAI of 100.'

'Jimmy . . . it's only the first semester of Year 11. You've only just started studying after years of not doing anything. It's going to take you a little while to adjust, going to take you a little while to get in the swing of things.'

'My marks are shithouse. They're fucking terrible.'

'Jimmy don't say that! You're just starting to learn exam technique and how to study properly. I think that all things considered you did really well.'

'I did shithouse.'

That night, one of our friends had a party. I rocked up on the dot of the 7:30 starting time and began pounding shots of bourbon. I just wanted to numb the misery, numb the pain, escape what I perceived to be my failures. By a quarter-to-nine I was lying face-down on the bathroom floor, puking my guts out into the drain. By ten o'clock, I'd passed out. Olivia – who'd been taking care of me all night – took me home. When we got there I started throwing up again before eventually passing out for good at eleven or eleven-thirty.

I woke at a quarter-past-nine to a shocker of a hangover and Olivia beside me. My parents had just started letting her spend the night, and under usual circumstances, I would've wanted to start the day by making love to her. But that morning, my head throbbed in agony; I felt weak, lethargic and queasy; and above all else, I was still consumed with devastation about my exam results. With great difficulty, I dragged myself into the bathroom and brushed my teeth to remove the aftertaste of vomit before pouring myself a glass of water and taking it back to my room. By then, Olivia was awake.

'How are you feeling?' she asked.

'Fucked,' I said.

'Hungover?'

'My marks.'

'Jimmy you can't be serious!'

'I am. I got nowhere near my goal. I did terribly. My marks were *so* shit.'

'Jimmy how can you say that? You've improved 80 places in half a year! You've done amazingly well! And if you keep working this hard you'll keep on improving, and by the end of Year 12 you'll be at the top of the grade!'

'I did terribly. I failed. I can't get a UAI of 100.'

I shook my head furiously.

'I'm useless . . . I'm worthless. Everyone was right . . . I'm an idiot. I'm nothing more than a washed up surfer.'

'Oh my God! Jimmy – '

'Liv shut up!'

'Jimmy – '

'Shut up Liv!' I grabbed the glass from my desk and hurled it across the room. It hit the wall and shattered into shards. Olivia ran towards me, held me tightly.

'Jimmy calm down! What's the matter? Why are you this upset?'

'I failed,' I stressed through gritted teeth. 'I'm a failure. Everyone was right – I'm nothing but a washed up surfer.'

'Oh my God! Jimmy you are being *so* hard on yourself! How can you possibly think of yourself as a washed up surfer? You still beat over two-thirds of the year! In your first full semester of even trying! That's amazing! And if you keep this up you'll keep on improving, and in Year 12 you'll be at the top of the grade!'

She paused for a moment, shaking her head incredulously.

'My God, Jimmy . . . how can you possibly be so hard on yourself?'

But that's how I thought. The way I saw it, I'd worked really hard to achieve a goal, and I hadn't even come close to doing so. So I'd failed. Big time. It was as simple as that.

I was feeling miserable for the next week, just stewing and stewing about how badly I'd performed.

You did shockingly . . . you failed . . . you completely screwed up. Fucking hell, fucking hell, fucking hell!

But with Liv's help, I was able to pick myself up by the following weekend.

Maybe she's right, I was finally able to rationalise. *You* have *come a long way in the last several months. And if you continue working this hard and keep honing your study skills and your exam technique, then you'll be in a good position to achieve your goal. You just have to keep working hard. Just keep working hard, every single day, and then you'll give yourself a shot of getting 100.*

The second half of the year was similar to the first – hard-core studying, seeing plenty of Olivia, hanging out with the boys and getting trashed on weekends. Most Saturday nights I'd go to a party and get wasted playing drinking games with the fellas and Liv and her friends before we'd all dance the night away. Other nights it'd just be Liv and me, having dinner in The Corso before making love at one of our houses. If we were at Liv's place, I'd often listen to her tickle the harp strings to the tune of Bach, Mozart or Tchaikovsky. In one of our more promiscuous moments, I stuck my prick through the strings and she gave me head while kneeling on the other side of the harp.

In terms of school work, Olivia was right when she said that my marks would get better the more I got into the swing of things. Over time, I honed my study skills and my exam technique, and in the end-of-year exams I scored over 90 in maths, business studies, and beginner's Spanish; 97 in economics; and I ended up coming 19th out of 156 students. Once again I'd hoped to do better, but since there was now evidence to support everything Liv had said last time, I was hardly as devastated. Instead, I was encouraged by my improvement, and convinced that I was on the right track to achieving my goal. *Just keep working hard and you'll end up doing it!* I kept telling myself. *You'll get a UAI of 100 and prove everybody wrong!*

I never took my foot off the gas pedal. After school had finished for the year, I gave myself one day off to chill out by the beach with Liv and get blind with the fellas at night before pumping out six hours of intense, gruelling study on day two of the summer break.

'You're such a nerd!' Liv joked. 'I can't believe you're studying this hard on the second day of the holidays!'

'I want to get 100, baby. You have no idea how badly I want it.'

That was how hard I pushed myself all summer long. I didn't take one day off – not even Christmas, New Year's Eve or New Year's Day. I knew Year 12 was going to be the mother of all academic challenges, and I was determined to meet it with everything in me. So I studied fanatically, and when the year started, I studied even more fanatically. I increased the amount of work I did after school from three hours a day to four, and the amount of work I did on weekends from six hours a day to seven. The workload was huge, but I was organised and on top of things, ceaselessly prepping for those final year exams.

Year 12 was also the year we all started pubbing and clubbing. In May we met a bloke who scratched us all fake IDs, so we began hitting up the town. The first time we went out was on Oxford Street to a club called Havana. The fellas and I and Liv and her friends arrived at eleven, had some shots, threw back a few beers and a few vodka Red Bulls for energy before everyone started going crazy on the dance floor. It was a wild night, purely hedonistic, everyone just living in the moment. Sean fingered a chick on the dance floor. Chris claimed he copped head in a cubicle right after the chick snorted a line of coke off his dick. One of Liv's friends went home with a dude she met at the bar. Another one drank too much and was puking in the toilets. I was just going nuts on the DF, drinking non-stop, jumping up and down and blowing off some steam. After an arduous week of study it was just what I wanted – good times and pure, self-indulgent escapism.

We were kicked out at three after we found Brent sitting in the piss trough passed out with his pants around his ankles. Liv's friend was still throwing up, so she took a cab home with her and the rest of the girls. The fellas and I had planned to do the same before Brent pulled himself together and suggested an alternative.

'Fuck going home, boys. Let's go to a gay bar.'

'A *gay* bar?'

'Yeah. It'll be hilarious!'

In our drunken state we all agreed.

We ended up at a place called the Stonewall Hotel. It was going off – Euro pop music blared from the speakers, topless men danced on the bar, and drag queens flirted left, right and centre. Within five minutes of being there, a bloke without pants grabbed me by the hips and tried to dance with me.

'You're so gorgeous!' he exclaimed.

'I'm straight, man.'

'No,' he slurred, running his fingers through my hair. 'You just *think* you are.'

'Seriously, man,' I said, pushing him away. 'I'm straight.'

'Fine,' he pouted, and walked away.

Corey then spotted a girl who he liked.

'I'm going to hook up with her,' he said, pointing to a skinny blonde chick standing by the bar.

'We're in a gay bar, bro. You reckon she's straight?'

'If she's not, then fuck it. I'll convert her.'

We all laughed.

Corey then approached the girl as we all watched on. He introduced himself, and they talked for about thirty seconds before a six-foot-three chick with muscles bigger than all of us put together got up in his grill.

'What the fuck are you doing?' she yelled.

Corey mumbled something inaudible before the girl punched him in the face. His head shot to the side, and she hit him again before security jumped in to break it up and kick them both out. We caught up with him outside.

'I can't believe you got beaten up by a chick, bro!' we all laughed.

'Fuck off, dickheads,' he winced, wiping the blood from his face. 'She would've beaten the shit out of any of you cocks too.'

We all kept on laughing before we picked up some Hungry Jacks, stumbled in a cab and went home to crash.

That was the routine I got myself into – working hard and playing hard. Saturday nights were wild, but for the rest of the week I was obsessively focused. As the year wore on, I inched closer and closer to my goal, and by the end I was so close I could almost taste it. In the Year 12 mid-year exams I finished 7th in the year, and in the trials before the final thing a few weeks later, I finished 3rd. At the award's presentation night, I won the Mathematics Prize, the Economics Prize, the Business Studies Prize and the 'Peter Willoughby Award for the Best All-Rounder,' and based on my trial exams, I was predicted a UAI of 99.75. I was stoked with how I was going, but I knew that I still had a lot of work to do to achieve my goal of coming first in the year and scoring a UAI of 100. It was English that was weighing me down – I had to improve my essay writing skills and get a better grasp of the prescribed readings. It was a subject that I didn't enjoy at all, and as I've already said, one that I found completely pointless. But at the same time, I knew it was probably the only thing standing between me and my goal. I genuinely believed I could get 100, and unlike at the start of Year 11, I was open about that belief.

'Damn Jimmy, you've been ripping up school lately,' someone would say. 'What UAI do you want to get?'

'100,' I'd reply deadpan.

'100?'

I'd nod.

'What do you need to get into your course?'

'For commerce/law at Sydney Uni you need 99.55.'

'Why not just aim for that?'

'I want 100.'

I remember somebody once asked me if I'd be happy if I got, say, 99.70 – good enough to get into commerce/law, but obviously below 100.

'Nah,' I said. 'I'd be pissed.'

They laughed. 'You're kidding?'

'No. I want to get 100.'

The final exams came and went. Everything went more or less according to plan except for English, which I wasn't entirely sure how I'd gone in. After the exams, Olivia and all my friends and pretty much everyone from our year headed up to Byron Bay for "Schoolies" – a week-long party where everyone drinks and takes drugs. I shacked up with the boys, and Olivia and her friends were staying in the same apartment complex too. We all had a great time, going out every night and partying until the early hours of the morning. I'd also taken to smoking weed, and would usually have a couple of cones in the afternoon before drinking 20 or 25 bourbon and colas at the club and eventually passing out beside Olivia (or on one occasion, down on the beach – and on another, in the gutter on the side of the street). Olivia kept saying that I was drinking too much and that I should try to cut down, but I figured I deserved it after working so hard. Discovering bud was nice too. *Sitting on the beach, watching the waves break in the distance and wash up on the shore of Byron Bay's beautiful Clarkes Beach while dragging on a joint with a few mates is surely one of the most relaxing things anyone can do,* I remember thinking. Olivia never smoked, but she said she didn't mind if I did so I figured what the hell. We only fucked once that week. With all the booze and the weed and the lack of sleep, my libido was pretty zapped.

The wait for our UAIs was long and nerve-racking. I desperately wanted to know my mark, and the days, while enjoyable spent chilling out by the beach and clubbing every weekend, seemed to last forever. I felt like my life had been put on hold. It was almost impossible to focus on anything else. I'd never wanted something so much in my entire life – not even to become the surfing world champion. I just kept thinking back to the University Seminar and that whole hall of people laughing at me and yelling out abuse. I wanted to prove them wrong with every fibre of my being, to get 100 and stick it to them all in the most emphatic way possible. The thought that my opportunity could be just around the corner filled me with glee. I'd picture myself doing it – getting 100 and jumping up and down, screaming off the balcony 'I got 100! I got 100! Hell yeah! Hell yeah!' I imagined sauntering through the door of Brent's post-results celebration party and saying 'I got 100. What are you motherfuckers going to say to me now?' I knew it would be one of the most satisfying moments of my life – being able to drink from the ethereal fountain of vindication. I craved it so badly. In the week before the marks were due to be released it was hard to sleep. I'd been waiting for this moment for two-and-a-half years and it was fucking hard to sleep.

Then the day finally arrived: January 4, 2007. The marks were to be posted online at 10:00 a.m. Before logging on, I prayed:

> *Dear God,*
> *Please let me get 100. Please . . .*
> *Amen*

With a thumping heart I typed in my username and password. With trembling fingers I clicked "log in." For a few long, torturous seconds the webpage was blank, the words "LOADING, LOADING" flashing on the screen. I was breathing heavily as sweat drenched my body, as an amalgamation of excitement, nervousness, fear and hope swirled around inside of me. Then finally, my mark appeared on the screen.

WARNING SIGNS

I was crushed. Completely and utterly crushed.

You didn't get 100, I lamented bitterly to myself. *You didn't reach your goal. You missed your opportunity to prove everybody wrong in the most affirmative way possible. You fucked up. You failed.*

I was shattered. I sat wallowing in disappointment before my parents both called me. Each conversation was fairly similar.

'So Jimmy . . . how did you go?'

'I got 99.60.'

'Wow! Jimmy that's fantastic!'

'No it's not.'

'What do you mean it's not?'

'It's shit. I wanted 100. It would've been the perfect way to prove everybody wrong.'

'But Jimmy you still proved everybody wrong! 99.60 is a great mark! That'll definitely be enough to get you into commerce/law at Sydney Uni.'

'But I didn't reach my goal. I screwed up English – totally mucked it up.'

'But you still got 99.60! How can you possibly be upset with that?'

'Because I didn't reach my goal. Because I blew my opportunity to stick it to everyone.'

My parents were flabbergasted. We discussed it for a while, but there was nothing they could say to ease my devastation. Eventually they had to get back to work, promising that we'd talk more about everything when they got home. We hung up the phone. A little while later, Olivia rang.

'Baby! Guess what! I got 97.00! I got into psychology at Sydney Uni!'

'That's great, Liv. Congratulations.'

'Thanks! How did you go?'

I told her my mark.

'Wow! Sweetie that is *so* good! You must feel incredible!'

'I feel shithouse. I didn't reach my goal. I missed my chance to really stick it to everyone.'

'Jimmy you can't be serious!'

'I am. It's not the mark I wanted. I fucked up. I failed.'

'What!' she exclaimed. 'Jimmy how can you possibly be so hard on yourself?'

'I'm not being hard on myself.'

'Of course you are!'

'No I'm not. I didn't reach my goal – so I failed.'

Just like my parents she was shocked as hell. She kept telling me how good my mark was, but I couldn't see it. In my head, I didn't reach my goal, so I'd failed. To me, it was that black and white – there were no shades of grey. Seeing that my feelings couldn't be changed, Olivia eventually let the matter drop.

'What time do you want to go to Brent's party tonight?' she sighed resignedly.

'I don't know if I'm going.'

'What? Come on, Jimmy. Everybody's going.'

'I'm not in the mood.'

'Jimmy . . . please?'

'Just go with the girls. Maybe I'll meet you there later.'

She tried to talk me into it but I really wasn't in the right headspace. We eventually hung up the phone and I was left to my misery.

Fucking hell, I thought. *Fuck, fuck, fuck, fuck, fuck. You really fucked this up. You really blew your chance to end high school on the perfect note and stick it to everybody.*

I just kept thinking back to the University Seminar and that whole auditorium of people laughing at me, and I felt so defeated for not achieving my vow. It didn't matter that I'd almost done it, that I'd still done well. In my books there were no moral victories or brownie points for getting close – you either succeeded or you failed. That's how it was when I was a surfer, and that's how I viewed my UAI result too.

I spent the day stewing before eventually dragging myself to Brent's party. When I got there, everyone was already wasted, either out of joyous celebration or overwhelming disappointment. Olivia was over the moon with her mark and was as drunk as I'd ever seen her, giggling and stumbling around as she danced with her friends. I started taking shots to numb my dejection, to temporarily silence that voice in my head telling me that I'd failed. Throughout the night I was inundated with praise and congratulations, with 'good on ya, Jimmy's and slaps on the back, but it all meant nothing. All I could think about was the 0.4% I'd missed out on until I passed out with the rest of the devastated in Brent's back garden.

Over the next few weeks, my self-perceived failure continued to weigh on me, filling me with a maddening dissatisfaction. It would drive me crazy – the imperfection, the fact that I hadn't achieved my goal. I couldn't let it go. And I couldn't shake that memory of everyone laughing at me at the University Seminar, of everyone yelling out abuse and calling me "Washed Up Wharton." All that anger still burned furiously inside me, and my desire for the ultimate vindication was as strong as ever.

English . . . fucking English, I thought. *If only you'd done well in that subject – then everything would be absolutely perfect. If only you could go back and re-sit that exam. If only you had a chance to rectify your failures . . .*

Another few weeks passed, and the nagging disappointment didn't abate.

You didn't reach your goal. You failed. You fucked up. You didn't prove everybody wrong in the purest way possible.

Finally, I couldn't take it any more.

You need to rectify this, I eventually concluded. *Somehow, some way, you need to rectify this. You need to make up for your shitty English mark by proving your worth in this field. The only way to stick it to everyone from this point forward is to conquer the "English World."*

I thought and thought about how I could do so, and eventually came up with an idea that I thought was a winner.

You could write a novel! If you could write a novel and get it published, then that would definitely make up for the fact that you screwed up your English exam. If you could get it published, then you sure as fuck would've proved that you can master any subject, and be exceptional in any field you wish to pursue. And what a spectacular way to stick it to everyone who laughed at you at the University Seminar and called you a washed up surfer! Imagine it – getting a UAI of 99.60 and then getting a novel published to make up for your shitty English mark! What an achievement that would be! It would be even better *than getting a UAI of 100!*

I started planning my novel straight away. I tried to think of something to write about – ideas that interested me, concepts that I'd like to read about (if I did read, that was – I hadn't touched a book since school, and I didn't intend on picking one up anytime soon either). When I really thought about it, the few novels that I'd actually enjoyed reading were ones where people had succeeded against all the odds, like *Angela's Ashes* by Frank McCourt or *Finding Fish* by Antwone Fisher. *So that's my theme,* I thought. *Now for a setting.* I thought about the books I'd read in the past and the kind of time periods and places that I liked. After a few minutes, *Of Mice and Men* by John Steinbeck – a novel I'd read in Year 9 and had, again unusually for me, enjoyed – came to mind. *America in the Great Depression of the 1930s? Sure, I could do that.* And then it hit me: *ah! I could write a novel about a boy growing up during the Great Depression who's really poor and destitute but somehow against all the odds he survives and makes a good life for himself! That's it! That's my story!* And just like that it all came together. Or in hindsight, all fell apart.

At around nine o'clock that night, my parents arrived home from work.

'Mum, Dad, check it out! You know what I'm going to do?'

'What, Jimmy?'

'I'm going to write a novel!'

They both frowned.

'A novel? *Really?*'

'Yeah!'

They were shocked.

'But . . . but why? You've never shown any interest in creative writing before.'

'If I could get it published then it would rectify my crappy English mark, and then I would've stuck it to everyone who called me "Washed Up Wharton" and laughed at me at the University Seminar.'

'Are you serious? Jimmy your school marks were great! There's nothing at all to rectify! And you already stuck it to everyone by getting 99.60!'

'But I still screwed up English and didn't get 100.'

We'd had this conversation before. They were both shaking their heads in disbelief.

'Jimmy . . . this is getting ridiculous,' Mum said. 'You need to get over the fact that you didn't get 100. You need to stop obsessing about the 0.4% you missed out on. It's not healthy.'

She paused for a moment.

'And this business about you writing a novel to prove your doubters wrong . . . I mean it's just *nuts.*'

We debated the matter for the next hour. It wasn't that they were trying to be unsupportive – rather, they just thought I was doing it for all the wrong reasons. But I was sure that my logic was flawless, and 100% confident that I could write a novel of publishable quality, even if I didn't read and knew sweet fuck all about writing or getting a book published. I didn't think it mattered. I knew I had a tireless work ethic and relentless determination, and in my mind, that was all I needed to do something successfully.

I spent the following day surfing the net and printing off information to read about the Great Depression before heading over to Liv's place at night. She'd been reading *Cosmo*, and wanted to try having sex in the "amazing butterfly" position. I stood in front of her as she lay down on the bed, lifted her legs onto my shoulders. Hands under her hips, I held her bottom as we thrust with passion, Liv clutching my wrists, her nails digging into my flesh as she loudly climaxed. A few minutes later I did the same, and just after I'd done so, I told her that I was going to write a novel.

'Really? Why?' she asked.

I told her why and about the idea for the novel itself. Olivia's response was the same as my parents'.

'Your school marks were so good, though! There's not a single person that you didn't prove wrong!'

'I didn't get 100. I fucked up English.'

That was our first debate, and just like my parents, she thought I was obsessing. She thought I needed to let it go. She thought the idea behind me writing a novel was just plain crazy. But I couldn't be convinced, and eventually, we agreed to disagree. Then came the second part of the discussion.

'But Jimmy . . . you writing a novel . . . it's just so . . . so *random*.'

I shrugged.

'Yeah, I know. But I still want to do it.'

'What if you don't like it? You've never shown any interest in writing before.'

'I'll enjoy the challenge of trying to get a book published.'

She looked at me seriously.

'Jimmy . . . you know that getting a book published is like . . . *really* hard. Right?'

I frowned.

'Are you saying you don't think I can do it?'

'No, I'm not saying that. I just hope you realise how difficult it's going to be.'

I shrugged.

'Yeah, but I'm a hard worker. I'll be OK.'

Our eyes met before Olivia quickly looked away.

'When do you plan on writing it?' she asked.

'In my free time.'

'What free time? Uni's about to start.'

'I can write a book and go to uni too.'

Liv raised her eyebrows.

'You're going to study commerce/law full-time, work as a high school tutor part-time, spend time socialising with me and your friends, *and* write a novel?'

'Yeah.'

'Don't you think that'll be too much?'

I shook my head.

'No. I think I'll be able to handle it.'

Olivia looked away.

'How long do you think it will take?' she asked.

I thought about it.

'Well . . . it's February now . . . I'll probably do a month of research . . . spend a year writing and editing it . . . so it will probably be done around April of next year.'

'Really? Just over a year?'

'Yep.'

'That quick, huh?'

'Sure. I don't think it'll take too long. I'll spend the whole summer holidays working on it too.'

Liv shrugged sceptically. 'I guess we'll see.'

I leapt straight into it. After spending a week reading a bit about the Great Depression and 1930s America, I decided to start writing:

Page 1, Paragraph 1:

There it is again – that black cloud. The huge, long, dark black cloud. The same one that has been hanging over my head, my city and my country for the entirety of this decade. I stare up at it with hopeful eyes, but it just remains motionless, like an ancient statue lying in its grave. My instincts tell me that this dark cloud is ominous of the future, that its presence is to establish this hardship for a long time to come. When I was younger, I remember my father telling me that the weather is God's way of foreshadowing future conditions, sort of like the way a heated argument between friends foreshadows violence and assault. I don't know what scares me most about this cloud – its piercing blackness or its static equilibrium. Whichever, I really hope my father was wrong. I'm sceptical as to whether I can psychologically handle any more of this persevered suffering.

I didn't really know if it was good or not, but it wasn't like I gave it too much thought: *the storyline's interesting*, I'd convinced myself, *so I'm sure if I just whack it all on paper and edit it a bit then it'll be a great read and be ready for publication.* So I trucked along with the first chapter, writing about how a young boy and his parents live in a Manhattan mansion and have it all during the "Roaring Twenties" before losing everything in the stock market crash of 1929 that sparked the Great Depression. The boy's father gets fired from his job as a stockbroker, and for lack of available jobs is forced to travel for work until he finds some as a farmer in Tuskeegee, Alabama. A couple of years later, poverty forces the 13 year old boy to quit school and start working on the farm too.

Before I'd first put pen to paper, I'd scribbled down a plot outline:

- After working for a while, the boy's father contracts prostate cancer and dies a slow and painful death. The boy and his mother then face the prospect of having to pay the medical bills on top of the standard food, rent and utility expenses. After being threatened with eviction, to the boy's horror his mother starts working as a prostitute to help support them.
- Even so they get evicted and are forced to live in a shantytown. The boy's mum keeps working as a prostitute but eventually reaches the end of her tether and kills herself. The boy – horribly upset – works terribly at the farm and gets the sack.

- The boy then considers ending his life too. He stands on a bridge, contemplating jumping before a black girl called Nicola – who also lives at the shantytown – talks him down.

- After a few days of sleeping and thinking, the boy then vows to turn his life around. His first step is to find work. During his search he spends his evenings with Nicola. They grow close.

- The protagonist finally finds a job as a construction worker about 30 miles away. Despite being of different races, he's able to convince Nicola to leave the shantytown with him so that they can start a new life together. But when they arrive at his new job, he's immediately beaten for showing up with a black girl. Nicola is told to 'either leave or be killed.' Terrified, she runs away.

- As soon as he's finished his shift he searches the city for her but can't find her anywhere. Then all of a sudden, he hears screaming. Moments later the town is in chaos – a tornado has hit. He runs frantically for cover and ends up in a house that has already been destroyed. Another person soon enters, and it turns out to be Nicola. They stare at each other, hug, kiss for the first time. Then, amidst the commotion and pandemonium, they strip off each other's clothes and make love.

- The story then ends with them holding each other, naked, and thinking that no matter what befalls them, they'll be able to overcome it, because they are strong, courageous and have each other. Regardless of the Great Depression and the racism and everything else, so long as they are strong, courageous and have each other, they believe that everything will work out and that they'll go on to live happily ever after.

Despite not being anything of a reader and not showing the outline to anyone, I was convinced it was a cracker of a plot: *a protagonist who never gives up and who falls in love with a beautiful girl? What's there not to like?* I wasn't really fussed about writing style or structure or anything like that – I figured all you needed was a good plot and interesting characters and then you'd be fine.

And contrary to everyone's assumptions, I was really enjoying writing it. I loved the creative aspect of it – being able to put my ideas on a page and see them come to life. Also, it was a story that I obviously found interesting, unlike an English essay where I was forced to write about topics that I really didn't care about. What's more, when word spread that I was writing a novel, everyone's lack of belief in me came roaring back. *"You can't do it,"* some said. *"You'll never finish it."* Others: *"you're a maths person – you can't write."* *"Stick to commerce/law."* *"It'll never get published."* *"You'd be a terrible writer."* They were the same people who doubted me in school, and it got me even more fired up to write a quality novel and get it published. I'd picture myself walking into Dymocks or Borders and smiling proudly at my book resting on the shelves, or speaking about it on TV shows or on the radio. I'd fantasise about hosting book signings, autographing copy after copy for all my readers. I'd imagine how good it would feel, conquering my final demon. *A published author! That would be amazing! What a way to stick it to everyone who's ever doubted you!* I got so excited, so wrapped up in it. I was like a pig in shit.

AVERAGE MAN ON CAMPUS

Uni started off with a bang in March of 2007. Before we'd even set foot in a lecture theatre, we had five straight days of solid partying during orientation week. Olivia and all my mates were also going to Sydney Uni, so I was lucky enough to share the experience with the people I was closest with. Every night we were out on the piss, and I worked out that over the course of the week, I'd had three bottles of bourbon and a case of beer. On Monday, we went to hear Sneaky Sound System play at Manning Bar. I remember jumping up and down to *UFO* with Olivia and the boys and a few random chicks they'd picked up and thinking about how exciting the uni nightlife was and how awesome the year ahead would be. After Sneaky had finished at eleven, we bar-hopped for a few hours before heading home at three (Corey and Sean with girls, and me, of course, with Olivia). I was trashed and passed out in the taxi, and when we got back to my place, Liv and the cabbie had to carry me inside. I was too heavy to get up the stairs to my room, so they plonked me down on the living room couch where I lay until morning.

The next three nights were standard party nights. A few of our friends from school were boarding on campus at residential colleges, so on Tuesday, Wednesday and Thursday we went to their parties. I was blind for all three. The other boys were smashed too but not to the extent that I was, and Olivia only had a few drinks each night. Then on Friday, it was Sean's turn to be the mess. It was his 18th birthday, so the boys and I thought we'd take him out for a big night where he could use his real ID for the first time. We started at a shitty run-down pub in the city where we all got wasted and shot the shit.

'What's your favourite position?' Sean asked.

'Doggy. Definitely doggy,' said Chris.

'Standard being on the bottom,' Corey slurred. 'I'm a lazy fucker in the bedroom.'

We all laughed.

'I don't know what it's called or anything,' started Brent, 'but doing it when you're both kneeling down. Fuck that's good.'

'What about you, Jimmy?'

'Missionary position.'

Sean laughed. 'You're so boring, man.'

I shrugged.

'Seriously, you've been with Liv for two years and you're telling us that the best sex you've ever had was in the *missionary* position?'

'Yep. Standard missionary, boys. Nothing better.'

'You're so boring, man,' Sean repeated.

'What about you, Steve?' Brent jeered.

'Come on, man,' I interjected. 'You know he's saving himself for his first love.'

The boys all laughed. 'Aww, Steeeve, that's so sweeeet!' they teased. Steve laughed it up. We all knew it didn't bother him. Still, having had the same philosophy myself, I felt the need to defend him.

'Go easy on him, boys. I reckon that's cool, saving your first time for a chick you actually care about.'

'Of course you do, Jimmy,' Brent said. 'You and Liv are on your way to the bloody altar!'

I laughed, knowing it was true.

'Hey let me ask you something, Jimmy,' Corey began. 'Say you got Liv pregnant – what would you do?'

I answered straight away.

'Keep it.'

His eyebrows jumped.

'You serious?'

'Absolutely.'

'You wouldn't get an abortion?'

'I'm not going to murder it!'

'You're not murdering it. It's just a foetus.'

It was the classic "is getting an abortion right or wrong?" debate. Is it murder? Is it not? Who knows? Personally, I thought of it as murder. If you're pregnant, you're pregnant. There's a kid inside of you. A living baby. In my and Olivia's case, a product of our unbridled love. How could we possibly get an abortion? But I hated those kind of debates where everyone judges everybody else and it turns into an argument, so I just stuck to my original answer and hoped there'd soon be a change of subject.

'Yeah, man. No way I'd be cool with Liv getting an abortion.'

Corey shrugged.

'What about you boys?'

'Abortion – no doubt,' said Brent.

'Ditto,' agreed Sean.

'I'm with Jimmy,' Chris slurred. 'I don't think I'd be down with an abortion. Maybe adoption.'

'Would you get it adopted, Jimmy?'

I shook my head.

'Nah, man. I understand why people do it, but I'd never be able to do it myself.'

'What about you, Corey?' Steve asked.

'I'm not sure,' he said thoughtfully. 'I've seriously got no idea.'

We drank for another couple of hours and then took a cab to the Cross. Being a boys' night and Sean's 18th, we decided to go to a strip joint called Bada Bing. We stumbled up the stairs and then sat lethargically around the small circular platform dance floor where the girls did their thing. They rubbed their tits, pushed them together, spread their legs, played with their G-bangers and flashed us their cunts as we drank beers and smoked and watched on drunkenly. Eager to get Sean a private show, we slipped a blonde girl with big tits $120 and were taken to a secluded room the size of your average living room. We sat against the wall on either side of Sean, still smoking and drinking as we waited for the magic to happen.

'Right,' the stripper said routinely. 'Who's the birthday boy?'

'I am,' Sean slurred. He was hammered.

'All right then.'

The music was pumping, some house shit. About two feet away from Sean, the stripper began to circle her hips as she removed her top and flung it across the room. She licked her fingertips, rubbed her tits, turned around, hips still circling as she slipped off her skirt. Slowly tip-toeing closer towards him, she shook her ass only inches from his face. She slapped each bare cheek, hard, then bent all the way forwards, blew him a kiss between her straight spread legs. She moved towards him, sat on his lap, swirled her hips to the music, rubbed his hands all over her tits.

'Yeah, Sean! Get in there, matey!' we cheered drunkenly. Sean was so fucked his eyes were barely open, but he had a slight smile on his face so I knew he was enjoying himself.

The stripper slid off him, twirled around, danced slowly, just out of reach. She stretched her leg beside him, knelt forwards, and starting at her ankle, ran a finger slowly up her leg before pulling her thong to one side and flashing her pussy to a few rowdy cheers. Her leg then dropped, and she ran her thumbs from the sides of her breasts down to her waist, hooking them inside her G before slowly removing it while circling her hips to even louder cheers. Completely naked, she straddled Sean, undulated her hips, held his head between her breasts before lithely arching backwards, balancing on her hands and the balls of her feet. Her legs were spread, muff exposed, and Sean, drunk as he was, reached out and stroked her pussy.

'Hey!' she warned. 'No touching.'

But instead of stopping, Sean, so blind he probably didn't hear her, decided to shove two fingers up her cunt.

'Hey!' she yelled, leaping to her feet. 'I said no touching!'

She quickly grabbed her clothes and stormed out of the room.

'Sean – what the fuck was that?' Brent asked loudly.

Sean just laughed. So did Chris. The rest of us just sat there, not quite sure what to do.

A few seconds later a bouncer stormed in and grabbed Sean by the collar.

'Get the fuck out of here,' he growled. 'And the rest o' youse, too – piss off.'

We quickly left. Outside, Sean started laughing, and the rest of us laughed too. We finished the beers we'd snuck out of Bada Bing before Sean started hurling in an alley. We decided to call it a night and take a cab back to Sean's place to crash. After some more puking in the cab and the consequential $100 fine, we stumbled through the door and within ten minutes had all passed out in his living room.

I was looking forward to starting classes, from the point of view of being eager to get my investment banker, management consultant or lawyer career off to a start so that in five years' time I could start pulling in the big bucks, just like my parents did. I was taking Foundations of Law, Introductory

Accounting, Introductory Microeconomics and Introductory Statistics, which Olivia was also taking as part of her psychology degree. It was exciting, walking through gorgeous Victoria Park in front of Sydney Uni's famous sandstone building, past nine story Fisher Library and down lively Eastern Avenue where students would be strolling to classes, spruikers would be encouraging you to sign up to clubs and you'd be getting handed fluoro-coloured paper telling you to vote for so-and-so in the upcoming student election. My first class was Foundations of Law, which turned out to be a general lecture about the degree itself. We were told what subjects we could choose from over the five year duration of our degree, and what career options we'd open ourselves up to at the end of it. The marking system was also explained to us: a "Fail" consisted of a mark less than 50%, a "Pass" was between 50% and 64%, a "Credit" was between 65% and 74%, and a "Distinction" was between 75% and 84%. The highest grade was a "High Distinction," which equated to a mark of 85% or greater.

'Now I know that all of you were accustomed to coming first in high school,' the lecturer said, 'but this is Sydney Law School, which has the highest entry requirement of any law school and practically any other course in the country. So now, you're competing against the cream of the crop. There are nearly 300 of you, and not all of you can come first. For most of you, you'll have to adjust to being just one of the pack, with an average mark in the vicinity of 75%.'

That won't happen to me, I remember thinking. With my obsession to be the best, there was no way I could ever settle for being just "one of the pack." It went against every fibre of my being. So right then and there I set myself the goal of getting a High Distinction average across all of my subjects.

I was convinced that I could do it, but I was so wrapped up in my novel that over the course of the 13 week semester, my degree managed to get pushed to the side. The urge to rectify my high school English mark and shut all the naysayers up was strong enough to trump everything else. So throughout the semester, I found myself missing lectures and tutorials to write. I kept telling myself that I'd catch up, but the weeks sped along and the workload mounted, and before I knew it, the end of semester exams were upon me. I pulled all-nighters and lived off Red Bull for their duration trying to cram, but I'd fallen too far behind, and had to resort to sitting them badly prepared on hardly any sleep. When I received my marks in the mid-year break, I was extremely disappointed.

Introductory Microeconomics:	79 (Distinction)
Introductory Accounting:	75 (Distinction)
Introductory Statistics:	74 (Credit)
Foundations of Law:	67 (Credit)

Fucking hell, I sighed when I saw them. *Fuck me dead. You got nowhere near your goal. And not only that, but your marks would be below average when compared with other law students'. That's ridiculous. That's hopeless. You fucked up this semester. You failed.*

At that moment when I was stewing in frustrated dejection, Olivia called me.

'Hey,' I answered dryly.

'Baby! Guess what! I topped Intro Psychology! I got 89%! And I got over 80 in my other subjects too!'

'Wow, that's amazing, Liv. Good on you.'

'Thanks! I'm so excited! Come over and we'll go to dinner.'

'Yeah, all right.'

'I'm sorry – I forgot to ask how you went.'

I told her. She sensed my despondency.

'Jimmy . . . that's still really good considering all the writing you've been doing. You didn't exactly study that hard . . .'

'It's still fucked,' I said angrily. 'I got nowhere near my goal.'

'Jimmy . . . you're going to be fine. You'll do better next time.'

I didn't say anything.

'Do you not feel like going out to dinner tonight?' she asked.

'It's fine. You did so well. We should celebrate.'

'Are you sure?'

'Yeah. Where do you want to go?'

'How about Garfish? We can eat barramundi and get a bottle of champagne. Maybe even a few oysters, too.'

'Sounds good.'

'Great. Swing by mine in an hour?'

'Yeah.'

88

There was a moment of silence on the other end.

'Are you sure you're OK to go out, though?' she asked. 'We can always do it another night.'

'It's fine – we should celebrate. I'll be over in an hour.'

'Are you sure you're sure?'

'Yes.'

'OK. I'll see you then.'

We said our goodbyes and hung up. Truth be told, I really wasn't in the mood to go out, and would've rather just been by myself – or gone somewhere and gotten drunk. But I knew Olivia was really happy about her marks, and I didn't want to ruin her big day by being a shit boyfriend, so I took a shower, put on a nice collared shirt and a new pair of jeans and met her at her place. I rang the doorbell and she answered looking beautiful, wearing a cream strapless dress and white high heels. We kissed for a few seconds before walking from her house to the beach and then crossing the road to The Corso, where couples and groups ate on either side of us or hopped from bar to bar. On the way to Garfish, a lady handed me a business card – Stephanie Jones, male casting agent at Flowtop Modelling – and asked me to give her a call. Olivia teased me about it for the rest of the night, calling me a "pretty boy" and a "princess" and what not, but I must admit that it did feel nice and gave me a much-needed boost of confidence.

At dinner, we both ordered the wood-roasted shellfish bouillabaisse with tomato and saffron and shared a half-dozen oysters. I'd brought a bottle of champagne from home – *Mumm Rosé* – and Liv had a glass and I had four. It was a nice meal, and obviously I always loved spending time with Olivia, but I'd be lying if I said that throughout the meal I wasn't bothered by my marks. It gnawed at me the entire time.

Those marks are way below your potential. They're terrible. They're a disgrace. They're an embarrassment to someone of your ability. You wanted to get an average of 85% and you only got 73.75%? That's not even close. That's fucking pathetic.

I tried my best to forget about it and just be wholly in the moment with Liv, but I must've seemed preoccupied because not long after we'd finished eating, she leaned across the table and kissed me. I was caught off guard.

'What?' I said.

'It was really sweet of you to come out and celebrate with me tonight,' she said appreciatively. 'I know you're upset about your marks and stuff.'

I shrugged. 'It was nothing.'

'No, it was sweet.'

I shrugged again.

'I'd tell you how well I think you did considering you didn't study that much, but you don't want to hear that, do you?'

I shook my head. The way I saw it, it made no difference *why* I got such terrible marks. *They are what they are,* I thought, *and there are no excuses. Shit marks are shit marks and that's all there is to it.*

Liv sighed. 'Is there anything I can do to cheer you up?'

'Not really,' I said. Then after a few seconds I added, 'well, it would be nice if you could play me a piece on the harp when we get back to your place. You know how much I like that.'

She smiled. 'Of course.'

We paid the bill and went back to Liv's house. She kicked off her heels and played Bach's *Jesu Joy of Man's Desiring*. It was soothing, listening to the melody, the harmonious euphony, watching Liv's fingers dance along the strings. I had another glass of champagne, and as I continued listening to her, I found myself mellowing, and better able to take stock of my situation.

OK, I said to myself. *You fucked up this semester. You failed. This is what failure feels like, and it feels pretty fucking bad. You never want to feel this ever again. Never, ever again. So next semester, you need to work harder. You need to work harder so that you can get your writing done and still have time to study for your exams and get good marks. If you work harder, you won't feel this pain ever again. If you work harder, you'll end up getting your High Distinction average and writing a great novel of publishable quality and then everything will be fine. It really is that simple. Just work harder.*

And then I felt better. Good, even. Determining a plan of action usually does that for me.

When Liv had finished her piece, she hopped off the stool and sat down on the couch beside me. We kissed, fell into each other's arms, tumbled to the floor. We sipped champagne from each other's bellybuttons, and Liv lathered some on my prick and sucked it before we had sex in the missionary position.

NAMES WE'D THOUGHT OF WERE JIMMY JUNIOR AND RACHAEL

I started the second semester with two goals in mind. First, I wanted to achieve a High Distinction average across all of my subjects. Second, I wanted to finish the first draft of my novel. These were two goals that I thought were entirely achievable, provided that I worked hard. And for the first two-thirds of the semester, everything went according to plan. I was doing it, studying and writing seven or eight hours a day, and it was paying off – I'd gotten High Distinctions in my mid-semester exams and was about two-thirds of the way through the first draft of my novel and on track to have it completed by the end of the semester. And as a result, I felt totally vindicated.

See, I told myself, *this is all you have to do – just work hard, every day, and you'll achieve your goals. It really is that simple. Whenever you don't achieve your goals, it's because you're slacking off. And under any circumstance, that is inexcusable.*

Such was my thought process, and up until that point in my life it had served me well. Throughout all the years I'd been surfing and in the couple of years I'd been studying hard, nothing external had ever happened to distract me. Life outside of the sea and the classroom had always been nurturing, so when it came to achieving my goals, it was always just a matter of working hard. I never really had much else to worry about besides that.

But in October, Liv missed her period. Then in the morning she started getting sick. We were aghast.

'J-Jimmy . . . I th-think I'm pregnant,' she wept.

'No . . .' I stressed. 'No, baby, that can't be . . . you're on the pill.'

'You know it doesn't always work . . .'

I pulled at my hair. 'Fucking hell.'

'What . . . what're we going to do?'

'I don't know, Liv.'

We were holding each other tightly. She buried her head in my chest, crying loudly. I felt utterly helpless. All I could do was hold her on the couch, stroking her thin brown hair.

'We'll be OK, baby,' I kept repeating. 'We'll be OK.'

For the next hour we just stayed there, silent and motionless as we stewed in terror. Eventually, Olivia spoke.

'We should go to the doctor's . . . find out for sure.'

So we went. Having no appointment, we had to wait over an hour to see Olivia's GP. We initially tried to read those trashy lifestyle magazines, but reading about how the Beckhams bought a new house in L.A. or why Britney Spears shaved her head failed to distract us from our predicament, so after a while we gave up and just sat there, anxiously holding hands. Finally, Olivia was called. We went in together.

She told Dr Shawl about the symptoms she'd been feeling.

'Do you use a condom?'

'No,' Liv said. 'But I'm on the pill as you know, and I've never missed it.'

'It's still safer to use a condom too,' said the doctor. Olivia and I were both silent. Dr Shawl wrote a few things down in Liv's file before filling out a form and handing it to her.

'OK, here's how it works from here,' she began. 'You need to do a blood test, which you can do tomorrow morning at Douglas Hanly Moir across the road. Fast for 12 hours before you take it. They'll send me the results later that day, so make an appointment to see me tomorrow evening. By then, we'll know if you're pregnant or not.'

We nodded, said our thanks and left.

We didn't speak on the way home. I was imprisoned in a cell of worry. *I'm not ready to become a father,* I thought. *We're only 18! How the fuck are we supposed to raise a child?* I was petrified. When I pulled up in front of my house I finally looked over at Olivia, and saw that there were tears streaming down her cheeks. I held her hand, stroking it softly. We stayed in the car but didn't say a word.

When my parents arrived home together at around half-past-eight, we finally went inside.

'Where have you two been?' Dad asked. 'At uni all day?'

'Yeah,' I lied.

'Studying for your statistics exam tomorrow, huh?'

'Fucking hell,' I muttered.

'What'd you say, Jimmy?'

'Nothing, Dad.'

'Either of you hungry?' Mum asked. 'I'm going to make spaghetti.'

Liv had to fast for her blood test in the morning, and I didn't think I could keep anything down.

'We're fine thanks, Mum.'

'That busy, huh?'

'Yeah.'

We went to my room and closed the door.

'Liv,' I said sternly. 'We've got to forget about this shit tonight. We've got to study for tomorrow's exam. It's worth 30%.'

'Are you serious?' she shrieked. 'How can you study at a time like this?'

'Keep your voice down!' I hissed. 'Liv, this semester's going really well for me so far. I don't want to screw it up now.'

'I'm fucking pregnant, Jimmy! I don't give a fuck about the exam right now!' She collapsed on the bed and burst into tears. I fell down beside her, hugged her tightly.

'Liv, baby . . . we don't know if you're pregnant yet,' I whispered, stroking her hair. 'You might not be. All I'm saying is that we should try to forget about it tonight – study for our exam. After the exam we'll know for sure, and then we can take it from there. OK?'

'I c-can't study now, Jimmy,' she sobbed. 'What if I'm pregnant? Seriously . . . what if I'm pregnant? What the hell are we going to do?'

'We'll work it out, baby . . . I promise . . . we'll work it out.'

Olivia continued crying, and after a while, I started crying too. The truth was that I had no idea how we were going to manage. I just couldn't picture us as parents. *For fuck's sake!* I fretted. *How can we go to uni and take care of a kid at the same time? How can I write a novel and take care of a kid at the same time? What the fuck are our parents going to say?* I was scared as hell.

When we'd finally stopped crying, I checked the clock. It was already 9:15, and we still hadn't moved from the bed.

'Olivia we've got to start studying,' I said, standing up. 'We still have the whole course to review.'

She didn't say anything, didn't do anything except lie there with her head buried in her hands. I softly pulled them away. Her eyes were bloodshot, cheeks dripping with tears.

'Come on, baby,' I whispered. 'We've got to start studying. I'll go make you a cup of coffee and then we'll start, OK?'

She eventually nodded. I kissed her forehead and went to the kitchen.

'You two OK?' Mum asked. 'I heard yelling before.'

'We're fine, Mum.' She obviously couldn't make out what we were saying.

'Would you mind making Liv a cup of coffee, though?'

'Coffee? At this hour?'

'We've got a long night ahead of us.'

'Really?' Mum asked as she turned on the kettle. 'You've been so well prepared this semester – I didn't think you'd need any all-nighters.'

I sighed. I really felt like shit.

'Tonight's an exception.'

I opened the fridge, rummaged around for a can of Red Bull before eventually finding one and downing it quickly. I then took an extra Red Bull and the coffee back to my room.

By then, Olivia had unpacked her books from her bag and was shuffling through her notes. Her eyes were lacquered, cheeks still wet. I gave her the cup of coffee.

'Everything will be OK,' I tried to reassure her. 'We'll worry about it tomorrow – after the exam.'

Olivia took the cup of coffee but didn't say anything.

She sat with the textbook at my desk, and I tried to read the lecture slides propped up on my bed. That had become my regular study routine the day before an exam: read over all the lecture slides, then the relevant parts from the textbook, and then read over the tutorial questions and answers. Since I'd been busy with the pregnancy fiasco for most of the day, I hadn't had a chance to start studying until then. I knew I had a lot of work to do, so I tried my damnedest to tune out of what was going on around me and just focus on sampling distributions and regression modelling. But I was finding it hard as hell to concentrate.

We're only 18! I kept panicking. *How the fuck are we supposed to raise a baby right now?*

And whenever I'd catch myself getting distracted like that, I'd get angry with myself.

Get a fucking grip! You don't even know if Liv's pregnant yet. Focus on your exam tomorrow, then deal with this shit.

But I just couldn't do it. And the more I struggled, the angrier I became.

Fucking hell! You've done so well all semester, and now you're going to fuck it all up by getting worried over something that may not even be an issue? Focus, you fucking pussy, focus! Revise this material, get some sleep, sit the exam, and then worry about everything else after that.

At 10:30, Liv and I took a break, deciding to watch some *Friends*.

'How's the studying going?' I asked.

'How do you think?' she snapped.

'Sorry.'

She looked away dismissively.

'Look . . . do you want to talk about it?' I asked, secretly hoping she wouldn't want to so that we could study.

She sighed deeply.

'No, you're right – we need to study for the exam. We'll worry about everything else after that.'

'Are you sure?'

'Yes.'

'OK,' I said, relieved.

We watched two episodes and then resumed studying. By 12:30 in the morning, I'd finally finished reading through the lecture slides. Before getting stuck into the textbook, I sculled another Red Bull.

'Sweetie, you want another cup of coffee?' I asked.

'Yeah, thanks.'

I made it for her and opened the textbook. It must've taken me an hour to read the relevant bits in the first chapter, which wouldn't have amounted to more than four or five pages. *Work, for fuck's sake, work!* I yelled in my head. *You're getting distracted about shit that isn't even a reality yet! You need to study now, you fucking idiot!* By three o'clock I'd gotten through another couple of chapters, at which point Liv said she couldn't study any more and wanted to go to sleep. I embraced her tightly.

'We're going to get through this, baby,' I whispered. 'And I'll be there with you, every step of the way. I promise.' She hugged me back and I kissed her forehead.

'I love you,' I whispered.

'I love you too.'

She crawled into bed and tightly clutched the covers. After guzzling a third Red Bull, I went into the spare room to continue studying.

At 5:00 a.m. I was done with the textbook, but I had to get up at seven and the exam was at nine and I was tired as hell, so I dejectedly decided to give the tutorial problems a miss.

Like I did every night before going to bed, I prayed:

Dear God,

Thank-you for blessing me with food, shelter, companionship, talents and the opportunity to pursue my dreams.

I pray for everybody – particularly those less fortunate than myself – and I pray that you take care of them, just as well as you take care of me.

I paused for a few seconds, gritting my teeth, desperately trying to replace the images of a baby bump exploding from Liv's thin belly, the little thing crying while we'd be trying to study or make love, and both of us always drained and run-down struggling to support it.

And I pray that Liv's not pregnant. I pray that she's not pregnant and that life can just stay the way it is.

Amen.

When I opened the door to my room, I realised that Olivia was still awake. She was just lying on her back, staring up at the ceiling.

'Liv,' I whispered. 'You been awake all this time?'

She nodded.

'Are you sure you don't want to talk?'

There was a long, long pause.

'I just . . . I just don't know . . . what we're going to do if . . .'

'I know, baby, I know,' I said, crawling into bed beside her. 'But we'll work it out.'

Another long, long pause.

'Let's just try to get some sleep,' I suggested. 'We've got to be up soon.'

Liv nodded. She turned to face me and we held each other tightly. I could feel her shaking. We both sweated abundantly.

At six o'clock, we finally nodded off. At 6:45 my alarm started blaring.

'Shit,' I groaned. I reached over and smacked the snooze. My alarm went off again at 6:55.

'Fucking hell.' I switched it off, then noticed Olivia had slept right through it.

'Liv,' I said reluctantly. 'Liv . . .' I shook her gently.

'What is it, Jimmy?' she murmured.

'Liv it's five-to-seven – we've got to get up, baby.'

She groaned and rolled out of bed. We quickly got dressed, packed our bags and got in the car. As soon as I stuck the key in the ignition and gave it a turn, my head lolled back on the headrest. I shut my eyes for a second.

'Hey,' Liv said. 'Are you OK to drive? You've hardly slept.'

I rubbed my eyes.

'Yeah. I'm fine.'

'Are you sure?'

'Yeah.'

We drove to uni. Kyle and Jackie O were doing the morning show on the radio. Some woman had rung up wanting to know if they thought it was a good idea for her to leave her husband and her five- and seven year old children because even though she *"loved her family"* and they were a *"happy household," "apparently when kids become teens they can become a real handful and ruin a family."* They said that leaving her family was stupid before opening the phone lines to see what the public thought, and pretty much everyone else agreed. It was decent to listen to. Maybe it took our minds off our own problem for a bit. Either way, we hardly talked.

When we got to uni, we parked the car, walked slowly to our exam room and sat down to wait with the other students. I was restless, wanting nothing more than to just get the exam over and done with so that I could get Olivia to Douglas Hanly Moir to do her blood test and find out whether or not we'd soon be parents. I looked at her beside me. Her eyes were closed, and her head leaned lethargically back against the wall behind her. We were both exhausted.

Before long, the instructor called us in and we all sat down. After he told us that it was a 'one hour exam,' that we could 'leave before the hour was up but not in the final ten minutes,' and that 'as soon as we were told to stop writing, we had to stop, otherwise our papers would not be graded,' we were allowed to start. The first few questions were multiple choice, and I thought I answered them decently. Then there were a few longer ones that required working out. I read the first question, but I was too stressed to properly process it. *What if Liv's pregnant, what if Liv's pregnant?* My heartbeat sped up and I started sweating. *What if Liv's pregnant, what if Liv's pregnant?* And then I caught myself panicking. *Focus! You have forty minutes left in this exam – focus on the exam for the next forty minutes and then worry about the baby!* I read the question again and did my best to answer it. I had to read the next couple a few times each to make sense of them, but I thought they went all right too. Yet as the exam continued, my concentration deteriorated. *What if Liv's pregnant? How am I going to provide for the baby? Will Mum and Dad help me? I think they probably will, but they're going to be pretty fucking upset that I got Olivia knocked up in the first place. What about the sex? Is it going to be a boy or a girl?* I thought back to the time Liv and I once hypothesised about future baby names for when we eventually did have kids. If we had a son, I wanted to call him Jimmy Junior, which Liv said she'd agree to if we called our girl baby Rachael after her late grandmother.

Remembering this exchange made everything seem even realer.

Who will Jimmy Junior or Rachael look like more – Liv or me? Will Jimmy Junior or Rachael like surfing? Will Jimmy Junior or Rachael like the harp? What school will Jimmy Junior or Rachael go to? The questions kept assailing me until I realised there were only ten minutes left in the exam and I still had to answer three five mark questions. I exasperatedly rushed through the first one but knew my answer was crap. Then I read the next question about the Poisson Distribution. My mind was drawing blanks. *What the fuck is the Poisson Distribution?* I remembered reading about it the previous night, but I couldn't for the life of me recall what it was.

'You have five minutes left,' the instructor announced.

With three minutes to go I was finally able to remember and started scribbling something down, but I was forced to stop mid-working when the instructor announced 'time's up!' I didn't even get to attempt the last question.

'Fucking hell!' I swore under my breath. 'Fuck me dead! I'd be lucky to get 65% on that fucking exam!' I was furious. I quickly packed up my things and stormed out of the room, waited for Olivia outside. When she came out a minute or so later I started ranting.

'I totally fucked that exam! I couldn't concentrate during the whole fucking thing! Seriously, what the fuck is wrong with me that I can't even concentrate during an exam that's worth thirty-fucking-percent?'

'Jimmy I don't care about the fucking exam!' Liv exploded. Everyone around us was staring, but neither of us gave a shit. 'Let's just go and do my fucking blood test and get something to eat.'

I paused for a moment, feeling guilty.

'I'm sorry, sweetie,' I finally said. 'I'll stop talking about the exam. We'll get your blood test done and then get something to eat. No problem.'

We walked to the car then drove straight to Douglas Hanly Moir in Manly. We had to wait ten minutes when we got there, once again attempting to read tacky magazines before Liv was called in. When she was done we drove a couple of minutes to The Corso.

'What do you want to eat?' I asked.

'Who cares,' she muttered.

I was trying to be calm.

'All right,' I said. 'How about we go to Wood and Stone Wood Fired Pizza? They have a pizza that has five different types of cheese for its topping. What do you say?'

'Fine.'

We ordered a pizza each and quickly wolfed it down. Olivia had been fasting and hadn't eaten since the previous day's lunch, and come to think of it, I hadn't either.

'What time's your appointment with Dr Shawl tonight?'

'Eight o'clock.' I couldn't believe it. In eight hours' time, we'd know if we were going to be parents or not. I was crippled with anxiety. I knew Liv was too. We were hardly talking.

'What do you want to do now?' I asked.

'Sleep,' she muttered. 'My place.'

We went back to Liv's house, crawled into bed and set the alarm for half-past-seven. We stayed on separate sides, not even touching, trying to sleep and dozing off here and there before the alarm started beeping incessantly.

My heart instantly started racing. I looked over at Olivia and she burst into tears. We hugged each other tightly, sobbed, held back further tears before throwing on some clothes and walking shakily to the car.

'Sure you're not too tired to drive?' Liv asked.

I was still exhausted, but I sure as hell couldn't be bothered walking.

'I'm fine.'

We drove, parked, went inside, waited.

'Olivia?' Dr Shawl called.

We both stood up, walked apprehensively into Dr Shawl's office. My legs were trembling, heart thumping. I looked at Olivia. Tears filled her eyes. We held hands tightly, sweating profusely. I fingered the cross hanging around my neck. *Please, God, please.*

Dr Shawl didn't waste any time getting started.

'Olivia – I've seen your blood test results, and you are indeed pregnant. Seven weeks.'

Olivia collapsed into tears, cried into her hands. I just sat there stunned, utterly aghast. The only thought that ran through my head was: *how the fuck can this be happening?* It still came as such a shock. I gritted my teeth, fought back tears of my own, felt my whole body shake. Just felt awful.

Time passed. Liv's crying eventually reduced to a quiet sob, and I tried to pull it together too. We clutched each other's hands. Finally, Dr Shawl spoke.

'Now, I recommend you both tell your parents about this. Then you can all decide what you want to do with the baby.'

'I've got to get an abortion,' Olivia wept.

'An abortion!' I exclaimed. 'You can't get an abortion!'

'Jimmy look at me!' she shrieked. 'Does it look like I'm ready to become a mother?'

'It doesn't matter! We can't kill it!'

'Kids, *please!*' Dr Shawl stressed, reaching forward to touch our knees. 'This is something you really need to think about.'

She paused for a moment.

'What you do with this baby . . . it's one of the biggest decisions you'll ever make in your life. Don't take it lightly.'

She then told Olivia a few routine things – not to drink alcohol, to see an obstetrician, that sort of stuff – before Liv made an appointment to see her again in a few days' time. Then we left. As soon as we were outside I hit the roof.

'An abortion, Olivia? You can't be serious! We can't just kill a baby because it's inconvenient for us to have it!'

'I can't do this, Jimmy! I can't become a mother right now!'

'You have to!'

'Don't fucking tell me what to do!' We got in the car, slammed the doors shut and started speeding home.

'Murder? That's your solution? Cold-blooded fucking murder?'

'It's not murder! The baby's only seven weeks old – it's still just a foetus!'

'It's a kid, Liv! It's already got a brain, a spinal cord, arms and legs! It's already got a heart! It's already got a *face*! How the fuck can we just kill it?'

'We can't be parents!'

'We can't kill – '

'Jimmy stop!'

We both screamed as we crashed into the car in front of us. Airbags blew up in our faces and we were both thrown forwards. Pain attacked my spine and the top of my neck, but my first thought was Olivia.

'Liv! Are you all right?'

'Yeah,' she panted. 'I'm fine.'

She saw me wincing.

'Jimmy how's your spine?' she exclaimed.

I groaned as I leaned back in the seat. I wiggled my fingers and toes, patted my feet on the floor, slowly moved my arms as if I were jogging, rotated my torso from side to side.

'I'm fine,' I sighed with relief.

We took a few seconds to compose ourselves before the overweight driver of the car we'd hit stormed up to us and pounded on the driver-side window. I wound it down shakily.

'What the fuck was that? Didn't you see me stopping? It was a red light, you idiot!'

'Sorry,' I muttered.

He was livid. We swapped insurance details while Liv stayed in the car sobbing. The guy then left. I got back in the car and tried to start the engine, but it wouldn't work.

'That's just fucking perfect,' I muttered. 'We'll have to call our parents.'

I rang my mum and told her that no one was hurt but that we'd been in a car accident. She was there within five minutes. The first thing she noticed was the smashed-up bonnet.

'What the hell happened?' she demanded.

I sighed.

'I crashed, Mum.'

'How fast were you driving to damage the car this badly?'

'I don't know,' I said dismissively.

'You *don't know*?'

I shrugged distractedly. She was furious.

'Jimmy, this is *so* irresponsible! You could've been hurt! You could've been – '

'Not now, Mum!'

'What do you mean not now?' she yelled. 'You could've died!'

'Mum shut up!' I exploded.

She grabbed me by the shoulders.

'Jimmy – what the hell's the matter with you?'

And it was then that I broke down in tears. I sunk to the ground, hugged my shins, cried into my knees – all in the middle of the street. Mum quickly knelt to my level.

'Jimmy . . . what? What is it?'

I just kept crying. Mum was holding me.

'Jimmy what is it?' she stressed.

I tried to say it firmly but it came out high-pitched and squawky.

'Liv's pregnant!'

Mum gasped. She pulled my head from my knees, looked at me frantically.

'Jimmy . . . tell me it's not true . . .'

'It's-it's . . .' I stammered. 'It's true.'

She threw her arms around me. Both of us cried. Olivia got out of the car and cried with us. Mum called my father and Olivia's parents. Everyone came. We all cried together. It must've looked ridiculous to everyone passing by.

After arranging for the car to be towed we all went back to my parents' house to try and figure out what the hell to do. At first, everyone just sat silently around our living room table. Then Dad finally spoke.

'So . . . where to from here?'

'We've got to keep it!' I stressed. 'We can't just kill it!'

'I'm not ready to become a mum yet, Jimmy!'

That argument continued for the next 15 minutes, both of us yelling at each other and our parents watching on silently. We were both firmly entrenched in our positions, and it appeared to be a stalemate. To me, abortion was murder – plain and simple. For whatever reason, Olivia just didn't share the same view. And she said there'd be no way she'd ever be able to put our baby up for adoption. Since she didn't want to be a mother, where did that leave us? The yelling continued.

'You're not listening to me, Jimmy!'

'I am listening to you! All I'm hearing is, "I want to kill my fucking baby!" '

She looked at me, horror-stricken, before bursting into tears and running out the door. Her parents glared at me before following her.

'Jimmy – that was below the belt,' Mum condemned me.

'Well what am I supposed to say when she's saying shit like that?'

'Jimmy – she's right. You're not listening to her.'

I was shocked. 'Huh?'

'Do you have any idea how hard it is to be a teenage mum? I know you say you're going to be there to help her, but it's still much harder on her. Who's going to be the one waking up at all hours of the night to feed it? Or change its nappy? Or cradle it when it's crying? If you have this baby, Olivia would probably have to drop out of uni. I know you mean well, but you can't force her into this. You just can't. You have to somehow reach a compromise.'

My parents and I talked well into the early hours of the morning, and after a while, I came to see Mum's point, which Dad also agreed with. And what's more, I knew it was me who would have to give in. As much as it would pain me to have the baby aborted, I knew I couldn't pressure Olivia into keeping it.

After another near-sleepless night, I picked up some flowers and went over to Liv's place. When she answered the door, a few seconds passed where we just stared at each other. She looked exhausted. I awkwardly gave her the flowers. She smiled weakly, put the flowers in some water before we sat down on her living room couch. Our eyes met but then she looked away, stared down at the ground. I took a series of deep breaths to compose myself before finally finding the courage to speak.

'Look, Liv – I'm sorry about last night. I wasn't thinking about how much it would affect you.'

I paused, scrunched up my face, gritted my teeth.

'I really, really, really feel strongly against you getting an abortion.'

I paused again, wiped my eyes.

'But if you really want to do it, then I'll support you. One hundred per cent.'

She broke down in tears and cried into my chest. I cried too.

'Jimmy . . .' she wept. 'J-Jimmy . . . you know . . . you know I don't *w-want* to get an ab-abortion. But I just c-can't be . . . I can't b-be a mother right now. I just can't . . .'

'I know, baby,' I sobbed. 'I know . . .'

We held each other for a long, long time. Finally, I pulled away.

'We should get an abortion right away then. As soon as possible.'

Olivia's face was still drenched with tears. She nodded softly.

'Yes . . . I'll work it out with Dr Shawl.'

I tried to sound strong.

'I'll be there with you, Liv. I'll be there with you every step of the way.'

She kissed me.

'I know you will be.'

Later that afternoon, Olivia's parents came home from work and we told them our decision. I then called my parents and told them, and they came over straight away. We all ate dinner together and discussed the situation. They all seemed to agree that an abortion was the best possible solution.

The next day, we saw Dr Shawl and told her what we'd decided. She set us up with an appointment at a clinic to get the abortion the following day.

The day itself was one of the hardest of my life. It's all kind of a blur. I remember driving Liv to the clinic, and reading the information pamphlets with her in the waiting room. I remember holding Olivia's hand, squeezing it tightly, feeling her squeeze back, feeling both of us tremble. I remember her being called in, and hugging her tightly. I remember placing my hand over Liv's belly.

'Goodbye, baby,' I whispered.

I remember Olivia crying, and I remember me crying too. I remember waiting three hours for her, trying to write in the meantime but finding it impossible to think clearly. I remember going to a nearby café and eating a sandwich, and then throwing it up on the way back to the clinic. I remember seeing Olivia finally come out, looking exhausted. I remember running towards her, hugging her, holding her, crying with her.

NEW YEAR'S RESOLUTION

To put it bluntly, the abortion fucked me up. To me, it was tantamount to murder, and the pain, the guilt, incessantly ate away at me. Even though on some level I knew that the only reason I gave in to it was for Liv's sake, and that for that reason, it was probably the selfless and caring decision to make, I still found it horribly difficult to deal with. I could hardly sleep, on countless nights only dozing for a couple of hours. I'd have this harrowing dream where I'd be taking Jimmy Junior to school. I'd be holding his hand, walking along the street, but when we'd arrive there'd be nobody there.

'Where is everybody, Daddy?' he'd ask.

'They're in class, Jimmy. Come with me.'

I'd take him to the classroom but there'd still be nobody there.

'There's nobody here, Daddy. Where is everyone?'

But instead of answering him, I'd throw him to the floor and start stomping on his face. Blood would gush out of his nose and mouth and ears and he'd be crying 'Daddy! Daddy! Stop it, Daddy!' but I'd keep going and going and then when he was finally dead, I'd stop and look at my bludgeoned son on the floor surrounded by all the blood and wake up screaming. I'd spend the next half-hour crying and would usually be too disturbed to sleep for the rest of the night. I'd lost my appetite too, often only eating one regular meal or two light meals a day. I couldn't finish main courses at restaurants with Liv any more, so after a while we just stopped going. Olivia was devastated too, and pretty quiet and moody and all over the place for the following few weeks – but she was nowhere near as distraught as me. Then again, to her it wasn't murder.

Liv and I got pretty similar marks that semester. Both of us were doing so well at the start, but we really tailed off towards the end. I found it nearly impossible to concentrate, so I wasn't well prepared going into the exams. Struggling to sleep didn't help either. I felt exhausted during the exam week and was even drawing blanks during exams themselves, forgetting simple things I knew I'd learned before. As a result, I started to loathe myself.

Focus Jimmy, you fucking idiot! Stop being such a bitch! Stop being such a pussy! It happened. Get over it. Move on. Be a man and get through this.

But no matter what I told myself, I just couldn't shake the guilt and sorrow that continued to engulf me. My average plummeted from over 85% after the mid-semester exams to 77%, bringing my average for the year to just over 75%.

What a fucking failure, I berated myself. *You came to uni wanting to get an average of 85% and you only got 75%? That's bullshit. That's not even close. You didn't work hard enough. You slacked off. You were a fat lazy fuck. It doesn't mean shit that Liv got an abortion. You still failed. Plain and simple.*

December was a rough month too. Olivia was working as a waitress at a pizza parlour five nights a week and was actually feeling a lot better about everything, but my month was hardly as constructive. I'd originally set the goal of finishing the first draft of my novel by the end of the semester, but since that also didn't happen, I figured I'd try to at least finish it by the end of the year. But once again, I was too disturbed to focus properly. I couldn't concentrate for longer than half an hour before crumbling to pieces. At the time the abortion happened, I talked about it at length with Olivia and my parents, and that helped ease my burden slightly. But by then – three months later – the matter had been discussed to death. After a while, I knew I'd just have to sit with the pain until I could eventually move past it. And that pain dominated most of December. There were a few bright moments, like when two different modelling scouts approached me on Manly Beach (although I forgot to ever call them), and when Olivia and I made sweet love on a restaurant table after closing time (this time, and all future times, wearing a condom, even though Olivia was still on the pill). But they were small illuminations in an otherwise dim and sombre month.

My coping mechanism was pot and booze. Since I'd stopped surfing I'd always been a heavy drinker, and I smoked weed from time to time, but during December, you could count on one hand the number of days that I didn't get stoned off my ass or drink myself into oblivion. I never got high in front of Olivia – only with the boys – but she knew I was doing it. She told me I was far better off seeing a psychologist or someone else who could help me instead of pulling bongs all the time, but I told her that I didn't want to see anyone and that smoking bud was only temporary and not to hassle me because I was trying to handle everything as best as I could. She reluctantly let it go, probably perceiving it to be a relatively minor issue considering what we'd just been through. However, then came New Year's Eve, which was a defining point when I realised that I was spiralling down the wrong path and needed to make some changes.

I woke up at eleven and walked to Brent's house, picking up a bottle of bourbon and a case of Toohey's Extra Dry on the way – I planned to spend the day drinking with the boys before we all headed over to an old schoolmate's party in Northbridge, where I'd organised to meet up with Liv and some of our other friends. At Brent's, we cracked open a few beers on the patio and talked for a while before deciding to play a few drinking games. Our favourite one was where we'd make teams of two and then play ping pong; when a team won two consecutive points in a row, they could either make the losers each drink three shots of beer, or take off their shirts and turn around, giving the winners a free shot at smashing the ball against their backs. Because we all wanted to get wasted, we usually made the losers drink, and by 2:30, the six of us had ploughed through two cases and were feeling pretty mellow. A few of our other mates from school came over then and we decided to watch a couple of old Bond flicks and crack open the spirits. Four hours later, I'd finished all 700 ml of my bottle of bourbon and was blind as anything. I passed out on the couch, during which time a very drunk Chris decided he wanted his head shaved, so after finding the dog clippers, Brent did the honours. At 7:30 we called a couple of cabs and went to the party.

Olivia and her friends were already there. I staggered up to her and gave her a kiss.

'Hey, baby,' I slurred.

'Jimmy . . .' Liv said disapprovingly. 'You're tanked already?'

'It's New Year's Eve, baby. You've got to loosen up!'

I was a mess, stumbling all over the place, tripping over myself, having to lean against the wall for support as everyone around me drank and danced and enjoyed the night. Olivia drank four Smirnoff Double Blacks and had a couple of glasses of champagne, which got her pretty drunk. She was letting her hair down, dancing with her friends and having a great time. Meanwhile, someone pulled out a bong. I'd been drinking heavily for eleven hours, so weed was the last thing I needed. Nevertheless, when it was doing the rounds, I knocked back two cones. Then I was beyond fucked. Legs trembling, I stumbled outside, fell down on the road, puked in the gutter. I lay there shaking, curled up in a ball as bile dribbled from my mouth into the drain. *Look at you*, I thought. *What a fucking mess.* And then for a few moments my mind felt clear and I was able to take stock of my life.

This is a fucking disgrace, I thought. *Curled up puking in the gutter? This is pathetic. Sure, Liv got an abortion, and that's been hard as hell to deal with, but it happened three months ago — you need to move past it. Because all this shit that's happening at the moment — this needs to stop. This needs to change. Now. This year, you achieved none of your goals. It has been a giant failure of a year. And look where it's gotten you: having so much weed and booze that you're curled up puking in a gutter. You've failed. This feeling sucks. You never want to feel this ever again. Never, ever again. Starting January 2, things will be different. No more weed. Nowhere near as much booze. You'll work hard on your novel until March when uni starts, and then you'll work hard on both during the semester, just like you did before Liv fell pregnant. In one years' time, to the day, instead of throwing up on the side of the street, you'll be celebrating getting a High Distinction average at uni, publishing your novel and sticking it to everyone who ever doubted you. You can do this. You* will *do this — if you work hard and stay focused.*

I rubbed the cross around my neck, looked up at the sky.

Please, God, I whispered. *Please give me the strength to move past this, to have a better year in 2008 and achieve my dreams.*

And then I blacked out. The next thing I remember is waking up the following morning in bed. When I called Olivia, she told me that just before midnight, she was looking for me so that we could kiss on the dot of twelve and ring in the new year by watching the fireworks together. When she found me passed out in the gutter, she got Corey to watch me while she said goodbye to her friends before calling a taxi to come and get us. Corey was able to heave me into the cab, and the driver helped me into bed at my place before dropping Olivia home. I asked her why she didn't spend the night with me. She said she was angry that I'd ruined her evening, and in any sense had to go home to shower and change because I threw up on her in the cab.

Part II

AND THEN OLIVIA FINALLY LET THE CAT OUT OF THE BAG

For the first couple of months, I did a good job of sticking to my new year's resolution. After spending New Year's Day shaking off the mother of all hangovers, having a long lunch with my parents, and taking Olivia out for a seafood dinner at Bluewater in an attempt to make up for my appalling behaviour the previous night and to tell her that I was going to quit taking drugs and ease up on the piss, I started getting seriously stuck into my novel on January 2. For once, my head was relatively clear – I made a conscious effort not to think about the abortion, and for the first time in a while there was neither weed nor booze. That day, I got a solid eight hours of good quality writing done, which was the most I'd done any day of the holidays to date. I slept better that night – satisfaction with a good day's work makes for the most comfortable pillow.

My hard work continued for the next ten days, at which point my first draft was finally finished. I spent the next month editing it ruthlessly before I started thinking about trying to find a professional editor. I browsed the New South Wales Writers' Centre website and discovered they ran a mentorship program, where aspiring authors could pay mentors to read their work and provide feedback on their writing. It was perfect. I looked through the list of names and a mentor by the name of Pierce Broadwater, author of two bestsellers and the ex-mentor of two writers who ended up signing major publishing deals jumped out at me. I gave him a call and we met for coffee. I told him that I'd been working on my novel for about a year, and that after he was done reading it, I'd make the changes he suggested and then submit it for publication. He nodded along, saying that he couldn't comment on that line of reasoning until he'd read the novel, and I said that that seemed fair enough before excitedly handed over my 400 page, 113,000 word manuscript. He told me he'd have his feedback ready within the next six weeks and that he'd contact me again then. 'Great,' I said. We shook hands and parted.

On the way home from my meeting with Pierce, I went to uni to buy my textbooks for the next semester. There were still two weeks before classes were due to begin, but I wanted to get an early start on learning the material, just like I'd done before the start of Year 11. While I was there, I called Olivia.

'Sweetie, you want me to get your books for next semester?'

'Sure, baby. That would be great.'

'No worries. You want to have dinner tonight too?'

'Ahuh. Where do you want to go?'

'Don't mind. What about you?'

'Hhmmm. Maybe Sugar Lounge for a pizza?'

'Good choice, hun. Pick you up at seven?'

'Done. See you then, baby.'

While I was buying our textbooks, a woman approached me.

'Hi – you look really familiar. Are you a model, by any chance?'

I couldn't help but laugh. 'No. I'm not a model.'

'Well! Then it's good we ran into each other!' She took a business card from her purse and gave it to me. Her name was Sarah Jeffries – she was a modelling agent at Folio Talent Management. Who knows what she was doing at the Sydney University Co-op Book Shop.

'You've got a good look – handsome tanned features, a nice smile and broad shoulders. You should give me a call.'

I said I'd think about it before we parted ways.

At dinner with Olivia, I told her about the incident. She laughed.

'That's . . . what? The fourth time you've been asked to model?'

I shrugged.

'You should do it!'

'You reckon?'

'Yeah, definitely!'

'I guess I could.'

'Yes! Do it! Give her a call tomorrow!'

'OK,' I laughed. 'I'll do it.'

'That's kinda cool. My little Jimmy's a model!'

'Shut up.'

We both laughed. Since New Year's Eve, things had been great between us. She wasn't dressed up or anything that night – only wearing a crop-top, skirt and thongs with hardly any make-up on – but she still looked stunning. Our legs rubbed together beneath the table, and within moments I was filled with lust. I leaned towards her and whispered in her ear:

'I'm so horny, baby. We've got to have sex as soon as we get back to my place.'

'Have some self-control, sweetie,' she teased, before softly nibbling my ear. I leaned back in my seat as we shot each other flirtatious looks. Some of our most exciting sexual experiences then came to mind: losing our virginity, making love on the restaurant table, and another time when she went down on me while we were stuck in a traffic jam. I was rock-hard, but then for some reason, I thought of the abortion. Consternation struck. I was inundated with guilt. It must've shown on my face.

'What is it, baby?' Liv asked.

I hesitated.

'Liv . . . do you ever . . . do you ever think about the baby?'

She looked shocked. We hadn't mentioned it all year – it was taboo to talk about it. She hesitated too, then nodded slowly.

'Yeah . . . sometimes. Sure.'

'You'd be due in three months.'

'I know, Jimmy.'

'Do you regret doing it?'

'I regret getting pregnant, yeah. But not the abortion. I'm just not ready to be a mother yet, Jimmy.'

I sighed, nodding slowly. She reached across the table and held my hand.

'It still bothers you, doesn't it?'

'I don't . . . I mean . . . I don't know. Not as much as it used to. But sometimes . . . you know? I get that dream and I just feel so disturbed.'

'Are you sure you don't want to talk to a psychologist?'

I sighed again.

'Yeah, I'm sure. I think I just need more time.'

Olivia nodded thoughtfully, kissed my hand.

The pizza came, and we ate in silence. We didn't have dessert, instead just paying the bill and leaving. I didn't feel like having sex once we got back to my place. That night was one of those nights when the abortion would get to me and I'd feel nothing but despair.

When the semester started a couple of weeks later, I felt energised, ready to work hard to achieve my goal of getting an 85% average. I was happy with the state of my novel, too – I was due to hear back from my mentor within the next four weeks, after which I planned on spending the rest of the semester editing it as per his suggestions and then trying to get it published during the mid-year holidays. It all seemed so simple. Yet the first couple of weeks of the semester didn't go according to plan. I hated both my electives – Regression Modelling and Corporate Finance – and in week three decided to change them to Intermediate Microeconomics and Mathematical Economics. Because I started both of them two weeks late, I was behind in each of them. Then a few days later, I received a hysterical phone call from Corey.

'Jimmy, Sarah's period's late!' (Sarah was his girlfriend).

'Fuck, man.'

'I need your help! What am I supposed to do?'

'Corey . . . you know I hate talking about this shit, right?'

'I know man, but I have no one else to talk to. I can't tell my parents – they'll freak! Just tell me what I'm supposed to do.'

I sighed. 'Just take her to a doctor, do a blood test and you'll know the next day.'

There was a long pause. Corey cleared his throat, once, twice, three times.

'J-Jimmy . . .' he finally stuttered. 'If she is pregnant . . . what am I . . . what am I supposed to do?'

'It's up to you and Sarah, man. You guys have to decide what's best for you.'

'Fucking hell – I've got no idea what to do. Sarah's freaking out, saying she wants to get an abortion. But I'm not sure, man. I don't know if I want to do that. Fuck, Jimmy. Why can't we just get it adopted? We can make sure a good family gets it, and then when we're older, we can see it and still be a part of its life. Doesn't that sound like a good idea, Jimmy? Doesn't that seem best for everyone?'

'I can't answer that, man. You've got to work it out with Sarah.'

'I just have no idea what to do,' he stressed. 'I just don't . . .'

'Corey – you want me to come over? We can talk about it properly?'

'Nah that's cool, man. I know you hate talking about it.'

'It's OK,' I said. 'I can if you want.'

'It's sweet, really. Don't worry about it.'

'Well give me a ring if you do.'

'Yeah, thanks.'

'Just get Sarah to take the test. She might not be pregnant – you never know.'

'Yeah, will do. Might go to the doctor now, actually. I'll call you a bit later, bro.'

'No worries. Good luck, mate.' We hung up.

It turned out Sarah wasn't pregnant, which was great, but that conversation with Corey made me relive the whole experience. That night, I had that dream again, and I had it a couple more times that week too. It was distracting me at uni, and just like before, it made it difficult to concentrate. And that really, really made me mad with myself.

Do some work, you fucking pussy! I'd yell in my head. *This shit happened six months ago! There's no way it should still be bothering you now!*

But it did, and after the third straight day of being so distraught I could hardly study, I did something I'd never done. My parents were away in Bali for their 20th anniversary, so I had the house to myself. I retrieved a bottle of bourbon from the liquor cabinet, and grabbed a large bottle of Coke and a glass from the kitchen. I slouched down in a beanbag on my bedroom floor, and poured a fifty-fifty mix into the glass. For a while I just stared at it, wondering if what I was about to do wasn't just a terrible idea. But I was so consumed with pain: *I murdered my baby . . . murdered . . . murdered . . . murdered it.* I just felt so tormented and I craved some relief, even if it was only temporary.

And what difference does it really make? I thought. *Drinking on your own or drinking with other people? If I was out with the boys and got drunk, that would be fine. So why can't I get drunk on my own? It's really just the same thing, isn't it?*

I took my first sip from the glass. It felt pleasant going down my throat, and the taste of booze was soothing. So I continued drinking. For the next couple of hours my whole body grew heavy, and then it felt numb as my lolling head flopped back against the wall behind me. My eyes flickered open and closed like a circuit on the fritz before I managed to drag myself into bed and pass out until morning.

I woke with a headache the next day, but even though I was hungover, I felt more mellow, less tense than before. I managed to stop thinking about the abortion so much, and was able to put in a good day of study. Feeling decent as a result, I rang Sarah Jeffries and booked an appointment to see her the following week. Then I called Olivia.

'Feel like coming over for dinner tonight?'

'Sure. Want to just order pizza and watch a movie?'

'Yep. I'll pick something up. Come over around seven.'

I went out and rented *Sherrybaby* and then did a couple more hours of study. It'd been a long day, and by then, I felt drained and worn out.

I could really go for a beer, I thought. *It's not like I haven't earned it – I've worked hard today. I deserve to relax now.*

So I cracked open a bottle. It was six-thirty, so I figured I'd just have one while watching Nadal smoke some wildcard in the French Open. By six-forty-five I'd finished my first beer and felt like another, so I had a second. Liv rang a touch after seven while I was onto my third.

'Going to be a little late, baby. Just finishing up some study.'

By the time she'd arrived, I'd had five beers. She saw the empty bottles on the table as soon as she walked into the kitchen.

'Jimmy,' she said sternly, picking up one of the bottles. 'What's this?'

'I had a hard day, baby – so much studying.'

'I had a hard day too, but you don't see me drinking alone.'

'I was just trying to relax, OK?'

'No, it's not OK. You shouldn't be doing this.'

'Just chill, Liv. It was only a few beers. Don't make a big deal out of it.'

She shook her head disapprovingly.

'Fine, I'll drop it. But please don't do this again, OK?'

I sighed. 'Fine.'

We ordered pizza and watched the movie. The whole time, I found myself feeling tense, anxious, wanting a drink.

'What's wrong?' Olivia asked.

I knew getting another beer would start a fight.

'Nothing,' I said.

'You don't seem yourself.'

'I'm fine.'

The movie finished. We fucked almost straight away. Then we had a shower, brushed our teeth and got into bed. As soon as we were under the covers, I kissed her, rubbed her breasts.

'Again, baby?'

'I'm in the mood . . .'

We had sex again, and at my initiation, once more the following morning (I needed the relief). Olivia then left to go to uni for an early class, and I logged onto my computer to check Facebook and my emails. Straight away, I saw there was one from Pierce. Nervous tension built within me. I'd been dying for his feedback from the minute I'd given him my manuscript, and now, the time had finally come. I apprehensively opened the email and read:

> *Dear Jimmy,*
>
> *Below is my assessment of your work. On the plus side, I think your story has potential — it has a clear plot and the power to be inspirational. However, you have **a lot** of work to do in order to get your manuscript up to a publishable standard.*

He then went on to detail all the problems with the draft. *"The writing style is terrible — way too many clichéd similes, unnecessary big words, awkwardly worded sentences, melodramatic scenes and too much repetition."* It was *"very poorly researched — the kryptonite for any work of historical fiction."* Nicola's character had to be deeply rethought, as *"the racial aspect of the novel isn't dealt with well at all, nor is her love with the protagonist believable — they don't share nearly enough experiences for them to fall in love."* The motifs I'd employed were *"extremely amateurish."* The poetry I'd written and inserted here and there was *"awful."* My use of punctuation was *"neither proper nor effective."* The ending was *"extremely contrived."* He then continued:

> *I recommend that you rewrite the novel from scratch, using what you've written as a guide to writing it again. You have so much research to do and you need to improve your writing style to such an extent that I actually think it would be easiest to rewrite it as opposed to editing what you've already done.*
>
> *In terms of how to improve your writing style — you need to read. That's all there is to it — just read. The more quality books you read, the better your writing style is going to be. It's that simple, really.*

I hope this advice has been of some help to you. I have been very hard on you, Jimmy, but you must understand that getting a novel published is very difficult. It is not for the faint-hearted or for those not willing to work hard.
Warm regards,
Pierce.

I read it through several times until words like "terrible," "poor," "amateurish," "awful," "contrived" and "rewrite" began to sink in, and the self-abuse made its way to the fore.

How did you think this would be so easy? Waking up one day and deciding to write a novel. No training, no practice, nothing – just waking up one day and deciding to write a novel and thinking you can have it done and dusted in a year writing it part-time. That's ridiculous. How the fuck could you be so stupid?

I felt like such a failure, both for having produced something that I thought was excellent when it was riddled with flaws, and also for being naïve enough to think that writing a novel would be so easy. *And this isn't the first time you've failed recently,* I reminded myself. *What about all of last year? That was just a whole damn year of failure – your marks were the epitome of mediocrity, and it's not like you can even say that you used the time to write a great book – all you did was churn out 400 pages of shit that was badly written, shockingly researched, employed amateur motifs and terrible poetry, had a failed love element, used punctuation poorly and had a contrived ending.* My self-confidence was shaken, and I felt overwhelmed by the goals I'd set for myself. *How am I going to get an 85% average and get my novel published?* I panicked. *I struggled all of last year trying to juggle the two of them, and all it got me was average marks. Now, I have to do it all over again, and it will be harder this time around because second year subjects are much harder than first year subjects.* I had no idea what I was going to do, but I knew I needed to blow off some steam. I craved an escape, some temporary relief. Something to clear my head. I rang up Corey.

'Hey mate, let's head out tonight.'

'Yeah, all right.'

'Huge night, man. We'll get the other boys involved too. Let's start at Brent's house, get trolleyed, then head to the Cross for a wild one.'

'Yeah? How wild are we talking?'

'Wild, man. Anything goes.'

'I like it. I'll ring the other boys. Assuming Brent's cool with it, let's get to his house at 7:30. I'll call you if there's a change of plan.'

'Too easy, bud.' We hung up.

By then, it was 10:00 a.m. I tried to study for the next few hours but couldn't stay focused – I was too anxious, too tense, and it was almost impossible to think about anything other than the review I'd just received. At three o'clock, I decided to mellow out by having a beer. I continued studying, doing my contract law readings as I sipped away. The booze helped me to relax but didn't help me focus, and by five, I'd had six beers, and while nowhere near wasted, I wasn't sober enough to be able to study properly. So I stopped. After having a couple more beers in front of an episode of *Law and Order: SVU*, I had a shower, got dressed and walked the few blocks to Brent's place.

When I got there, I drank some more with the rest of the guys. I can't remember who, but at some point someone floated the idea of doing a "Century," which involved downing 100 shots of beer – equivalent to about three litres – in 100 minutes. Everyone agreed.

An hour and 40 minutes later, the guys were reasonably drunk. I was fucking blind, puking in Brent's garden.

'Jimmy you lightweight, what's going on?'

'He was drinking before he got here,' someone said.

'With who?'

'Probably Liv.'

'Nah, couldn't have been Liv – I saw her at uni today.'

'Then who were you drinking with, Jimmy?'

I threw up again. Brent patted me on the back.

'Dude, are you all right?'

'Yeah I'm cool, man.'

'You want to just stay here and chill for a bit?'

Gagging, I nodded.

'Can we wait an hour? Leave then?'

Brent checked his watch. It wasn't even nine yet.

'Sure,' he shrugged. 'But try and sober up a bit. You won't get in anywhere otherwise.'

A couple of minutes later I stopped vomiting and re-joined the rest of the boys on the patio. They were talking about which club to go to and which girls to ring to see if they'd like to come out with us before giving a few of them a call. I didn't say anything, didn't do anything but sit there nodding along, feeling heavy and drunk and lazy, thinking about the mess that was my novel. At a quarter-to-ten, they started getting ready to go.

'Jimmy, you all right mate?' Corey asked.

I got up slowly. 'Yeah. I'm fine.'

'You sure? You look pretty fucked.'

'I'm good, man.'

He nodded. 'Maybe don't drink any more tonight.'

I didn't say anything.

We rode the ferry to Circular Quay and then took a couple of cabs to World Bar in the Cross, where a few girls from school were waiting for us.

'Where's Liv?' Sarah (Corey's girlfriend) asked.

'At work,' I slurred.

'She going to come out after?'

'Yeah, I'll give her a call later.'

'Cool. I'm going to go get a teapot of Long Island Iced Tea. You want anything?'

'Yeah, the same thanks,' I said, giving her some cash.

Just after Sarah left, Brent returned from the bar.

'Got you a water, mate,' he said, handing it to me.

'I don't need water,' I slurred.

'You're fucked, mate. Drink some water.'

'Nah. Sarah's getting me a teapot.'

'Fuck, man. You shouldn't be drinking any more.'

'Fuck that. Hey, where's that chick you're trying to bang?'

Side-tracked, Brent looked around.

'I don't know, mate. She was here a minute ago.' He checked his phone. 'She just messaged me – she's upstairs.'

'So what are you doing down here?'

'Checking up on your drunk ass. You going to be all right here til Sarah gets back?'

'Yeah. No worries.'

He looked at me sceptically, shook his head and left.

Sarah then came back with two teapots. She poured some of hers into a glass to drink. I sculled all half a litre of mine from the spout.

'Getting loose tonight, eh Jimmy?' she laughed.

'Fuck yeah.'

Corey and Steve came back from the dance floor. By then, my vision was so blurred I struggled to make them out, and I felt so heavy that I thought I'd never want to move. Then again, I did want another drink. I just wanted to plunge myself into oblivion and forget all about my novel and uni and how difficult it would be to juggle both of them and achieve my goals. I staggered up.

'Jimmy, where are you going?'

'Bar. You guys want anything?'

'Got beers already, mate,' Corey said.

'Damn, Jimmy's getting loose tonight,' I heard Sarah say.

Corey sighed.

'He's always getting loose.'

I lined up at the bar and ordered two more teapots. I sculled them both, one after the other, straight from the spout like before. Then, a bouncer came up to me.

'You're not allowed to drink them like that,' he growled. 'You've got to leave.'

'Sorry, I didn't know.'

'There are signs everywhere – get out.'

I was so drunk and the music was so loud that I couldn't process what he was saying. I turned around to walk back to where the guys were sitting but he grabbed my shirt.

'Hey – I told you to fuck off.'

Leading me by the shirt, he escorted me out of the club. As I was thinking about how I could sneak back in without him seeing, those last two teapots really hit me. I tried to walk but stumbled, fell over on the road, lay there dizzily.

'Get up, mate.' A stranger. He helped me to my feet.

'You right to stand?'

I mumbled 'yeah' and then staggered away. Feeling kind of hungry, I bought a piece of Hawaiian pizza from New York Slice and sat down on the side of the street to eat it.

The next thing I knew it was the following morning, and I was lying in my front garden covered with dirt.

How the fuck did I get here? I thought, confused as hell, and simultaneously glad that my parents were in Bali and would thus be none the wiser. I stood up, wiping the grass and the dirt off myself before checking my phone.

I had 36 missed calls.

Eight from Corey, nine from Brent, and 17 from Olivia. *What the hell?* I thought. I rang up Corey.

'Hello?' he answered drowsily.

'Corey – it's me.'

'Jimmy!' He sounded relieved. 'Fuck man, what the hell happened to you last night?'

I shook my head. 'Man I . . . I really don't know.'

'Where are you?'

'At home.'

'How'd you get there?'

'I have no idea. Last thing I remember was eating pizza outside New York Slice.'

'What happened at World Bar?'

'Got kicked out.'

'Too drunk?'

'Nah. Sculling teapots from the spout.'

There was a pause.

'I'm just glad you're all right,' he said. 'We spent ages looking for you and couldn't find you anywhere. We thought you might've gone back to Liv's place, but when we rang her she said she hadn't heard from you all night. We were all trying to call you but you weren't picking up. We were starting to get a bit worried, mate.'

I was still in a state of shock. I genuinely had no idea how I'd gotten home.

'Look,' said Corey. 'I'll text the guys and let them know you're all right. Meanwhile, you should give Liv a call. She was pretty stressed out, man.'

'Shit,' I said. 'I'm sorry.'

'It's cool bro, these things happen. Just give Liv a call now.'

'Yeah, will do. Thanks, mate.'

We hung up. I rang Olivia straight away.

'Jimmy! Thank God you're all right!'

'I'm so sorry I had you worried, baby,' I said guiltily.

As soon as she'd established that I was safe, her concern turned to anger.

'What the hell happened, Jimmy? I was worried sick all night!'

'I was out with the guys . . . and I drank too much. Then I got kicked out of World Bar . . . and then I woke up this morning at home.'

'Why didn't you tell anyone you were leaving?'

'I didn't mean to leave. I just woke up and I was at home.'

'What? How?'

'I . . . I have no idea.'

She was furious.

'You were so drunk that you don't even remember how you got home?'

I didn't say anything.

'Is that right, Jimmy? You were so drunk that you don't even remember how you got home?'

I sighed. 'I'm sorry, Liv.'

'Sorry's not good enough,' she said angrily. 'This is inexcusable. And it's not the first time your drinking's gotten out of control.'

She paused.

'Why do you do this?'

I told her about Pierce's comments and about how overwhelmed I was at the prospect of having to juggle rewriting my novel and getting a High Distinction average at uni. Her anger mollified slightly.

'Jimmy, you're becoming too dependent on alcohol. You can't use it to solve your problems. That's what alcoholics do.'

'I'm not an alcoholic!' I retorted quickly.

'Well you sure are acting like one. Who else do you know who drinks alone? Two nights ago you'd had five beers before I'd even arrived!' (Not to mention that I'd also gotten blind by myself the night before that, which Olivia still didn't know about.)

'Liv . . . I'm sorry. What . . . what do you want me to do?'

'You need to stop using alcohol to solve your problems. You need to stop getting so drunk all the time. And if you don't think you can control yourself when you drink, then you should stop drinking altogether.'

I was silent. I didn't know what to say.

'Jimmy?'

'Yeah?'

'Do you agree that this needs to stop?'

I sighed.

'Yeah,' I said. 'It needs to stop.'

'OK. Now I've got to go and help my mum do the shopping. But Jimmy, please think about what I've said. I love you *so* much, and you have *so* much going for you – but you'll ruin everything if you keep going down this path.'

'OK, baby, OK. I'll stop, all right?'

'OK. I'll call you later tonight.'

We hung up. I felt terrible. *What's happened to you?* I thought. *When you first started uni you were on top of the world, but now, your marks are way below what you know they can be, your novel is nowhere near complete, and Liv's on your case about being too dependent on alcohol . . . and let's not forget that she had to get an abortion, which goes against some of your strongest beliefs. Let's be honest here: everything's a fucking mess right now. You've got to fix this,* I told myself. *Plain and simple – you've got to fix this. At the start of the year, you envisioned getting a High Distinction average and having your novel published by the end of the year. You can still do that – you just have to work hard for it. Just work hard. Do whatever it takes. Anything less than a High Distinction average and a published novel by the end of the year is a failure – and you know what that feels like. Hell, remember last New Year's Eve? Lying in the gutter, shaking and puking? That's the way you started this year. Now, imagine ending it with a High Distinction average and a published novel! How amazing would that be? That's something that would really stick it to all your doubters. It'd be fucking brilliant! And you can do it. You're not a quitter. Things may seem overwhelming right now but you're not a quitter. You'll overcome this and achieve your goals. You just have to work hard – do whatever it takes – in order to make it happen.*

Despite being in the same predicament I was in the previous day, my hopeful enthusiasm had revived. I felt newly fortified. I had a plan, and I believed that if I could stick to it, then everything would turn out OK.

My first task was to reply to my mentor's email:

Dear Pierce,

Thank-you for your assessment of my novel. It appears that I still have a lot of work to do, so I'll get cracking right away. I'm not sure how long it will take me to rewrite my manuscript and get it ready for you again, but I'll work extremely hard, and will hopefully have it finished by the end of the year. In the meantime, I'll keep you up to date with my progress.

Thanks and kind regards,

Jimmy.

Second on my to-do list was to call Sarah Jeffries and cancel my appointment – there was no time to screw around modelling with all the work that I had to do. Once that was done, I got straight to it. I had an economics exam the following Monday that I had to study for, so I started reading through the lecture slides for that. When I was done a couple of hours later, I took a break and watched an episode of *Friends* before sitting down to read the relevant sections of the textbook. At around five in the afternoon, Olivia rang.

'Hey, Jimmy. Have you had time to think about what I was saying?'

'Sure have, baby. I think the reason I've been drinking heaps is because I've been feeling so stressed out wondering how I'm going to get a High Distinction average and get my novel published. And I figured the best way to solve this problem is to just work harder to make sure I achieve my goals. If I can do that, then I won't feel the need to drink so much.'

Olivia pondered my response.

'I guess that makes sense,' she eventually said. 'But you know, you shouldn't feel the need to drink so much anyway – regardless of whether you're achieving your goals or not.'

I shrugged. 'I guess.'

There were a few seconds of silence on Olivia's end. It was as if she wanted to say something more but was holding it back.

'Anyway, enough about that, I guess,' she finally sighed. 'What do you want to do tonight? Dinner somewhere? Or maybe a movie?'

'Don't think I can, Liv. I need to study for this economics test that I have on Monday.'

'Is this part of your new plan to work harder?'

'Ahuh.'

'Fair enough. Well maybe I can come over and we can study together, then?'

'Sure.'

I stuck to my plan of working hard for the rest of the semester. I cut down my socialising to only a couple of nights a week, leaving me with more time to study and write. At a guess, I'd say that I was working between 50 and 55 hours a week. It was draining, being solely focused on something for that long and not being able to talk to anyone during it. I found it so arduous, and while I knew there were more hours in the week and that I could theoretically be working harder, I felt so exhausted at the end of each day that in reality, I didn't think I could. But even though I was trying my best, it still wasn't enough to achieve my goals. Once again, I was battling to maintain an adequate balance between uni and writing. Whenever I'd study hard enough to get the marks that I wanted to get, I'd hardly get any writing done. Whenever I'd try to write more, I'd fall behind at uni. No matter what I tried I couldn't find a combination that worked. It was so frustrating. So disappointing. And as the weeks dragged on, I found myself slipping into a state of almost permanent despair. I found myself feeling unhappy, almost every day. Almost every day, I felt burdened by my goals and the thought that I wouldn't be able to achieve them, so much so that I became filled with an anxious dread. As usual, my solution was to simply work harder.

The harder you work, the more chance you have of getting a High Distinction average and the less time it will take you to finish your novel and get it published. Once that's done, you'll feel better again.

But at times, that constant misery weighing me down was too heavy a burden to bear. As a result, instead of drinking less, I started getting smashed much more often. My night out at World Bar with the guys became a weekly occurrence (except for the forgetting-how-I-got-home business and damn near having a search party out looking for me). It was just that relief, that escape I craved – the numbness that comes from being so plastered that you forget about how miserable and unhappy you are. Olivia was worried, and after a while, started to seriously believe I was an alcoholic. Even the boys, who weren't aware of the reasons behind my drinking, were growing concerned.

'You've got a great life,' they all said. 'You have so much going for you. Why do you feel the need to drink so much?'

I'd just shrug it off. I knew what I was doing wasn't great, but when you need an escape that badly, it's easy to stop caring and just do whatever it takes to get it. Ironically though, all drinking was doing was exacerbating my despair. Alcohol is a depressant, after all.

Of even greater concern was the fact that drinking on my own was becoming a habit. On numerous occasions I'd pick up a bottle of bourbon and a bottle of Coke on the way home, and after telling my parents at around eight o'clock that I was going to write for a couple of hours before going to bed and for them to please not disturb me, I'd sit down at my desk and drink as I'd work on my novel. I'd inevitably pass out 20-30 standard drinks later, depending on how much I'd eaten for dinner. Some nights I'd make it into bed. Other nights I'd sleep with my head on the desk. Once I puked on the floor. Another time I puked on the desk and fell asleep in it. No one – not even Olivia or my parents – had the slightest idea.

That semester, I was feeling my worst around the time of the final exams, which lasted for two weeks. I was so overworked, and because I couldn't find the right balance between studying and writing, I wasn't nearly as well prepared for them as I needed to be in order to get an average of 85%. The fear that I'd fall short multiplied with each day passed, and after each exam that didn't sail as smoothly as it could have. My self-confidence continued to wane, as did my self-esteem. I hated myself more and more after every exam, and after every exam I'd go and buy that bottle of bourbon and the Coke and drink it alone in my room before passing out until morning.

Then there was what became known in my circle of friends as the "Star City incident" – a night where I was so blatantly out of control that it became glaringly obvious to myself and everyone around me that I was an alcoholic and that if I didn't stop drinking I would ruin my life.

The exams had finally ended, and the law faculty was hosting a big party at a club called The Gaff on Oxford Street. Olivia couldn't make it because it was her mum's birthday and she was having dinner with her parents, but all the boys were coming so I figured it would be a good night where everyone could go wild and celebrate the end of the semester. I hadn't had a drink in 44 hours and was desperate to get on the piss, so it was convenient that upon paying the cover charge, there was unlimited beer, wine and spirits from eight until midnight. Typically, we all arrived dead-on eight o'clock to start abusing the bar tab. My policy was simple: I'd line up, get a drink, go to the back of the line, drink it on the way to the front of the line, and then get another drink before joining the back of the line again. I did this for the first couple of hours, talking to whoever I knew who happened to be lining up at the same time. By ten o'clock, I'd had around 20 bourbon & colas and was feeling pretty fucked. After spending half an hour on the dance floor and having a chat to the boys outside for a bit, I returned to the bar and sculled another ten bourbon & colas. We then decided to leave.

'All right, boys,' Chris slurred. 'It's nearly midnight – what do you say we get some food and then head to Star City?'

'I can't afford to be gambling, bro,' Corey said.

'Mate fuck gambling. Do you know how many women there are at the casino just looking for a root?'

'What are you talking about?'

'I'm serious, man – like half the chicks there just want to pick up.'

'Maybe the rich dudes – you're not going to get any.'

'Nah, I reckon they want the young meat. I'm going to go for it.'

'This I got to see.'

'All right then – food then Star City?'

We all agreed and then went across the road to Hungry Jacks.

By then, I was a mess. As soon as we walked in, I started yelling.

'Bacon Deluxe Burger, bitch!'

'Jimmy, what the fuck?'

'Bacon Deluxe Burger, bitch!'

'Dude, stop yelling!'

'Nah man, I want a fucking Bacon Deluxe!'

Corey and Brent took me aside and shoved me in a corner.

'Man why are you yelling?'

'I'm fucking hungry, man!'

'Dude he's blind as anything,' Brent said. 'Just keep him here and make sure he doesn't yell. I'll go get his burger.'

'Bacon Deluxe, bitch!' I yelled.

'It's coming, man!' Corey stressed, cupping his hand over my mouth so I couldn't yell again. 'Just chill.' I pulled his hand away.

'Corey you're so stressed out, man,' I slurred. 'You've just got to relax!'

He shook his head.

'Jimmy, you know I love you, bro, but you're acting like a fucking idiot right now. Seriously, man – just stop yelling, all right? Brent's getting your burger, then we'll get you some water, and once you've sobered up a bit we'll go to Star City. All right?'

'Yeah, sounds good man. I fucking love you, Corey, you know that? I fucking love you, man.'

Corey shook his head. 'I love you too, bro. But try and spend the next hour sobering up, all right?'

'You got it, man! No worries!' I said enthusiastically. He shook his head again.

The food came a couple of minutes later and we all sat down to eat. After taking a bite of my burger, I started yelling again.

'Dude, there's fucking tomato in my burger!'

'Take it out if you don't want it.'

'There's fucking tomato, man!'

'Jimmy, shut up! Just take the tomato out.'

'I don't want this fucking tomato!' I took a piece out of the burger and pegged it towards the counter, hitting a chick in the back of the head. She turned around and gave us the finger.

'Jimmy don't throw shit, man!'

'I really don't want this fucking tomato, though!'

I threw the other piece towards the counter as well, and this time, the security guard saw me. He pointed to our table.

'Oi youse cunts! Piss off!'

Everyone, fairly irritated with me now, grabbed their food and left.

'All right! Star City then, boys!' I yelled outside.

'I think you need to go home,' Chris said.

'Naahh, man. What are you talking about?'

'You're fucking out of control. That's not cool.'

'You're so high-strung, man. You've just got to relax!'

Chris walked ahead angrily. I turned to the boys and laughed, completely oblivious to everyone's frustration towards me.

'Jimmy, you've got to stop acting like this, man,' Corey said. 'Seriously, bro – you're pissing people off.'

'All right,' I said. 'I'm sorry.'

'Now, if you come to Star City, are you going to act normally? Or do you need to go home?'

'Nah I'll be right, man.'

'All right. Now go catch up with Chris and tell him you're sorry.'

I apologised to Chris and we hailed a couple of cabs to Star City. And it's around this time that my memory gets blurry. I remember getting out of the cab, getting some water to drink from a convenience store, and taking a long piss. But that's it.

The next thing I knew I was waking up in Olivia's bed with a throbbing face. She was asleep beside me. I gently shook her awake.

'Liv . . . what . . . how . . . what happened?' I murmured hazily.

She looked at me.

'Oh my God, Jimmy!'

'What?'

'Your face . . .'

'What about it?'

She handed me a mirror. I gasped.

It was covered with cuts and freshly developed bruises.

'What . . . what happened?'

I could tell she was furious. She was always blunt when she was furious.

'Someone beat you up.'

'Huh? When?'

'Last night.'

'What happened?'

'Jimmy!' she suddenly exploded. 'What the hell were you doing so drunk in the first place? Are you trying to kill yourself?'

'What? Liv, what are you talking about?'

'You can't control yourself when you drink! You're a disgrace!'

Her words assailed me as I sat there silently, processing what she'd said. And then it's as if the severity of what I'd been doing — the incessant alcohol abuse — all sank in, and I realised how much of a problem it was. Hell, staring back at my bludgeoned face, it was pretty bloody obvious.

'You're right, Liv,' I sighed.

'What?'

'I'm an alcoholic.'

'Jimmy . . . I'm not saying you're an alcoholic, but I — '

'No — Liv listen to me. I am.'

And then I told her about how I'd been getting wasted all by myself. She started crying. She asked me why, asked what could possibly drive me to do such a thing. I told her how despondent, how miserable I'd been feeling. She couldn't believe it.

'But how can *you* feel this way, Jimmy?' she wept. 'You have such a great life! You're studying commerce/law at a top university, you're a great looking guy who gets approached by modelling scouts, you have great friends and a girlfriend who loves you . . .'

She continued weeping.

'You've got a great life, Jimmy. How can *you*, of all people, be so unhappy that you feel the need to drink so much?'

I fought back tears of my own.

'Because I feel like such a failure,' I said. 'My marks aren't what they should be . . . my book's nowhere near finished. I just feel like such a failure . . .'

'How can you think of yourself as a failure?' she asked, flabbergasted. 'You've achieved more than any 19 year old I know!'

I shook my head.

'I feel like such a failure,' I repeated. 'I feel like such a failure . . .'

And then Olivia let the cat out of the bag.

'Jimmy . . . you're showing classic signs of depression.'

'Huh?'

'Depression.'

'What are you talking about?'

'Clinical depression. It's an illness, Jimmy.'

I frowned. I was confused. I'd heard of clinical depression before, but I didn't really understand what it was.

'What . . . what is depression, exactly?'

'It's basically a state of intense unhappiness, experienced over a prolonged period of time.'

'But . . . but doesn't everyone feel unhappy from time to time?'

'From time to time, yes. But not for prolonged periods. People with depression often feel constantly miserable, almost without relief. And the intensity of their despair is usually far greater than that experienced by a non-depressed person. Some people with clinical depression hate themselves. Some self-harm. Some kill themselves. Clinical depression is an illness, Jimmy, and it can be very serious.'

I nodded. The description seemed to fit.

'So you think I've got depression, then?'

'It sounds like it, yes.'

'What . . . what do I do about it?'

'You need to see a doctor. Then you need to see a psychologist.'

I shook my head.

'I don't want to see a doctor or a psychologist.'

'I think you need to, Jimmy.'

'No, I just need to work harder. If I can just work harder then my marks will be better and my book will be finished quicker and then everything will be OK.'

'Work harder? Jimmy, you already work really hard!'

'I could be working harder.'

'But if you do you're going to run yourself into the ground!'

'No I won't. I'll be fine.'

'What about the drinking? What are you going to do about that?'

'Yeah . . . that I need to stop.'

'Altogether?'

I paused, then nodded slowly.

'I'm an alcoholic,' I admitted. 'I have to.'

Later, Olivia told me how I got all the cuts and bruises on my face. The boys were going up the escalators to Star City when they suddenly noticed I wasn't with them. They went back down to try and find me, and saw me standing still while some guy was punching me in the face (maybe I said something to piss him off? Who knows?). Too drunk to defend myself or to even feel him hitting me, I just stood there and took it. The guys ran towards us, and a fight broke out between my friends and his before the bouncers at Paddy Maguire's next door saw the incident and jumped in to break it up. The bloke that was hitting me left, and then it was just me and the boys. Blood was dripping down my face. I was dazed. The guys took me into the bathroom and cleaned me up before calling Olivia to come and get me. She took me back to her place, washed my face, dabbed Betadine over my cuts and prayed that I'd overcome my drinking problem before leading me to bed and kissing my forehead goodnight.

COLD TURKEY

After confessing the extent of my alcohol abuse to Olivia and promising that I was going to stop, I went home and told my parents. Because they never saw me drunk (I'd arrive home from a night out well after they'd gone to sleep, and like I've said, they never saw me drinking alone), they were completely oblivious to what had been happening. When I told them they were shocked as hell. They asked me how it had happened, how it had gotten to that point. I told them how much I'd struggled trying to juggle uni and my writing, and that I thought I might be suffering from clinical depression. I don't think I'd had a long, involved talk with my parents since Liv had gotten the abortion, and I must admit that it was cathartic and that I was glad I'd told them. They weren't judgmental, my parents – they loved me for who I was, whether that was a commerce/law student or a depressed alcoholic – and they said they'd do whatever it took to help me get better.

We all agreed that the first step to take would be to see a doctor. I saw my regular, Dr King, a thin middle-aged man with brown hair, and told him everything.

'Let's first focus on the part about you wanting to stop drinking entirely, OK?'

'OK.'

'Right. Now there are a few ways that you could try to do this. You could go to a detox program in a private hospital as either an in-patient or an out-patient, or you could see a psychologist or a counsellor. Each of these options will help you get to the bottom of why you've been drinking so much and give you techniques to cope with the cravings that you'll likely experience from abstaining. You could also go to Alcoholics Anonymous, which would give you an outlet to talk about your experiences with alcohol and give you the opportunity to draw strength from other people who may be going through the same things as you. Alternatively, you could try to stop on your own – no help or anything. Now, from what you've told me, you seem to have a strong dependence on alcohol. For this reason, I recommend that you either attend a detox program in hospital or start seeing a psychologist who specialises in treating addictions. That way, you'll get the maximum support and give yourself the best chance of being able to abstain.

I thought about it. To be honest, the idea of a detox program or seeing a psychologist didn't appeal to me. It just didn't seem necessary. *You're a strong-willed, determined person capable of doing anything you set your mind to,* I thought. *You can get over this problem by yourself. You don't need to go to a detox program or see a psychologist or anything like that.*

'I think I'll just do it by myself at home,' I said.

The doctor raised his eyebrows.

'I wouldn't recommend it, Jimmy. It's much harder at home. It's less formal – more tempting to break the rules. And you wouldn't be getting the help that I think you need.'

I thought about it a little more, before concluding that my determination was strong enough to conquer anything.

'I'd rather do it by myself at home,' I repeated. 'I have a good support system, and I know that I'm strong-willed. I'll be able to tackle it on my own.'

The doctor nodded. 'If you say so. But if you do feel that you need some extra support or that the cravings are becoming too intense for you to manage on your own, then you should consider one of the other options I've recommended.'

I nodded.

'What do cravings feel like?' I asked.

'Well . . . I've never had them myself, but I've been told by patients that experiencing a craving is kind of like being really, really hungry. And fighting it's like not eating.'

I nodded slowly, trying to imagine what that must feel like. But I'd just eaten lunch so I found it difficult to do so.

'Will I definitely get cravings?' I asked.

'After a couple of days, almost certainly. They'll probably be at their worst three-to-ten days after your last binge. Then they'll gradually taper off.'

He then gave me a few tips that would help me to abstain, including removing all the alcohol from my house, and telling all my (close) friends about my decision to stop drinking in order to gain their support. The conversation was then steered towards the reasons behind my drinking.

'Now Jimmy,' he began. 'Judging by what you've told me, you are right in that it does seem like you've been suffering from depression. Now I'd like to look into this further, and diagnose you if I can.'

He filed through a drawer before handing me a checklist called *SPHERE*, a scale developed to increase the identification rate of mental illnesses like depression. I started reading it:

> *For more than TWO WEEKS have you:*
> 1. *Felt sad, down or miserable most of the time?*
> 2. *Lost interest or pleasure in most of your usual activities?*

I answered "yes" to the first option and then as per the instructions, I completed the "symptom checklist," ticking most of the "behaviours," "thoughts" and "feelings" associated with mental illnesses: "relying on alcohol and sedatives," "unable to concentrate," "I'm a failure," "it's my fault," "overwhelmed," "unhappy, depressed," "no confidence," "guilty," "disappointed," "miserable" and "sad" – although, interestingly enough, none of the "physical" symptoms: "tired all the time," "sick and run down," "headaches and muscle pains," "churning gut," "can't sleep," and "poor appetite/weight loss." After I was finished, I handed the test back to Dr King for him to tally up my score.

'You got a score of 11,' he said. 'According to the authors of the test, you are likely to have a depressive illness if you register a score equal to or greater than three.'

He then asked me a few additional questions, like whether I'd also experienced periods of mania or had had any hallucinations, for the purpose of ruling out whether I was exhibiting symptoms of other mental illnesses like bipolar disorder or schizophrenia. After being satisfied that I wasn't, he concluded that I was in fact suffering from clinical depression.

'What do I do about it?' I asked.

'Depression is usually treated by a combination of therapy and medication,' he said. 'Therapy is used for the purpose of getting to the root of your depression and then giving you techniques to overcome it. Medication is used to help you cope in the meantime.'

I frowned.

'Medication? For depression? How can that be?'

'If you have depression, it means that you have a chemical imbalance in your brain – a deficiency of either serotonin, dopamine, adrenalin or noradrenalin. It's an illness, Jimmy. We use medication to treat depression in the same way we use medication to treat physical illnesses. There's no difference, really.'

News to me.

'So should I start taking medication now, then?' I asked.

Dr King squinted thoughtfully.

'I'd like to leave it for a couple of weeks, see if we can't get your drinking under control first. Your body's about to experience some strange feelings, and I don't really want to add a medication into the mix that's likely to have side effects. However, I will write you a referral for a good psychologist named Dr Peter Kendall, who specialises in treating young people with a mental illness.' He typed one up, printed it off and handed it to me.

'Try and see him straight away,' he said. 'It's critical that you nip this illness in the bud before it gets any worse.'

I nodded. 'What about you?' I asked. 'When should I see you again?'

'Come and see me in a week's time – more just to see how you've been handling sobriety than anything else. But we'll talk about you taking medication for depression then too.'

And so concluded my visit.

The first three days of life without booze weren't actually too bad – I had a clear head, managed to get a lot of writing done, and didn't get any cravings. But the fourth day was fucking awful. It happened in the afternoon. I was home alone working on my novel, struggling to find some information on the Internet about American vernacular during the 1930s when gradually, I felt more and more like a drink. It started off mild at first, but I was definitely aware of the feeling. *You're just experiencing a craving*, I told myself. *Don't worry about it – you knew they were going to come.* I'd mentally tried to prepare myself for them and figured I'd be able to handle them. *Don't think about it. Just keep writing and try to forget about it.*

I tried to keep working but the craving intensified. *Fuck – the doctor was right*, I thought. *It really is like being hungry and not eating.* And that hunger only evolved, growing worse and worse until I was starving. I started sweating. My body felt weak and unsteady. I gripped my head, breathed deeply, loudly through gritted teeth. I kept fidgeting – sitting up straight, slouching, crossing my legs, leaning forwards – but no position satisfied my hunger. *Fuck*, I started swearing. *Fuck, fuck, fuck, fuck, fuck!* I stood up, started pacing the room . . . didn't work . . . went to the kitchen, ripped open a packet of dried chips and started shoving them in my mouth, but chips weren't booze. I ran back to my room and tried to sleep . . . couldn't do it. Then I was on the edge of the bed, squeezing my skull, pulling at my hair, ripping it from my head, all the while screaming through gritted teeth, 'fucking . . . cunt . . . mother . . . fucking . . . *cunt!*' But it was all hopeless. The craving was insatiable. I clutched the cross around my neck. *Please, God*, I begged. *Please . . . please help me get through this.*

By the time Olivia rang the doorbell an hour or so later, I was lying on my bed watching a movie. I felt dreadful, but lying down seemed the lesser of all evils, and watching TV seemed to make the time pass a fraction less slowly. I felt so lethargic. So drained of energy. The task of standing up seemed unbearable.

'It's open,' I groaned.

Olivia came inside and entered my room, and straight away realised that I wasn't well. She hurriedly knelt down beside me, held my hand.

'What's wrong, baby?'

'Craving booze . . .' I murmured. 'Really want to fucking drink.'

She squeezed my hand, kissed it softly. 'How long for?'

'I don't know . . . maybe one or two hours.'

She kissed my hand again.

'You're doing really well, sweetie. Just keep hanging in there, OK?'

I nodded.

'I will.'

'You're going to get through this, baby. And I'll be here with you, every step of the way.'

She hopped up on the bed beside me and we both watched the rest of the movie together. I felt better with Liv there, but that longing for grog was still overwhelming. My limbs now felt heavy. I sweated through the sheets. Liv got a towel and wiped me down. She gave me a back massage. It was nice, but I still felt shocking. Then all of a sudden she started licking my dick. It took me by surprise.

'Liv, what are you doing?'

'Something to take your mind off it,' she said in between licks.

She continued for a few minutes as my cock gradually hardened. Then she took me in her mouth, stretched me close to the point of climax before she stopped sucking and climbed up my body, took off her bra, shoved my face between her breasts.

'Go down on me, Jimmy,' she whispered in my ear. 'Make me moan . . . make me scream . . .'

Olivia wrapped her legs around my head as I started licking her honeysuckle. She clutched my hands, dug her nails into my flesh, cried out loud with every breath.

'Oh fuck . . . ! Fuck . . . ! *Fuck* . . . ! You're so fucking good . . . ! You're so fucking good . . . ! You dirty fucking boy . . . ! You're going to make me come . . . ! You're going to make me come all over your face!'

I eagerly moved to her clit, tonguing it rapidly before her thighs clenched around my head and with a high-pitched shriek she ejaculated all over me. I expected her to relax her legs and invite me inside her, but she wanted more.

'Do me again, Jimmy,' she panted. 'You're too good to stop . . . keep going and you'll make me squirt . . . you'll make me fucking drench you . . .'

Up for the challenge, I went in deeper this time, really getting my tongue as far into her as it would go, thrusting it in and out, in and out, in and out. Olivia was so loud that I felt like a porn star.

'You dirty fucking boy . . . !' she yelled. 'You dirty fucking boy . . . ! Keep going . . . ! Don't stop . . . ! Don't you dare fucking stop!'

Then I moved my tongue to her clit and put two fingers inside her, started rubbing them up against the back of her pussy.

'Oh my God . . . !' Liv cried. 'Oh my God . . . ! Oh fuck, oh fuck, oh fuck!'

I kept going, quicker and quicker until she screamed at the top of her voice and sprayed all over me.

Her legs slipped off me as she lay on her back gasping for air. My face was dripping wet. I wiped some of her juices onto my cock for lube in preparation to fuck her, but when I made to enter her, she stopped me.

'Not yet,' she whispered. 'You're not horny enough.'

'After *that*? Are you kidding me?'

She smiled flirtatiously.

'You're not horny enough, baby.'

I was about to object when she covered my mouth with her hand, pushed me down onto my back and grabbed my pulsing cock. She knelt down on top of me, breathing hotly into my ear.

'Just trust me . . .' she whispered.

Then she started massaging the head of my dick. Just the head, just massaging, just three fingers. It felt great, but after a few minutes, I wanted to fuck.

'Let's have sex now . . .' I panted.

'Not yet,' she said. 'You're not horny enough.'

'I am!'

'Not you're not. Just trust me.'

So she kept rubbing, kept squeezing the end of my prick. It felt amazing, but I still wanted to be inside her.

'Liv let me fuck you . . .' I puffed.

'Not yet.'

'Liv please . . . I want to come inside you.'

'You will.'

'Not . . . oh fuck! . . . Not if you keep rubbing me . . .'

'You won't come if I'm only touching the head. So long as I don't touch your shaft we can do this all day.'

'But . . . how do . . . how . . .'

I could hardly talk while she was touching me.

'How . . . how do you know?' I finally got out.

'I read it in *Cosmo*.'

I was too out of breath to respond as I kept on moaning.

'You can fuck me soon, baby,' she said. 'You'll be so horny you'll blow in 30 seconds.'

'Now . . . ! Now . . . ! Please let me fuck you now!'

'Not yet. You're not horny enough.'

'*Please*, Liv!'

'Not yet. Trust me.'

She continued for the next hour-and-a-half. By then I was dripping with sweat, shaking under her touch, gasping for air with every breath. Every minute I thought my cock would explode, shoot out come all over her hand. But Liv was right – it wouldn't happen. This was the most intense foreplay known to man. My horniness had been stretched to, without a doubt, unchartered territories.

Finally, I couldn't take it any more.

'Liv please!' I cried, grabbing her hand. 'Please let me fuck you . . . ! I'm fucking begging you . . . ! I'm fucking *begging* you!'

She studied me carefully.

'How do you feel?' she asked.

'So horny . . . so fucking horny . . . please let's have sex . . . please, Liv . . . *please*!'

'Do you still want to drink?'

'What?'

'Have your cravings gone?'

'Yes.'

'Are you sure?'

'Yes! Let's fuck! *Please*!'

Finally convinced, she grabbed a condom from the bedside table and slipped it on me. I lasted one thrust and then I came.

For the rest of the night, I felt OK. Pretty good, even. We ate dinner, had sex two more times and then went to sleep.

Withdrawals dominated the next ten or so days, coming and going and coming back again. Olivia – who'd rostered herself off work for the following two weeks so that she could support me through them – was there for every episode. She'd do whatever she could to ease my tension: give me a massage, play the harp, take me to the movies, or on one special occasion, to Oceanworld to go diving with the sharks. It goes without saying that we also fucked like animals.

It's no surprise, I suppose, that the strength of my cravings depended on my mood at the time. When I was feeling good – because my writing was going well or because I was having a great time with Olivia – the cravings were relatively mild or non-existent. But when I was feeling miserable – usually because I was struggling with my writing – they were almost unbearable. The worst case was when I received my first semester marks late one afternoon. My average was 76%, once again well below my goal. I felt awful.

You should've studied harder, you fucking idiot! You've failed again. Failed again. Again and again and again.

That urge to drink away all feeling erupted inside of me. I started out on the bed, tossing and turning as I ripped strands of hair out of my head, groaned loudly through gritted teeth. My whole body grew slippery with sweat and like she'd done before, Olivia wiped me down with a towel and gave me a massage. She sucked my dick but I couldn't get hard, and in any sense, after a few minutes of it I had to run to the bathroom. As soon as I sat down on the toilet I started crapping diarrhoea. For ten minutes it gushed out of my ass, during which time my head began throbbing incessantly. I stumbled back into the bedroom and collapsed on the bed. Liv held a cool towel to my forehead, rubbed it gently over my face.

'Stay strong, baby,' she kept repeating. 'You're going to beat this. Just hang in there.'

My headache heightened to a horrific climax as I moaned in pain before a queasy cyclone stirred in my gut, forcing me to run to the bathroom and start throwing up in the toilet. Olivia knelt down behind me, rubbed the back of my neck.

'This is so fucking bad, Liv,' I gasped through mouthfuls of puke.

'You'll get through this, baby. The cravings will pass. You're going to beat this.'

'This is so fucking bad . . .'

'I know you, Jimmy. You're so strong. So determined. You'll beat this. I know you will.'

I fell to the floor, coughed up bile, crawled into the foetal position, puked again.

'You're going to beat this, Jimmy,' Liv continued. 'Remember when I first met you, after you hurt your spine? No one thought you were smart, but you told me you were going to study really hard and prove everyone wrong – and then you did – you got 99.60 and got into commerce/law at Sydney University. You overcame your injury and everyone's doubt in you. And you're going to overcome this too. Great things are going to happen to you, Jimmy Wharton. You're going to get awesome marks at uni and go on to become a rich investment banker. You'll get your novel published. We'll get married one day and have a beautiful family.'

She paused, leaning down to kiss my cheek.

'You're going to beat this, baby. I know you will.'

She was right. While I did have a predisposition to slipping into alcoholism when I became depressed because I'd heavily relied on booze to relax since I was 15, I also had the right characteristics to overcome it: determination, discipline, and no tolerance for failure – which is exactly what I would've judged drinking during a heavy craving episode as being.

Olivia was also right in the sense that it did get easier. By the third week of the holidays, the cravings were becoming fewer and farther between, and by the fifth and final week, they were a memory. At the time, I was actually reasonably proud of myself, thinking that I'd done well to kick my addiction, particularly without needing to go to a detox program or AA or anything like that. Hell, I didn't even see Dr King again. *There's no need to*, I thought. *I've got everything under control, now.*

With regards to my depression, it was more or less forgotten about over the course of the break. I suppose there were two reasons for that. Firstly, I didn't have to worry about studying for uni, so that struggle to find the right balance between my writing and my degree – and my self-perceived failure in both that so gravely troubled me – just wasn't an issue during the holidays. As a result, that unvarying unhappiness with life and that constant, unfocused dread just wasn't there. Secondly, I was so focused on trying to conquer my alcoholism that I more or less forgot about what had caused it in the first place. In any sense, by the time the cravings had stopped, I felt fine.

I don't have depression any more, I thought. *There's no need to go to the doctor and talk about the possibility of taking medication.*

In what could quite possibly be described as the most ignorant thinking of my entire life, I figured I'd beaten it.

As the cravings abated, it became much easier to write. The first thing I'd done since receiving Pierce's feedback was research the Great Depression in 1930s America in far more detail than I had done previously. Another thing I did was read a lot of novels. Like Pierce had said, many of the problems I had as a writer could be ironed out if I read a lot of good quality books and studied the craft of writing, so that's exactly what I did. In the three months since I'd received Pierce's review, I'd read *Of Mice and Men* (again) and *The Grapes of Wrath* by John Steinbeck, *To Kill a Mockingbird* by Harper Lee, *The Colour Purple* by Alice Walker, *Wuthering Heights* by Emily Brontë, *The Outsider* and *The Plague* by Albert Camus, *Sophie's Choice* by William Styron, and *One Flew Over the Cuckoo's Nest* by Ken Kesey. Pierce was spot on – it really did help my writing. And what's more, I actually found myself thoroughly enjoying the act of reading itself, which came as a surprise since I'd always hated reading in school. I wasn't really sure why that was, but I chalked it up to there being some sort of a difference between reading for the purpose of writing a thousand word essay on the book, and reading purely for the sake of soaking up its brilliance. I was glad I enjoyed it, too – by default, reading became my substitute for alcohol as a means to relax, which was something I knew I'd need to prevent a relapse into uncontrolled drinking.

On the last day of the holidays, Olivia and I had dinner at Jellyfish in Manly. As I usually do at the end of something and before the start of something else, I reflected on the break and the experiences I'd had. I'd quit drinking, and I was excited with the improvements I was making to my novel.

This is how it's got to continue, I said to myself. *When the second semester starts, you've got to work really hard to keep making progress on your book and to get that 85% average. That's the way to solve your problems – by working hard, not by drinking. If you just work hard, you'll achieve your goals and then everything will turn out great.*

And then I thought about Olivia and all those times I'd been ripping hair out of my head, sweating so much the sheets were soaked and vomiting in the afternoon or at three in the morning. Not once did she abandon me. She stayed with me every minute, holding my hand, telling me that I was strong and that I'd get through it and that everything would be better soon. She was so understanding. So unbelievably supportive.

I love you, Olivia, I thought. *I love you so, so much. Finally, all of the dramas are behind us – the abortion, the depression and the drinking. Life can go on again. We'll spend every day together. We'll get married and have a big bunch of beautiful kids. We'll be together forever and live happily ever after.*

I guess it's true when they say that ignorance is bliss.

IT REALLY DIDN'T SEEM SICK TO ME

Within the first two weeks of the second semester, I felt that constant despair return with a vengeance. Striking the right balance between studying and writing had trumped me again. I'd already fallen behind in my subjects, and I wasn't getting much writing done at all.

How the fuck could you think this semester would be any different, you fucking idiot? I yelled in my head. *It's the same scenario, so how could you think it would turn out differently from the other semesters? What the fuck is wrong with you? Every semester you've had at uni has been a failure, and you're well on your way to failing this one too.*

I honestly felt beaten. *How am I supposed to overcome this?* I asked myself. *Seriously – how am I supposed to sort this out and achieve my goals?*

My answer was the same as it always was: work harder.

You're awake for 16 hours a day, I reasoned. *It's not unreasonable for you to be studying or writing for, say, ten of those hours – that still gives you plenty of free time. All you've got to do is stick to working ten hours a day – or 70 hours a week – and you should be fine. You can time how long you work too, just to make sure you're not slacking off. If you work that hard, then you should be able to get your High Distinction average and finish your novel by the end of the year.*

In weeks three and four of the semester, I worked 72 and 70 hours. I got back on top of my subjects and wrote three whole chapters – but I found it unsustainably exhausting. Working ten hours and getting eight hours of sleep in a single day doesn't give you much time for anything else. Brushing my teeth, having a shower and eating breakfast in the morning took me half an hour; driving to uni, parking and walking to class took me another hour; having lunch took, say, half an hour; walking back to my car and driving home took me another hour; and having dinner took half an hour – that was already three-and-a-half hours of the day that I couldn't spend working, which meant that if I was going to do other things – like see Olivia, hang out with the boys, work as a tutor or go to church – I had to fit it into that two-and-a-half hour window of free time I had each day. And two-and-a-half hours (say four-and-a-half on weekends, because I wouldn't travel to uni then), just wasn't enough time. If Liv and I were to go out, we'd spend, say, two hours at dinner and maybe a couple of hours at a movie, and afterwards, time in the bedroom. Travelling to and from tutoring took about an hour, and the session usually lasted two. And what about parties? They usually went for three or four hours, and longer if you went clubbing afterwards. And, don't forget that I couldn't just work, say, five straight hours on the weekend, have lunch for half an hour, work another five straight hours, and then spend the night with Olivia or go out or whatever. I needed a few breaks in between – I couldn't do ten hours of intense, intellectually demanding work in a ten-and-a-half hour period. So on those days when I had tutoring, spent time with Olivia, hung out with the boys or went to church, I'd work more like six or seven hours instead of ten, which would mean I'd be behind the 8-ball the following day. I'd lose sleep trying to catch up, and find that I'd need a Red Bull in the morning before I could function and then another in the afternoon, and that even then I'd still feel tired and rundown for most of the day.

Not surprisingly, I couldn't maintain working that hard. In the fifth week of the semester, I only managed to work 59 hours. I was sleep-deprived from the previous two weeks, so some nights I slept nine or even ten hours, which obviously meant that I had less time to work during the day. Then on Friday I did dinner and a movie with Olivia which took five hours, not to mention that we had sex three times that week, which, including foreplay and everything else, amounted to three or so hours. On Saturday night I went to a party at nine and then went out clubbing until four (which was boring anyway since I wasn't drunk), and then on Sunday I had tutoring in North Sydney from one to three (not including 30 minutes of travelling time each way). Additionally, I was so mentally exhausted from the previous two weeks that I needed more frequent study breaks, and usually longer lasting ones. Fifty-nine hours was the result, and at the end of the week, I was racked with disappointment. Once again I'd failed to reach my target, and as a result, I'd fallen behind at uni and not written as much of my novel as I needed to in order to have it finished by the end of the year.

You've finally found a system that works, but you don't work hard enough to stick to it? I ranted at myself. *That's so fucking lazy. That's so fucking pathetic. You should be ashamed of yourself, you useless fucking loser.*

I was furious with myself, but I vowed to work harder the following week and reach my 70 hour target, and thereby catch up on my uni work and get back on track with my novel.

But the next week I amassed only 56 hours. Given that I wanted to have a social life and also worked as a tutor to save money, studying and writing for ten hours a day was almost impossible unless I missed out on sleep or didn't have any breaks. Under such circumstances, I was probably doing the best I could. But at the time, I couldn't offer myself that compassion. All that registered in my mind was that I was failing to achieve yet another goal. Instead of compassion, all I felt for myself was hatred.

You know what you need to do to achieve your goals — are you that fucking lazy that you can't even do it? What sort of a man can't work hard to achieve his dreams? You're so fucking hopeless, I told myself. *You're so fucking pathetic.*

Late Sunday night I lay in bed, stewing in self-hatred. I couldn't sleep, but as the time ticked by, my thoughts gradually eased.

I hate feeling this way. I hate feeling like a failure and that I'm lazy and worthless.

I kept on thinking.

I never want to feel like this ever again, I concluded. *Never, ever again. What I need,* I figured, *is something to make sure I won't fail. Something to make sure I'll work my hardest to get things done. If I can do that, then I'll stop hating myself.*

It seemed simple enough, but what could I do? I mulled it over, evaluated a few options before I came across one that I thought was a winner.

I got out of bed and went to the kitchen, opened the cutlery drawer. I studied the knives, their size and sharpness. I picked up a thick steak knife with a two-and-a-half inch handle and a two-and-a-half inch blade. After being satisfied that it was sufficiently sharp yet small enough to fit into a pocket, I lathered it with soap and washed it thoroughly. After I was convinced it was 100% clean, I returned to my room, sat cross-legged on the bed. I stared at the knife, running my thumb back and forth over its jagged, serrated blade.

My plan had been formulated: I was going to cut myself every time I thought I'd failed.

It makes complete sense, I thought. *When you do something wrong — like not work hard enough so that you fall behind at uni or don't get as much of your novel written as you'd like — it's your fault. If it's your fault, then you deserve to be punished. Ergo, whenever you do something wrong, you will cut yourself, starting just above the wrist and then working up your arm. It's just simple punishment for a failure, in the same way that a child is punished for being impolite, disobedient, swearing, or for not cleaning his room.* I had it in my mind that this would make me fail less.

The following week, I worked 63 hours. I was on track to work 70 until Friday night, when I spent the evening with Olivia. Then on Saturday I had two hours of tutoring and went to a party on the other side of town, and then on Sunday I went to church and had another two hours of tutoring. So I'd blown it.

You were on track, you fucking idiot, and then you slacked off. You shouldn't have spent so much time with Olivia. You should've left the party earlier or not gone at all. You should've worked harder throughout the week to make up for the fact that you wouldn't get much done on the weekend.

I was so disappointed, so furious with myself. I stormed to the bathroom, rolled up my sleeve, held my arm over the sink. I retrieved the knife from my pocket and clutched it tightly in my hand.

'You deserve this pain,' I said severely to myself.

Then I plunged the knife into my forearm, and slowly, methodically tore it across my flesh. Blood trickled from the open wound, dribbled down my arm as I cringed, grunted, gritted my teeth in pain. I promised myself I'd never be that lazy or disorganised ever again before I pulled out the knife, washed it, and put it back in my pocket.

After cleaning the wound, I slumped on my bed, wholly consumed with self-loathing. *You're so fucking pathetic and so fucking lazy I fucking hate you, you fucking idiot.* I felt so angry. So dejected. Like nothing but a failure. For the first time in weeks I felt the urge to drink – to crack open a bottle of bourbon, mix it with some Coke and plunge myself into the abyss. But all the booze had been cleared from my house, and in any sense, I knew it was a bad idea. I needed something though, any form of relief. I decided to wank, and for the next 15 minutes I was able to escape. But after coming, I was back in the same pit of despair.

By then, it was nearly one in the morning. I knew Olivia would be asleep, but I really needed her support. So I rang. On my third attempt, she picked up her phone.

'Hello?' she murmured drowsily.

148

'Liv . . .'

'What is it, baby? Are you OK?'

I was silent. I didn't know what to say.

'Jimmy?'

'Yeah . . . no . . . no, I'm not OK.'

She was startled.

'Jimmy what is it? What's the problem?'

'I don't – I don't know . . . I feel so worthless . . . everything . . . everything just seems so hard. I hate myself.'

Olivia gasped.

'Jimmy I'm coming over.'

'What? Baby it's late – you need to sleep.'

'Forget about it – this is more important. I'll be at your place in five.'

Sitting on my bed, I told her what I'd been feeling (although I left out the part about cutting myself with the knife).

'I think you're doing too much, baby,' Liv said. 'You're putting too much pressure on yourself. You don't have to work this hard, you know.'

'I do if I want to get an 85% average and have my novel finished by the end of the year.'

'But Jimmy it's not worth it if it's going to make you so depressed!'

'I'm only depressed because I'm not working hard enough to achieve my goals.'

'Not working hard enough? Jimmy, you're working harder than anyone I know!'

'But it's still not enough!'

Olivia sighed.

'Baby . . . I really think you're doing too much.'

'No, I'm not. I'm just trying to achieve my goals. And if I work as hard as I should be, I'll be able to achieve them and then I won't be depressed. The problem's just working that hard. It's tough to do.'

'Of course it is.'

'But you think I can do it, right Liv? You think I can work 70 hours a week for the rest of the semester and get an 85% average and have my novel finished before the end of the year, don't you?'

Olivia nodded again.

'Jimmy . . . you know I think you can do anything.'

I gazed at her, staring intensely into her eyes as all the sorrow and the misery that was weighing me down seemed to melt and then slide right off my back. Hearing her say the words I so yearned to hear filled me with resolve and reenergised hope.

Yeah, that's right, I thought. *I am strong, I am determined, I am a hard worker. I can do this.* I felt refortified. *I will do this. I'm going to get a High Distinction average and have my novel finished by the end of the year.*

I leaned in to kiss her. Our tongues wrestled for a few seconds before she pulled away.

'Are you feeling better, baby'

'Yes.'

I went to kiss her again but she turned her head.

'Jimmy, this is serious. You shouldn't ever feel worthless, and you absolutely shouldn't hate yourself. It's not healthy. If you do feel that way, then you should be seeing a psychologist – they'll be able to help you. And if it's struggling to juggle writing and uni that's making you feel this depressed, then you should change something – maybe do one and not the other. I don't know. But you should never feel this way.'

But by then I felt resolved and my energy had resurged. I felt hopeful, confident, and certain that I'd be able to work 70 hours a week for the rest of the semester and not feel depressed ever again.

'I'll be fine, hun. Trust me.'

'You're not listening, Jimmy.'

'I am, baby. Don't worry about it.'

'How can I not be worried?' she exclaimed. 'You ring me up in the middle of the night and tell me that you hate yourself and that you feel like getting wasted and you expect me not to be worried?'

'I'm sorry, baby, I'm sorry. But I'll be fine,' I repeated. 'I'll be better from now on.'

She held my hands, stared into my eyes.

'Jimmy . . . I'm worried about you. I don't think you're heading down the right path.'

'I'll be OK. Just trust me.'

She sighed.

'Promise me you'll at least think about what I said.'

'OK.'

'Promise me, Jimmy.'

'OK, Liv. I promise.'

She was still staring at me, her face coated in trepidation before she finally looked away.

'All right hit the lights,' she sighed. 'It's three in the morning – we'd better get some sleep.'

The following week I worked 70 hours and 15 minutes, but it came at the expense of my social life. I only saw Olivia once – she came over to study on Wednesday night – and I didn't see the boys at all. I also had to cancel all three of my tutoring gigs, giving up $240 in the process. By the end of the week I was exhausted, and very highly-strung. I hadn't done anything purely enjoyable for seven days. It was just work, work and more work, and it had taken its toll. I was fractious and irritable around the house, and over the course of the weekend had had three fights with Mum and two with Dad, all over trivial things like leaving my notes scattered across the dining room table or forgetting to take the trash out. But I'd gotten a sufficient amount of work done, and I felt good about that at least.

But being exhausted and fractious is a terrible mindset in which to do anything productive, so even though I'd had a good working week, I'd set myself up for a bad one. On Monday, Tuesday and Wednesday of the following week, I managed to study and write for only 22 hours, and I despised myself for it.

'What the fuck is wrong with you, you fucking idiot?' I bellowed in my room. 'Twenty-two fucking hours in three fucking days is fucking pathetic! You're such a lazy, worthless piece of shit! You fucking need to work harder!'

For the next four days, all I could think about was that if I didn't work hard, then that would make me even more of a failure, and then I'd have to cut myself with the knife again. It occurred to me that, unlike when I was training for a big surfing contest or studying for my Year 12 exams, I was motivating myself by dwelling on the depression I'd feel if I didn't achieve my goals, rather than focusing on the fact that I could achieve them and that working hard was necessary to do so. But at the time, it seemed like a trivial distinction instead of one of crucial importance.

That week, I worked 58 hours, and once again barely saw Olivia or my friends. I did go to church, though. I prayed for the strength to work harder, the focus to work 70 hours a week. But I just couldn't do it.

What the fuck is wrong with you? I berated myself again. *You're such a fucking slacker. You didn't even see Liv or the boys, and all you could do was 58 hours?*

I pulled out the knife from my pocket and stood over the sink.

'You deserve this pain,' I said fiercely to myself. 'You sure as hell deserve this pain.'

I forced the blade into my skin, just above the previous cut which still hadn't healed. My arm hurt, throbbed in pain. I panted horrendously, my face tightening in desperate agony as blood seeped from the wound, dribbled thickly into the sink. I held the knife in there, dragging it across my arm as the pain intensified before lessening slightly when I finally withdrew the blade. I quickly washed the knife and returned it to my pocket before clenching my throbbing forearm. I held it tightly, breathing sharply through gritted teeth as I thought about its meaning.

It's your own fault, I said to myself. *If you didn't fail so much, then you wouldn't be in pain.*

I hid my cuts with a long-sleeved shirt. On days I knew that I was likely to have sex with Olivia, I wrapped a bandage around my arm and told her that I was developing eczema, and that I needed the bandage to stop me from scratching. I couldn't think of a better way to conceal my wounds. Since that day, I've met other mental health patients who've used foundation cream, make-up or cocoa butter for the job. Then there was one girl I met who would invent stories for why she always had bandages around her arms. She'd claim she was attacked by a cat, fell on a piece of glass in the playground, or sprained her wrist playing netball. She told me that every day, she'd make sure she fell over in front of everyone, just so she could develop a reputation for being a klutz and thereby make her injuries seem more believable. She was 12 years old.

The following week, I found myself being increasingly plagued by one of depression's many torturous symptoms: an inability to concentrate. Whenever I'd be reading a textbook, sitting in a lecture theatre or writing my novel, my mind would drift off. I'd find myself anxiously contemplating how the hell I was going to catch up on all the course work I was behind on, or stressing out wondering how the hell I'd ever finish my novel by the end of the year (by that time – September – I'd only written up to chapter seven, so it seemed impossible that I would finish it before then). Other times, my wandering thoughts were less depressive. Sometimes I'd think about how great it would feel to get straight High Distinctions, or about how amazingly satisfying it would be to walk into a bookstore and see my novel displayed on a shelf, knowing that I'd stuck it to everyone who'd ever doubted me. I thought about Olivia, about how much I loved her, about how lucky I was that she was part of my life – particularly during such a difficult time. I imagined us in the future, getting married, having kids, and growing old together. I pictured it all happening at the same time, imagining how spectacular, how truly and wonderfully glorious life would be if I did achieve all my dreams, marry Olivia, and start a family. But regardless of the tangents my brain would stray off on, I found it impossible to focus on the task at hand. And this turned my illness into a self-fulfilling prophecy: the worse my concentration, the less work I got done, and the more depressed I became . . . the more depressed I became, the worse my concentration, the less work I got done, and the more depressed I became . . . and so the cycle went. Consequently, I was only able to work 57 hours that week. At a quarter-to-midnight on Sunday, I retrieved the knife once again.

When will you learn? I asked myself furiously. *This is all your fault. When will you learn?*

I repeated what was becoming a weekly custom, ripping the knife through my flesh. I did the same thing for the next two weeks too after working only 61 and 55 hours. Then the following week – probably the worst seven day period of my life up to that point – I worked 52 hours. After viciously cutting myself once again, I added a new twist to my gruesome ritual. After telling my parents I was popping out to Liv's place, I trudged down to Manly Wharf and sadistically held my throbbing, bleeding arm under the saltwater. I gritted my teeth, breathed loudly, damn near yelled it stung so much. And then I did scream. And then I pulled the knife out of my pocket and cut myself repeatedly.

You fucking cunt! I yelled. *You lazy! Mother! Fucking! Cunt!*

Blood oozed from my arm. I screamed in pain, rolled onto my back, gripped my arm tightly, bled all over my shirt, let my cries be swallowed up by the vast, callous darkness.

No one knew about my pain. That's one of the most perverse realities of depression, or of any mental illness for that matter. With a physical illness, the symptoms are much more evident, so family and friends are aware of the patient's suffering and often do their part to help. But depression? No one can see that. When you're cutting yourself alone, no one can see that. No one can read your thoughts and see how unhappy you are – or in the worst cases, how much you hate your life and want to die. That's why suicide usually comes as such a shock – because no one knows what's going on inside the victim's head. Their mind is a closed book, with a cover that blends in with all the others. Even Olivia and my parents – they knew a little bit – what I'd told them – but they had no concept of its severity. No one knew I was cutting myself. No one knew that I'd gone from perceiving myself as a good-looking, intelligent young man with the world at my feet to a lazy, pathetic, worthless loser who'd trade lives with anyone in a heartbeat. But it was inevitable they'd find out sooner or later. I was like a balloon of pus that was about to burst. I needed help, and I was thankful it came on the worst night of my life to date.

It was a Wednesday evening, and I had a statistics exam the following day at ten o'clock. I was three weeks behind, and I'd also had a criminal law assignment due that day that I'd been working on until the 5:00 pm deadline, so I hadn't started studying yet. Point being: I was in for a long night. At seven o'clock I chugged a Red Bull and sat down at my desk to learn the most recent material, but with depression continuously whispering inside my head, I found it impossible to focus.

You're so far behind, the voice tormented. *You should've learned all this ages ago. How the fuck could you let this happen, you fucking loser? You're so fucked for this exam. You're going to get a bad mark and then you'll have to cut yourself again.*

Overwhelmed with terror, I ran to the bathroom sink and threw up my dinner. After I'd gathered my breath, I caught sight of myself in the mirror. I hadn't shaved in a week. My eyes had bags under them from the constant lack of sleep. Vomit dribbled down my chin.

'You're a fucking mess,' I said.

I worked unproductively for another hour until I became so overwrought with stress and fear and self-hatred that I went downstairs to the rumpus room and raided the liquor cabinet, which had recently been restocked since my parents were convinced that my alcoholism was under control. Knowing they weren't home from work yet, I cracked open a bottle of bourbon and had six shots, one after the other. I was preparing myself to take a seventh, but then I stopped, thinking about how far I'd come from the night at Star City and all those times I'd gotten cravings and been sweating through the sheets, pulling hair out of my head, crapping diarrhoea or puking my guts out. I thought some more. *Why are you drinking? This is weak, this is what quitters do. And you are not weak. You are not a quitter.* So I returned the bottle to the cabinet and went back to my room to try and study.

Half an hour later, nothing had changed. I was still too overwhelmed to concentrate and desperately craving a drink.

No, don't be weak, I kept telling myself. *Be strong. Don't give in.*

But I needed some form of relief. When you're that low, that despondent, you just want to feel good for a bit even if you know it'll be temporary as hell. Short-term trumps long-term, and all you're looking for is an escape. I may not have been able to drink, but I still had a dick – and trust me, when you're depressed, you're more grateful than ever that you have a pecker.

At my desk, I undid the buttons and slipped my hand inside my jeans. I seized my prick and rubbed it up and down, up and down as my breathing intensified. I pictured Olivia's warm eyes, beautiful smile. Slowly it hardened, stiffer and stiffer as I pictured her soft round breasts, wet honeysuckle, imagined being inside her and thrusting in ecstasy until in reality, I felt warm and my hand was sticky and it was all over. But after a few seconds my body had inevitably cooled again, and I was instantly engulfed by depression's familiar black waters.

Midnight: back to work. More stress, more fear, more panicking, more self-loathing. I could hardly function. In the next hour, I was able to read only seven pages. I was so angry, so frustrated, so laden with despair – and I had absolutely no idea what to do about it. For 15 minutes I just sat there, doing absolutely nothing, inundated with a wandering dread. Then I called Olivia.

'Sweetie . . .' she murmured drowsily. 'What is it?'

I couldn't even speak. I just breathed heavily.

'Jimmy?'

'Liv . . .'

'Jimmy?' She was startled. 'Jimmy what is it?'

'Liv . . . I feel so shit.'

'OK I'm coming over.'

She came. We sat on the edge of the bed. I couldn't really communicate. She asked me questions but I couldn't articulate answers. She put her arm around me, silently rubbed my shoulder after she realised I couldn't talk. A while later, I finally said something.

'I wish I was dead.'

Olivia gasped.

'What?'

'I wish I was dead.'

She held me tighter.

'Jimmy don't – don't talk like that.'

'It's the truth.'

'Jimmy!'

'I want to be dead!'

And at that, I exploded. Jumping up from the bed, I pulled the knife from my pocket and pegged it across the room. Then books, pens, deodorant cans, and a full glass of water that smashed into the wall.

'I want to die!' I yelled.

'Jimmy stop it! Stop it!'

She grabbed both my arms, trying her best to hold me but I pushed her away.

'I want to die!'

The commotion woke my parents. Soon they were in my room and all three of them were trying to restrain me.

'I want to die! I want to fucking die!'

Finally, I stopped struggling. They eventually let go of me and I collapsed on the bed, buried my head in my hands. I started weeping. They all surrounded me, asking all sorts of questions but I just lay there crying, crying, crying.

When I was finally able to speak, I told them what had been happening. They were all so shocked. So shocked I'd gotten so depressed. So shocked I'd been cutting myself. So shocked it had happened right under their noses and not one of them had suspected a thing. Olivia wept. So did Mum. Dad looked dismayed, seemed incapable of speech. We talked and talked. They all agreed that I needed to see a doctor as soon as possible. Try to get this sorted out.

'You shouldn't feel the need to cut yourself. Never, ever, ever, ever.'

I finally came to agree with them.

I got my exam postponed a week and saw Dr King the very next day. I told him what had been happening. He got me to take the *SPHERE* questionnaire again, and this time I checked, in addition to the boxes I'd ticked the previous time (although minus "relying on alcohol and sedatives"), "stopped going out," "not getting things done at work," "I'm worthless," "frustrated," "irritable," "churning gut" and "life is not worth living." I registered a score of 17.

'In light of what you've told me, and according to your *SPHERE* scores, your depression seems to have worsened in the last few months.'

He kept calling it an "illness," saying that I was "sick." More about the chemicals in my brain being unbalanced.

'You need to see a psychologist,' he reiterated. 'A psychologist will work with you to pinpoint what's triggering your depression, and then teach you techniques to manage those triggers. That's the best way to deal with your depression – *not* by cutting yourself.'

He also said he thought it would be best if I started taking medication to help balance the chemicals in my brain. He told me a bit about the different types before we got onto the topic of side effects.

'Antidepressants, while proven to be very effective, often have side effects. Most commonly, these include nausea, insomnia, ejaculation disorder, and/or erectile dysfunction.'

My eyebrows jumped.

'Did you say . . . *"ejaculation disorder and/or erectile dysfunction?"* '

Dr King nodded.

I recoiled. The thought of no longer being able to do it with Olivia – particularly during such a difficult time when sex was one of my only forms of escape – was utterly unbearable. For this reason alone, I pleaded with Dr King not to place me on medication, and while he stressed that I really should be taking it, he eventually relented.

'If we must,' he sighed, 'we can see how you fair for the next week without it. But if last night repeats itself, then I'm going to have to insist that you start taking medication. OK?'

I sighed too.

'Yeah. OK.'

When I arrived home after my appointment, Olivia came over. We had very mediocre sex. I just wasn't into it, being too laden with despair, too racked with uncertainty over how I was going to achieve my goals and accordingly, I thought, ever be happy again. Everything seemed so bleak. I talked things over with Liv. Like she had in the past, she told me that she thought I was doing too much and that I ought to make some changes. I'd always thought she was wrong and continually dismissed what she said, but in that moment, when everything seemed so consummately hopeless, I was less closed-minded. I found taking some of the pressure off myself to be a welcome, soothing concept.

'Maybe I could defer uni next year. Spend it writing my novel.'

'Yeah, you could. Then you wouldn't feel like you'd have to work so hard all the time.'

I mulled over the idea for a few more days, and the more I did, the more I began to warm to it. It was hardly ideal, but my parents, Liv and I agreed that it seemed to be my best option. So the following week, I lodged the paperwork with the university.

The semester dragged on. Exhausted in every sense of the word, I eased my foot off the gas pedal, slowing down to around 50 hours of work a week. Not surprisingly, my marks suffered as a result. My average was 75.5%. Once again I was miserably disappointed, although I was comforted by the fact that 2009 would be different. And overall, I did feel better. After deciding to take a year off uni to focus on my writing, I went back to see Dr King. He said he thought it was sensible, and agreed to hold off placing me on medication. He still strongly recommended that I see a psychologist to get to the root of my depression and to help me conquer it, but I wasn't wild about the idea and what's more, I didn't think it would help.

I don't need to see a psychologist, I thought. *All I need to do is start achieving my goals again. If I can do that, then I won't feel depressed.*

It would be months before I'd finally see a psychologist, and realise that the reason I was depressed was because of the way I perceived my circumstances, as opposed to those actual circumstances themselves.

You can blame everything that's happened thus far – and everything that's about to happen – on this deceptively simple misunderstanding alone.

DIARY ENTRY: DECEMBER 12, 2008

Somewhere along the way, I started keeping a diary. I got the idea from Luke Davies' novel *Candy*, where the floundering protagonist at one point tries to write his way out of his heroin addiction. That's how I felt — as trapped as an addict. At the mercy of my illness.

December 12, 2008:

I said the days are better, and they are, because I no longer cut myself. But I'm still far from happy. At the start, happiness and I were bundled together, but this year's been kind of like the Big Bang, with me and happiness stretching further and further apart until it seems like nothing more than a dim pinprick in the great blackness of space. It feels like I have no sun. In my world it's always winter. I try to write but my mind's so hazy. I have the focus of a bored child.

Sometimes, I find myself thinking of Olivia's dog — little Jack Russell, cute as can be. He spends his days in a tranquil slumber. I watch him, enviously, just lying there. And I feel jealous. Jealous that he's not burdened by despair. Jealous that a biscuit makes him happy. That he can just lie in bed, sleep all day. That his life expectancy is 14 years instead of 76. That his life is not mine. And then I realise just how fucked my life is. I'm jealous of a dog, for fuck's sake.

Olivia's going with her girlfriends to Europe, and I need to get away too. I need an escape — somewhere, anywhere. So I closed my eyes, stuck a pin in a map. South America it was. I went to a travel agent who threw around some ideas before I decided to go to Chile after Christmas; volunteer at an underprivileged school in Cusco, Peru in January; and then go to the Galapagos Islands for a six day tour before stopping off in New Zealand for a week on the way home. Maybe a change will help? Who knows? Hope still fills me. Every day I pray. Please help me, God. Please let me be happy, once again. *I stay positive no matter what. I don't know any other way to be.*

A TRIP TO NEVERLAND

The first thing I remember feeling when I arrived in Santiago, Chile was an intense loneliness. I didn't know a single person on the entire continent, so I felt as isolated as Robinson Crusoe or that guy from *Castaway*. *I need to meet some people*, I thought. *There's no way I can bear four days and nights of this, particularly New Year's Eve. That would be so unbelievably depressing that I'd probably buy a bottle of bourbon and take shots in my room until I passed out. I know that's the last thing I should be doing, but there's just no way I can spend New Year's alone.* I explored my hostel a little bit, loitering around the pool table and the dining room in the hope of meeting someone, but the snippets of conversation I heard were in Spanish, and while my grasp of the language wasn't bad, having studied it through to Year 12 and taken night courses all December, they were speaking so quickly and using so much slang that I could hardly make out what they were saying. So I decided to walk up the street and eat some beef *empanadas* for dinner before going to bed at 8:30 to wear off my jetlag and hopefully have a better next day.

Desperate not to spend another day alone, I woke up the following morning and walked around the hostel with the same boundless hope of meeting someone that had filled me the day before. On the top floor outside the bathroom, I noticed a 20-something year old blonde-haired bloke wearing a Billabong t-shirt. I approached him.

'You from Australia?' I asked.

'Yeah, Queensland. How about you?'

'Sydney.' I stuck out my hand. 'My name's Jimmy.'

He shook it. 'Pete.'

'How long you been here for?'

'Just got here today. How about you?'

'Yesterday. I'm telling you, mate, you're the first bloke I've met who speaks English here.'

He laughed. 'Yeah, there aren't too many of us. There are a couple of British chicks downstairs, though – I'm about to go to the *plaza de armas* with them now, if you want to come?'

'Sounds good, man.'

We both took a piss before Pete introduced me to the British chicks, Claire and Sarah, both thin brunettes with fair skin, also probably in their 20s. We talked for a while and then walked to the *plaza*, the main square in Santiago. We went to the cathedral and Santiago's governmental centre, *Municipalidad de Santiago*, but mostly, we spent the day just wandering around and watching the city live. At any given time there were artists painting the scenes around them; street performers acting out skits, performing comedy routines or juggling fire; and people playing chess (I even played a few games with the locals, and from memory won three out of four). In the afternoon, after we'd filled up on numerous *pastel de choclos* – pies filled with ground beef, chicken, olives and boiled eggs and topped with mashed corn – we took a train back to the hostel.

'What do you guys want to do tonight?' Claire asked.

Pete shrugged. 'Drink? Then maybe head out somewhere?'

'Sounds good,' said Sarah.

They turned to me. *Fuck,* I thought. *I'd love nothing more than a night on the piss, but apart from the six shots I had that night at home, I haven't had a drink in six months.* I grew nervous, unsure of what to do.

'Well, Jimmy?'

Shit, I really shouldn't be drinking, I thought. *But it's not like I can explain to these people why. And they'll think I'm weird if I don't drink.*

'Yeah, sounds good,' I said, figuring I could just have a couple of beers to get in the spirit of things but stop short of getting wasted.

We popped into a supermarket on the way back to the hostel and picked up some vodka and some beers, and also some steaks and sausages to throw on the barbeque for dinner. After we'd finished eating, a few Americans and a couple of Dutch people (all around the same age – early-to-mid 20s) joined us for a game of "never have I ever." It's a pretty simple game: basically, everyone takes it in turns saying, for example, 'never have I ever had sex in a phone booth,' and everyone who *has* had sex in a phone booth has to have a drink. The game started off with fairly standard statements: 'never have I ever smoked weed;' 'never have I ever hooked up with someone of the same sex;' 'never have I ever had a threesome.' The first few beers were glorious, cascading like a waterfall down my throat as the game went on: 'never have I ever fucked a prostitute;' 'never have I ever had a one night stand without protection.' I'd done my fair share of them, mostly the relatively tame ones (sex on a pool table, on a balcony, etcetera, all with Olivia of course). But the others had done a lot more. One of the Dutch blokes claimed to have had a foursome with three hookers, and also confessed to fucking his very own niece.

After a couple of hours of playing, I was well and truly wasted – in part due to having a low tolerance from not drinking for months, and of course – as is typical of all alcoholics – from not being able to stop once I'd started. Everyone else was pretty blind too, so instead of going out, we all decided just to stay in and shoot the shit.

'I'll tell you guys the most fucked up thing I've ever done,' Pete said. 'A few years ago I was travelling around Europe, and there was this one night in Prague when I got really drunk and went back to this chick's eight person dorm. After I fucked her I had to take a piss, so I went to the bathroom across the hall, and then got back in bed with her. I was still pretty horny, so I kissed her, rubbed her tits a bit, to, you know, let her know that I wanted to go again. But then she started clawing at my face and screaming like crazy. So I jumped out of the bed. Meanwhile, someone had gotten up and switched the lights on.' He paused for effect.

'What happened?' Claire asked.

He smirked. 'Turns out I got into the wrong chick's bed by mistake.'

Everyone burst out laughing.

'What happened then?'

'It was fucked. I was standing there butt-naked in the middle of the room, with the whole dorm wide awake and staring at me and the chick I'd actually slept with jumping up and down, trying to explain to everyone what had happened. So I just picked up my clothes and bolted. What else could I do?'

Everyone laughed again.

'Wicked story man, wicked story.'

'I'll tell you guys one,' Sarah said.

'Go for it.'

'Last year when I was in Barcelona, I was at this club called Golden Eye and I saw this cute guy on the dance floor, so I went up to him and started dancing. Pretty soon we started grinding, and I could feel his boner on my hip . . . and then he started grinding harder, and then he was thrusting like a bloody rabbit. So I looked at him, about to tell him to chill out, and then I realised . . .'

'What?'

'That he was . . . coming!'

'Shit!' we all yelled.

'That is *fucked*,' said one of the Americans.

'It's all right,' said Pete. 'He came while he was grinding on a hot chick. Who cares?'

'It's still pretty messed up,' said another one of the Americans.

'It's not that bad,' slurred a very drunk Claire. 'I'll tell you something that happened to me once – and consider this my "bad" story. So a few years ago I was giving this guy that I was seeing head, right . . . and just when I thought he was about to come, he pissed in my mouth!'

'What the fuck!'

'Yeah, I know. I chucked him straight away.'

'What did he say about it?'

'He said he thought it was . . . romantic.'

We all laughed.

And that's how the night went, everyone just drinking and swapping stories until three in the morning when we all said goodnight and went back to our rooms to crash. Sloshed as anything, I lay on my back and stared hazily at the slightly-cracked yellow ceiling. I knew I shouldn't have gotten as drunk as I did, but in that moment it was hard to care. *For the first time in ages, I've had a really enjoyable night!* I thought. *This is great! This is awesome! I hope the whole trip's like this – just meeting new people, shooting the shit and having fun! Fucking A!* And then I passed out.

The next day was also good. After waking up at midday, Pete, Claire, Sarah and I took a cable car up the *Cerro San Cristóbal* and had a late lunch while enjoying the 360° views of the city. In preparation for a massive New Year's Eve the following night, we took that one pretty easy, just playing some pool in the rec room and then turning in early. Before I went to sleep, I emailed my parents to tell them that I was safe and well, and then Facebook'd Olivia to say that I loved her and I missed her and to wish her a safe flight to London on New Year's Day.

The following afternoon, we met two other Sydneysiders, Johnno and Matt, and went to the markets at Bellavista. At around four o'clock, we decided to pick up some food and booze for the night and head back to the hostel.

'What time do you guys want to start drinking?' Claire asked.

'Soon as we get back,' said Johnno.

'It's too early. We'll crash before midnight if we start getting pissed at five.'

'Crash? As soon as we hit the clubs we'll start snorting coke. There's no way we're going to crash.'

Matt was nodding. Claire and Sarah looked at each other. Pete was silent. Finally, Sarah spoke.

'Cocaine, huh?'

'Hell yeah! We're in South America – it's the drug-fucking-capital of the world!'

Pete shrugged. 'I guess. Sure, I'll do it.'

Claire and Sarah then nodded. 'We'll do it too.'

'How about you, Jimmy?'

I'd had such a good time a couple of nights beforehand, and I just wanted to have a good time that night too. And it's hard to do that when you don't fit in.

'OK,' I eventually said. 'I'll do it.'

We went back to the hostel, had showers, got changed and then started drinking as we cooked up a feast. After eating, the hostel manager came around with a massive jug of Pisco Sour – a Chilean (some say Peruvian) cocktail of pisco, lemon juice, egg whites and bitters – and we all had a couple of glasses. It was potent, and it hit me straight away. By nine o'clock we were all shitfaced, and after a few more games of pool in the rec room we decided to hit the town.

'So where are we getting the coke from?' Claire asked.

'We know a place,' said Johnno.

We went to a bar in Bellavista and ordered a few rounds of Pisco Sour while Johnno and Matt went to get the coke. When they came back with smiles on their faces, we knew they'd scored. They sat back down at the table and were both handed drinks.

'OK, it's pretty easy to snort,' Matt began. 'Just make a line of it on the top of the toilet using your credit card. Then, roll a note, stick it in one nostril, block the other and just go for it.' He handed each of us two little folded pieces of paper.

'One for as soon as we get in there, one for later in the night.'

We went to a club and instantly headed for the bathrooms to take the coke. Matt and I got in the same cubicle where he immediately emptied the contents of one of his packages on top of the toilet and used his credit card to make two short, thick lines before quickly snorting them.

'Your turn, mate.'

Too drunk to feel anything but excited, I slowly emptied the contents of the package and used Matt's card to make two more lines. He rolled a note for me.

'Just do what I did,' he said. 'Take it real quick and you'll be sweet.'

I snorted both lines, waited a few seconds.

'How long does it take to kick in?' I asked.

'Wait a minute, then you'll be flying.'

We lined up to get some drinks, and I felt my mouth start to go numb. Then I felt a huge rush of energy. I looked at Matt.

'Is it hitting you?' he asked.

I nodded. 'Yeah, I think so.'

'Let's smash this drink, find the others and get on the dance floor. I'm ready to rip this place up.'

We ran into everyone else at the bar, all downed another round of Pisco Sour and then hit the DF. By then I was exploding with energy, and we all jumped up and down on the dance floor, bouncing to the beat and sweating our asses off but feeling so damn good we didn't care. I felt incredible, so full of life and vigour, just wanting to jump! Jump! Jump! Jump! Jump!

'Hell, yeah!' I screamed, punching the air. 'Hell, yeah!'

I turned to Matt and the others, all of whom were as hyped as I was.

'Yeah!' I screamed.

'Yeah!' we all screamed, arms around each other and jumping as one.

Apart from to keep buying drinks, to piss, and to take another hit at around three in the morning, we didn't leave the dance floor until closing time at five. After stopping for *empanadas* at a street vendor, we eventually arrived back at the hostel at six where I swapped Facebook details with everyone, hugged them all goodnight, packed my bags and then hailed a taxi to take me to the airport for my 9:00 a.m. flight to Cusco, Peru.

I was a fucking mess at the airport. Still drunk as anything, I somehow managed to navigate my way through customs and find the right gate, albeit with the help of several unimpressed airport employees. I boarded the plane, went to the toilet, chugged 15 cups of water, and then took a long, long piss. While I was washing my hands, I noticed the "DO NOT DRINK WATER FROM THE TAP" sign before returning to my seat and passing out until touchdown.

After I'd collected my bags and sleepwalked through customs, I crawled into a taxi which was similar in size to a Cooper Mini, but with tattered seats and a beat-up radio instead of a sleek Western interior and a six speaker CD player.

'Adonde vas?' he asked.

'La Rapa,' I replied, handing him a crumpled piece of paper with my host family's address on it.

'Si, si,' he said, accepting it. He put my bags in the backseat and we both got in. I reached for where the seatbelt would usually be before realising there wasn't one.

'Cinturón?' I asked.

'No, amigo,' he replied, shaking his head. I then noticed that he didn't have one either. *Shit*, I remember thinking. But I was too tired to really care.

Peru, being a Third World country, was considerably poorer than any place I'd ever been to. The first thing I noticed as we drove along the dusty brown roads was that some of them didn't have any lanes, meaning that if a driver wanted to veer in a particular direction, he'd just sound his horn and go. The second thing was the rectangular brown mud-brick houses scattered across the vast green mountains surrounding us. *How can houses be made out of mud?* I remember thinking. *What happens if it rains or if there's a flood or something?*

I asked the driver.

'Lo que ocurre con las cámaras cuando llueve?'

'Si hay un poco de lluvia, no es ningún problema. Si hay un montón de lluvia, las casas son destruidas.'

At least the (very simple, one story) brick houses on the sides of the streets wouldn't get destroyed, I thought morosely.

After about ten minutes of driving through the dilapidated town, we arrived at my host family's home, a place with three bedrooms and one toilet connected to a tiny dining room and kitchen. I met the "house mother," Dina – a lovely middle-aged woman with dark features and long black hair – and my roommates Carmen, Steph, and Humphrey – all from Sydney and all having just finished their second year of uni like me. Dina made me a beautiful chicken soup which did wonders for my hangover, and we all talked in broken Spanish around the kitchen table (Dina couldn't speak English) before I excused myself, saying that I was exhausted from not having slept the previous night. I went to bed and didn't wake up until the following morning.

The next day, I met the other 15 or so volunteers who were staying at other houses. After we'd all been introduced and had a chat, we drove a minibus up the dirt roads of the rugged mountains to the school where we'd be working for the next four weeks.

It was situated in the middle of a small farming village about 25 minutes out of the city. Each house in the area was made out of mud bricks like the ones I'd noticed on the way from the airport to Dina's place, and each had a front yard growing rows of vegetables that was fenced off from a pig pen and a chicken coop. The school itself was comprised of three mud brick classrooms and a field outside where children kicked around a soccer ball, jumped skip rope and happily chased each other around.

I spent the morning helping to build a coop so that the school could house chickens, and thereby have eggs as a constant source of food for lunch. Afterwards, a couple of the other volunteers and I organised a sport class for the third and fourth grades, which was dodgeball on the field. I was playing in the game, but at times, I found myself just watching the kids with admiration as they jumped and laughed and smiled and threw the ball around with such alacrity and joy, even though they were obviously poor as hell. Plenty had unevenly trimmed hair, and crooked teeth that would have "required" braces in First World countries. Some of them wore navy jumpers with the white and orange World Vision logo, and most of the children, if not all of them, had a rash on their cheeks, apparently due to having dry skin caused by the high altitude. It reminded me that even though I'd been suffering from depression for most of the past year, that being happy is always possible, and that I should never give up on it no matter what.

That night, the charity managers organised a welcome dinner for all the volunteers at a fancy restaurant in *la plaza de armas*. After having potato-cheese soup for our first course, we ate sumptuously from a buffet of beef, chicken, llama and guinea pig with sides of rice and vegetables. For dessert we had cake, fruit and ice-cream, and throughout the meal drank wine and Cusquena, Peru's most popular domestic beer. Then at ten-thirty, we hit the clubs in the *plaza*. After drinking more Cusquenas and a few Pisco Sours at Mama Afrika's and Mythology, I was pretty well wasted. But the fun was only just beginning. At around one in the morning, Eliza, a tall, brown-haired girl from Sydney who I'd been getting along well with all day, asked me if I'd like to do some coke with her.

'Yeah for sure,' I said. 'Do you know where to get it from?'

'Yep.'

'Sweet.' At that moment, Humphrey came out of the bathroom and joined us.

'You want to do some coke with us?' I asked him.

He considered it for a moment.

'I've only ever done weed before. What's coke like?'

I told him what it felt like when I did it a couple of nights earlier in Chile and he was instantly on board. I asked my other roommates, Carmen and Steph, but they weren't keen.

Humphrey and I each bought another Cusquena while we waited for Eliza to get the coke. Five minutes after she'd left she returned with three small packages, and discreetly slipped one to me and one to Humphrey. Eliza then went to the ladies' to snort hers, while Humphrey and I squashed into the same cubicle in the mens'. I took his packet and emptied about half of each of ours on top of the toilet and used my credit card to form four lines. I rolled up a ten sole note and snorted the first two to show Humphrey how to do it. He then took his two lines, and after flushing the toilet, we left the bathroom and found Eliza. The effect soon kicked in and we joined the other volunteers dancing wildly, jumping up and down and having the time of our lives.

'This shit's unreal!' Humphrey yelled in my ear over the music.

'Damn straight!'

We took another line an hour or so later. By that time, well and truly fucked out of our minds, we found ourselves dancing on top of the bar –

an acceptable custom in some Peruvian nightclubs. Despite being so consummately wasted, I distinctly remember looking out across the dance floor as I fist-pumped like a maniac to the music and feeling absolutely incredible. *Life is so good!* I remember thinking. *How was I ever depressed? Life is so fucking good! I'll never be depressed ever again!*

We snorted another line at three in the morning before partying until five, taking a taxi home, crashing for a couple of hours and then waking up the next morning to go to school.

Such was the typical day for the volunteers: going to school during the day, and then partying like crazy all night long. I really was having one hell of a good time. And cocaine! *Ah! What beautiful stuff!* I'd muse. *That white powder is just so thin and soft and yummy! And the high it gives you! It's like snorting pure happiness! Like sniffing glory and joy and bliss!* Whenever I took it I felt like I could run forever, fly, conquer the world. I felt so confident, vivacious and energetic. It just made me feel the exact opposite of depressed. In some twisted, unnatural way, it gave me the one thing I'd been desperately searching for all year – happiness – and it wasn't long before I started taking it at "inappropriate" times. A couple of binges later, I gave Eliza 40 extra soles (about 20 Australian dollars), and asked her to get me two grams on top of what we usually got.

'Why?' she asked.

'I just want to have some spare.'

She looked at me suspiciously, but then just shrugged her shoulders and said 'no problem.'

If it makes me feel so unbelievably good, then why do I only take it at night? I reasoned. *Why not take it in the morning and during the day as well?* With hindsight, I realise that this line of thinking must sound completely absurd. Using narcotics all day just to feel happy? Is there a more textbook way of getting seriously addicted and ruining your life? But depression bends straight lines, complicates simple equations. Don't you get it? I just wanted to feel happy – almost at any cost – and my judgment was significantly impaired by my illness – just like it was when I was drinking like an alcoholic or cutting myself every Sunday.

So I started snorting coke at random intervals throughout the day. I'd usually take a line as soon as we got to school just to give myself a buzz, another when we got back to the volunteer house, and then another after dinner before we'd hit the town. I'd usually also take one as soon as I woke up, since apart from weekends where I'd spend most of the day sleeping, I'd have to get up early after only having a few hours of sleep due to clubbing until late the night before. Of course, I'd also have somewhere between four and six lines at the club. Eliza was always suspicious when I asked her to get me more coke, but she was usually too drunk to really care and never remembered it in the morning anyway.

Without being conscious of it, I was well on my way to becoming a coke addict. I needed a wakeup call, and halfway through January, I got it in one of the most bizarre ways imaginable.

It all started when my roommate Carmen suggested that we both take a short trip to Bolivia. After a few of the volunteers who'd already been there told me what it was like, I was all for it. Carmen wanted to see the *Salar de Uyuni* salt flats in southwest Bolivia, and I wanted to go to Route 36 in La Paz, a club renowned for selling coke to the customers to snort on the bar; and, also in La Paz, San Pedro Prison, a jail that offers guided tours to foreigners and the opportunity to snort rack with the inmates. I wasn't sure how we were going to do everything since we had limited time and Carmen was dead against heavy narcotics, but I was excited for the adventure and figured that we'd just work it out along the way.

As soon as we arrived in La Paz and checked into our hotel room, I was keen to go to the prison. I told Carmen about it, and after I'd assured her it was safe, she was interested enough so off we went. We took a taxi to San Pedro Plaza and then experienced the disbelief felt by the majority of tourists when they're told that the yellow-walled building with windows instead of bars that's situated upon prime real estate right smack bang in the middle of town is the prison that houses some of Bolivia's most hardened drug dealers.

'*Está usted seguro de que esta es la prisión?'*

'*Sí,*' the driver replied, confirming that it was in fact the right place.

We paid him and then dubiously approached the arched entrance where two policemen guarded the door.

'*Disculpe señor, es está la prisión de San Pedro?'*

'*Sí, amigos, sí,*' he said eagerly. '*Ustedes son touristas, sí? Qieren un tour, sí?'*

'*Sí! Tour!'*

'*Sí, sí!*' he said zealously, ushering us inside. We had indeed found the right place.

We entered a wide passageway which led to a gate with vertical bars extending from the floor to the roof. On our side stood several guards wearing green uniforms chatting idly amongst themselves, as well as another dozen or so young people of different origins all wearing plain clothes, presumably tourists waiting for the tour to begin. On the other side, pressed up tightly against the metal gate and pushing and shoving each other to get to the front and stick their arms through the bars in attempts to sell us drugs or beg for money, was a loud frenzy of prisoners. Carmen and I looked at each other. We were both a little scared, but also excited to see what lay beyond the bars and learn about the prison's way of life.

We waited a few more minutes for another couple of tourists to arrive before each paying 20 bolivianos (about five Australian dollars) to the guards. After the prisoners were ordered to step back and make way for us, one of the guards opened the gate and let us inside. A moment later, a well-groomed man with black hair, dark skin and medium build, probably around 30, approached us.

'Hi, I'm Pedro,' he said, smiling warmly and shaking each of our hands as we introduced ourselves. He was wearing a clean light blue button-up shirt, dark blue jeans and polished black leather shoes. *How is he dressed so nicely?* I remember thinking. *These are the sort of clothes I wear to nightclubs back home.*

Well-dressed Pedro then showed us around the prison, which was, to put it mildly, nothing like I'd expected. Inside, there were restaurants, convenience stores and small businesses, all owned and run by the inmates themselves. Pedro explained that the prison was like its own small economy. At the top were the wealthy businessmen who continued to run their empires that existed on the outside, using fax machines and phone lines which they'd paid other inmates skilled in the trade to install. The prison's middle class was comprised of cooks, painters, carpenters, electricians, accountants, doctors, lawyers and other skilled workers who sold their services to fellow inmates, and the lower class was made up of unskilled workers who performed chores like cleaning the toilets and delivering messages. Of course at each class level, there were also plenty of inmates who dealt drugs or engaged in other forms of criminal pursuits to make their money.

When Pedro showed us his so-called "cell," I could hardly believe my eyes. There were no bars. From the outside, it looked like your average apartment – just a wooden door embedded in a concrete wall. As we stood there stunned, Pedro retrieved a key from his pocket, unlocked the door himself, and opened it for us.

'Welcome to my home,' he said.

My jaw dropped when we walked inside. It honestly was like a studio apartment – Pedro had a kitchen with a fridge, stove, microwave and oven; a large shelf full of books and magazines; a chest of drawers with clothes pouring out of them; a dinner table surrounded by chairs; a bedside table with CDs, cigarette packs, a toothbrush, toothpaste, a razor, shaving cream, deodorant, shower gel, hair gel, skin cream and cologne resting on top; and at the foot of his bed, he had a big screen TV and a six speaker stereo.

'How . . .' 'what . . .' 'this can't be . . .' were the shocked responses from the tourists.

Pedro laughed. 'Everybody, find somewhere to sit and I'll tell you a bit about our living conditions.'

Inmates had to buy their own cells. If they could not afford one, they slept outside in the freezing cold. The way Pedro explained it, the market for cells operated like any normal property market: prices fluctuated according to supply and demand, and commissions for agents and lawyers had to be paid for the transaction itself. After agreeing on a price, the buyer and seller would sign a sale-purchase contract in front of a witness and the section delegate. The section delegate and the witness would then sign the sale-purchase agreement too, and the section delegate would stamp it with the section stamp to make it official. After the sale price had been paid, the buyer then had to pay the title transfer fee, which was received by the section treasurer. The title document was then handed over to the new owner, who then had the right to live in the room.

'Are all the rooms this nice?' one of the tourists asked.

'No,' Pedro replied. 'In the more dangerous parts of the prison, there are long rows of tiny concrete cells lit by a dim bulb dangling from the ceiling. There are no windows, and up to five inmates live in each cell. They have no possessions and live off scraps.'

He paused.

'Some inmates die of starvation. Others freeze to death. Some are stabbed and bleed out.' He shook his head. 'This is prison. Life is cheap.'

The tour continued for another half hour or so as Pedro told us more about the workings of the prison and shared a few of his more interesting tales. Afterwards, he said that instead of leaving, we could choose to stay the night for an extra 30 bolivianos. A group of six Europeans instantly said they'd do it, but none of the other tourists wanted to. I'd heard from a number of people that at night was when the coke snorting started and things at the prison really got exciting. I'd also been assured that it was safe – the tourists brought so much money into the prison that no one wanted them to stop coming, which is exactly what would happen if any of them were robbed, hurt or killed. Tourists were thus very well protected, both by the prison guards and the inmates that had been hired by the tour guides for added protection. I looked at Carmen, hoping she'd want to stay but knowing she probably wouldn't.

She sighed. 'You want to spend the night here, don't you?'

'If you don't want to we can go back to the hotel. It's fine.'

'You don't have to come back with me.'

'I'd feel bad leaving you all alone.'

'Don't be silly! If you want to stay, stay. I'll be fine.'

'Are you sure?'

'Of course. I'm exhausted anyway – I hardly slept last night on the bus over here. I'll probably just have an early dinner and go to bed.'

'Are you *really* sure?' I repeated.

'Of course. Come back early in the morning though so we can go to the *Catedral Metropolitana* tomorrow.'

'OK. Thanks, Carmen.'

So then there were eight of us: Pedro, the six Europeans, and me. It wasn't long before Pedro pulled a bag of cocaine out of his pocket and started making lines on top of CD cases.

'This is where the best cocaine in the world is made,' he said as he lined it up. 'San Pedro Prison.'

'What do you mean?' one of the Europeans asked.

'Cocaine – some of the prisoners have laboratories in their cells. This is where it comes from – the purest cocaine in the world. You want to know how much coke we have here? Some of the inmates have cats that are addicts.' Pedro laughed at our astonishment and then we all started doing lines.

After a couple of hours I was higher than I'd ever been. I had no idea how much coke I'd had, but apparently it was more than anybody else.

'Whoa! *Australiano,* you've got to take it easy, man!' Pedro exclaimed (one of the Europeans was also called Jimmy, so he'd taken to calling us by our country of origin).

'Pedro man I fucking love this shit!' I said manically. 'This shit's so fucking good man I love being on coke, it just makes me feel so good and awesome and I fucking love it!' The shit I was saying was pretty stupid – we'd also been drinking.

Pedro studied me carefully.

'How long have you been in South America, *Australiano?*'

'Two-and-a-half weeks.'

'And how much coke have you had in that time?'

'No idea man . . . heaps eh? It's just so fucking good! Everyday all the time whenever I want! It's just so fucking good!'

Pedro shook his head.

'*Australiano,* you've got to stop taking so much, man,' he said firmly. 'Otherwise, you're going to get addicted.'

'No way man I'm not going to get addicted. I'll be fine!'

'*Australiano,* listen to me,' he said sternly, but I was way too hyped to concentrate, just thinking about how amazing everything was compared to when I was depressed. I reached for the bag of coke on the table to make another line, but Pedro cut me off.

'I'm serious, *Australiano!*' he said, raising his voice. 'You've got to stop this shit!'

'Chill out man I'm fine!' I laughed, reaching for the bag once more. But Pedro cut me off again and shook his head seriously.

'I would rather you didn't have to see this, *Australiano.* But if it's going to stop you from turning into a coke addict, then I'll have to show you.'

He told everyone to 'wait a minute' before he left his cell, taking the bag of coke with him. When he came back a few minutes later, he was accompanied by a shockingly groomed, emaciated, middle-aged man dressed in what barely passed as rags. It looked like he hadn't showered in days. He had scabs and bruises all over his body, a nose that was flat and crooked, and only five teeth. Conversation stopped as we studied him carefully.

'Everyone, this is José,' said Pedro. 'Say "*hola*" to José. He doesn't speak any English.'

'*Hola!*' we all said loudly.

José didn't say anything, didn't do anything except ravenously stare at the coke that Pedro was lining up on a CD case.

'Now everyone,' he began, looking directly at me, 'this is why you never, *ever*, want to get addicted to coke.'

He handed the CD case to José who zealously snatched it from his hands and quickly snorted the coke. For a minute or two, he didn't do anything but stand there. Then, he began to fidget . . . then the next thing we knew he was jumping up and down, frantically flapping his arms in the air before he fell to the floor and started convulsing wildly, shrieking in terror as he furiously scratched his body.

'*Arañas! Arañas! Hay arañas debajo de mi piel!*'

'What the fuck is he saying?' yelled one of the Europeans.

'He's paranoid,' Pedro replied. 'He thinks there are spiders underneath his skin.'

We all watched on aghast as José continued screaming, spasming violently on the ground and scratching himself vehemently, drawing blood with his dirty long nails. I wanted to stop him, pin him down so he would stop hurting himself, but Pedro held out an open palm, instructing us not to come any closer. But then José started pounding his head on the ground, slamming it so hard that his skin cracked and blood oozed from the wounds. It was more than I could bear. I lunged forwards to help him, but Pedro restrained me.

'No, *Australiano*! Leave him! He needs this.'

'But he's going to die!' I yelled, struggling to break free.

'No he's not. He needs this,' Pedro repeated.

A few seconds later, José stopped moving. Blood was dribbling down his face and was flecked across his body. His eyes were sealed shut, his breathing deep and heavy. There was complete silence as we watched him, panic-stricken.

It was several minutes before José's eyes finally cracked open. A couple of minutes later, he staggered to his feet, and Pedro gave him a towel, a small tub of ice, a plate of our leftover chicken dinner, as well as some Band-Aids.

'*Gracias,*' murmured José before leaving. Pedro closed the door behind him and looked at us sombrely. We were all horrified. It was a while before anybody spoke.

'What . . . what was . . . what was h-happening to him?' one of the Europeans finally stammered.

'Paranoia,' replied Pedro. 'He thinks spiders are crawling underneath his skin. But eventually he snaps out of it – when he hits his head on the ground. It's the pain that snaps him out.'

Once again, a while passed where no one spoke. Finally, looking directly at me once again, Pedro repeated:

'And *that*, everyone, is why you *never* want to become a coke addict.'

After another awkward silence, the Europeans got back to talking amongst themselves and drinking rum. I was too disturbed to socialise. Pedro came and sat beside me.

'I'm sorry I had to show you that, *Australiano*. It's just that I've seen so many people lose their lives to drugs. I didn't want you to make the same mistake.'

My eyes filled with tears as it all began to sink in. *Look what you've done,* I thought to myself. *You're going down the same path with coke as you went with booze.* And then all of a sudden everything came gushing out, and I was telling Pedro all about my depression and everything I'd been through and how taking coke just made me feel happy for the first time in what felt like forever. He listened patiently the whole time, never interrupting as I spilled my soul. When I was finally finished, he put his arm around me, patted me kindly on the shoulder.

'I don't know how to fix your depression, *Australiano*. But I can promise you that cocaine is not the answer.'

I nodded seriously.

'Yeah. You're right.'

We were silent for a while, absorbed in our own thoughts before Pedro checked his watch.

'It's nearly morning, *Australiano*. You should go back to your hotel and get some sleep before you go with your friend to the *Catedral Metropolitana*.'

I nodded in agreement, eager to get out of there anyway and be alone with my thoughts.

He walked me to the gate of the prison. Awash with emotion I hugged him tightly.

'Thank-you, Pedro,' I whispered in his ear.

'No problem, *amigo*,' he said, clapping me warmly on the back.

To this day, I'm still grateful for what Pedro did for me, and I'll have a go at anyone who says that all prisoners are scum who have no hearts.

The following night, instead of going to Route 36 as planned, I decided to go to an internet café and Skype Olivia.

'Hey, sweetie!' she exclaimed when she first heard my voice. We'd been sending each other messages on Facebook the whole time I'd been away, but that was the first time we'd managed to Skype.

'Hey, baby! How're you going?'

'Great! I'm in Austria now! It's so cold!'

We spent a while catching up on each other's news from the previous few days.

'Baby we took a cruise down the Rhine River!' she began excitedly. 'It was so beautiful! We passed all these castles and vineyards! And then we stopped in this lovely little village called St Goar where we went wine tasting in a candlelit underground cellar! I wish you were there with me, sweetie! It was such a beautiful little town! Gorgeous cobbled streets, medieval castles in the background, and the largest freestanding outdoor cuckoo clock in the world! Then at night we took the coach to Munich and spent the day at Maximilianstrasse. Oh, Jimmy! It was the prettiest boulevard I've ever seen! All the designer labels had stores there: Dolce & Gabbana, Gucci, Versace, Hugo Boss, Louis Vuitton, Dior, Chanel and Bulgari. They had the prettiest things, baby, the most beautiful dresses I've ever seen! But everything was so expensive – I spent four hours there and I didn't even buy anything! And afterwards, we went to this magnificent park called *Englischer Garten*. It was stunning, baby – snow sprinkled across the ground and flecked through the trees . . . ducks swimming in the water . . . so beautiful! And we saw so many things there! The Japanese Teahouse, the Monopteros, the Chinese Tower and the Rumford Saal! Then at night we went to the beer garden there and tried all sorts of German beers. I don't even like beer, sweetie, but I drank some! And then today we arrived in Austria!'

It sounded like she was having the time of her life. I also definitely noticed that she seemed to be back to her "usual self" – effervescent, relaxed and worry-free – as opposed to being, as I perceived it, burdened by concern for me. I became inundated with guilt whenever I thought about what I'd put her through, and even more so when I felt like I detracted from her happiness rather than added to it. Given that she was in such good spirits and was enjoying her holiday so much, it was surely the wrong time to tell her that I'd been snorting coke six times a day. But at the time, I thought she'd be pleased to hear that I'd decided to stop. Instead, a fight ensued.

'I can't believe you'd be so stupid as to take cocaine!' she shrieked.

'I know, sweetie,' I said softly, trying to calm her down. 'It was – '

'How have you not learned your lesson from your drinking? How can you start snorting coke in the middle of the day and not see anything wrong with it?'

I tried to apologise, I tried to explain, but there was nothing I could say to mollify her anger. When she started to weep, I became racked with guilt once again.

'J-Jimmy . . . I love you *so* much . . . so it h-hurts me to see you do these things to yourself. The drinking . . . cutting yourself . . . now the cocaine. I was so worried about you last year, J-Jimmy. Sometimes . . . s-sometimes I couldn't sleep . . . just thinking about how much pain you were in and the things you did to yourself. It hurt *me* too, Jimmy.' Her sobbing grew louder. 'And I th-thought you were b-better . . . these last few weeks . . . and now I find out you've been taking cocaine every day . . . and n-now . . . now I'm w-worried again!' She burst into tears.

'Liv please don't cry,' I begged.

'I love you too m-much to see you do this . . .'

'Please don't cry, Liv. Please don't cry . . .'

'I love you too much . . .' she trailed off, crying.

'Liv I'm going to stop. I promise. I'll never take cocaine ever again.'

She cried for what felt like an eternity before finally composing herself.

'Do you *really* promise?' she asked.

'Yes. I promise.'

We continued talking for a few minutes longer before we hung up and I was left alone with my remorse.

You've got to stop doing this, I told myself. *You can't keep fucking up and putting Liv through all of this. Otherwise, you're going to drive her away.*

I thought about José, and was confident that I'd be able to abstain from snorting coke for the rest of my life. *I'll be OK,* I told myself. *I know I can stop taking cocaine and be a good boyfriend to Olivia.*

The following day, Carmen and I were meant to take a bus to see the *Salar de Uyuni* salt flats, but she'd gotten food poisoning at dinner and was up sick all night. Instead of going to the salt flats, she preferred to just take the bus back to Cusco where she could rest before returning to school. We left that night and arrived the following day.

The rest of my trip was amazing. I continued having a great time in Peru, going out every night with the other volunteers and partying into the early hours of the morning. Keeping true to my promise to Olivia, I didn't snort any more coke. Then again, I did continue drinking a lot. I knew I probably shouldn't have, but just being in that environment with everyone partying all the time made it difficult not to. All I wanted to do was just fit in and have a good time, and I didn't feel like I could do that without joining in the fun. I made a rule, though, that this would purely be an "overseas thing" – that there'd be no more binge drinking back in Sydney. *If you can stick to this rule,* I figured, *then it doesn't really matter what happens over the next few weeks.*

The Galapagos Islands were serene. After the madness of Peru, it was nice to just lie on the beach, snorkel and relax on the boat that took us from island to island. I figured that week would be somewhat of a detox week for me, but most nights we were up late on the roof of the boat drinking and swapping travel stories. One morning, I woke up lying on a deckchair with rum spilt all over my clothes and no memory of what had happened the previous night. My fellow travellers snickered when they saw me at breakfast, but I never found out what it was all about.

In Auckland, New Zealand, I spent most of my time getting back in touch with my novel. Each morning, I'd wake up early and walk a couple of blocks to a coffee shop called Esquires, order an iced chocolate and a ham and cheese croissant and spend the morning writing. After having lunch at Subway, I'd return to Esquires to write some more, and would usually go back there after dinner too. Having spent six weeks away from my novel revitalised me, augmented my desire to finish it and get it published. When I'd first arrived in New Zealand, I was up to the part where the protagonist's mother was about to start working as a prostitute, and in the one week I was there, I wrote all the way up to the part where they had been evicted and were forced to live in the shanty town (three whole chapters!). I was ecstatic. I knew my novel was improving and that I was on the right track. The plot was much sharper now, and many of the other problems Pierce had drawn to my attention had been weeded out. My writing style had also dramatically improved, due to all the reading I'd been doing. In the previous six months alone I'd read another 12 or so of John Steinbeck's books; *Breath, Cloudstreet, Shallows* and *Dirt Music* by Tim Winton; and *The Catcher in the Rye* by J. D. Salinger. When I wasn't writing, I spent most of my time listening to "fire-up" songs like Nelly's "Heart of a Champion" and Survivor's "Eye of the Tiger," all the while imagining myself receiving that phone call where I'm offered a publishing contract and yelling, screaming, punching the air; or walking into a bookstore and seeing my novel on the shelves and being so steeped with pride, so happy that I'd proved all my doubters wrong that I could weep. It was an obsession that dominated my thoughts. *I must do this. I must!* I was so imbued with hope, so excited for the year ahead. *I get to spend the whole year writing, working on my dream!* I'd think exuberantly. *How amazing is that!*

When I arrived back in Sydney, my parents – who'd arranged to leave work early – picked me up from the airport and took me out to dinner. The next morning Liv flew in, and we spent the day at Shelly Beach, a few hundred metres south of Manly Beach. We lay together in the sand, paddled hand-in-hand by the reef, kissed in the cool ocean water that rippled around us. We went back to her place and made short, sweet love that barely lasted ten minutes, and afterwards, as we lay there in each other's arms, I remember feeling reborn.

My depression's over, I thought. *Done, finished, kaput. Now, I can get on with my life.*

For the first time in a long time, I felt free, like an eagle, wings mended and ready to soar through the sky, chase my dreams, marry Olivia, have a family, and live happily ever after.

IT'S A SNEAKY ILLNESS, DEPRESSION IS

Like I said, Olivia got back from Europe the day after I returned from South America. We spent the day together, but, eager to see all our friends who we hadn't hung out with in a while, Liv decided to have a few people over to her place to catch up over drinks. She invited her friends, and I brought Corey, Brent and the rest of the guys.

The night started off fine – everyone eating from the barbeque with a drink in hand, talking about their summers and the things they'd done. I was doing the same, but ploughing through the drinks at a much faster rate than anybody else. Like so many of the mistakes you have witnessed me make – and will, unfortunately, continue to witness me make – it seems like such an obviously stupid one. I mean, I had a history of alcoholism – so why was I drinking? To answer your question, I guess it was just a hangover from South America. I'd enjoyed myself so much over there, and, over there, my drinking hadn't gotten me into any strife. So I reneged on my promise to myself that binge drinking would only be a "South America thing."

Everyone had a good time and left around midnight, by which point I was well and truly plastered. I couldn't hold a proper conversation, nor could I walk in a straight line or help Olivia clean up. She was livid. When I tried to make drunken conversation, she ignored me. When I tried to spoon her in bed she pushed me away. She gave it to me the next morning, yelling at me for drinking so much and reminding me of all the trouble my boozing had caused in the past. She was so angry, so upset, so *frustrated*, as she put it, that just when she thought I'd stopped drinking and taking drugs, I'd start back up again. For the first time since the San Pedro Prison incident, I was filled with guilt and self-directed anger.

What the fuck are you doing? I chastised myself. *You've only been back for two days and you've already got Liv angry and upset and frustrated! What the fuck is wrong with you? How many more signs do you need telling you that you shouldn't be drinking? Stop doing this to yourself. Stop doing this to Olivia. Lay off the grog, for fuck's sake.*

I went out with the boys three of the next five nights, and didn't take a sip of liquor. It was fine in the sense that I was able to do it without experiencing any cravings, but sobriety made the nights if not boring, then certainly underwhelming. I just didn't fit in – everyone was smashed except for me. Have you ever been the only sober person amongst a group of carefree, skylarking drunks? It's not much fun. In fact, I found myself leaving the pub or the club even more anxious than when I'd first arrived. And this anxiety was compounded by a sickening fear: fear that all the joy I'd felt in South America was temporary. Fear that I'd never really conquered my depression at all. Fear that there were days to come where I'd feel nothing but an acute, unwavering dread; nothing but the urge to plunge that knife into my forearm; or worst of all, that there'd be days ahead where I'd wish for nothing else but death. With mounting terror, I could sense all my demons awakening from their naps, could feel depression retightening its grip around my throat. I hadn't even been back a week and I was already gagging.

So when I went out the following night, I was determined to have a good time. *I'll just have a few drinks with the guys before we go out, and then another couple at the club – just so I don't feel left out. I won't get drunk, though. I'll drink like a controlled, civilised human being – and there's nothing wrong with doing that. It's when you take it too far, drink so much that you can't control yourself – that's the problem. But if you just limit the amount you drink and keep a relatively clear head then you should be fine.* So I decided to have a couple of beers with the boys at Brent's house. After my first one, I felt a little more relaxed. The second one was great too. The third . . . beautiful. I was having a good time, just shooting the shit with the guys and telling them some of the other things I'd done on my trip that I hadn't already shared with them. It was great just to hang out with them and drink like old times, but before we'd even left for Darling Harbour, I'd had seven beers, and by then I couldn't stop. It happened once again. I arrived at Cargo Bar tipsy before drinking myself senseless for the sole purpose of escaping those demons, getting a little breathing room. By the time I left I was absolutely wasted. Corey had to put me in a cab.

'Tell the driver to take me to Liv's house,' I slurred.

Corey raised his eyebrows.

'You sure Liv's going to want to see you in this state?'

'Yeah, no worries man. She'll be right.'

'Are you sure?' he asked again.

'Yeah, man. Don't worry about it.'

He shook his head sceptically, gave the driver Olivia's address and went back inside the club. That's my last memory of the night. What happened next is what Olivia told me the following morning.

Apparently, I'd gotten out of the cab in Olivia's street, and rung what I thought was her doorbell. When no one answered, I started pounding on the door.

'Liv! It's me! Open up!' I kept banging and yelling and banging and yelling until someone finally answered.

'Who the hell are you?'

I stumbled away. On to the next house. Same story.

'Liv! It's me! Open up!'

'What the fuck?' another stranger answered. I tried to walk inside, but he blocked my path. Being bigger than him, I tried to push my way past him.

'No! Get the hell out of my house!'

'Liv! Where are you? I'm just trying to find Liv, man. You need to chill out!' He pushed me out of the house.

'I'm calling the police!' he yelled.

I crossed the street. The same thing happened at another house before I finally found Olivia's. She answered the door in her pyjamas, stricken with fury.

'Jimmy what the hell are you doing?' she hissed.

'Hey, baby!' I exclaimed, attempting to kiss her. She pushed me away.

'You're drunk again!'

I went to kiss her once more.

'No, Jimmy!' she shrieked furiously. 'I can't even look at you right now!'

'Come on, baby! I just want to spend some time with you.' I tried to hug her but she fended me off.

'Aw, come on Liv. Don't be like that!'

'Jimmy, seriously — get away from me. I don't want to be anywhere near you right now.'

'Come on, Liv,' I whined. 'Let's go to bed.'

'I said no!'

I groped her breast. 'Come — '

'Jimmy fuck off!' she yelled.

She ran outside, leaving me alone in the doorway. She sat on the side of the street and bawled her eyes out.

'Why do you do this, Jimmy?' she cried. 'W-why do you do this?'

Then, the cops arrived.

'Are you all right, Miss?'

Olivia looked up at them, her eyes filled with tears. Then she saw her neighbours standing outside, and instantly grew worried.

'Yes, th-thank-you,' she sobbed. 'Did something happen?'

'A few of your neighbours reported a young man banging on their door and trying to enter their home. Do you know anything about that?'

She gasped. She didn't know what to do. She didn't want to get me in trouble, but at the same time, she couldn't lie to the police. She figured that if she could just explain the situation, then hopefully everyone would understand.

'Yes, sir. I'm sorry, but that man is my boyfriend. He was trying to find my house, but he got the wrong ones by mistake.'

She sighed.

'He'd been drinking.'

'That son of a bitch woke my whole family up and tried to enter my home!' one of the neighbours yelled. 'I want to press charges!'

'No! Please don't!' Olivia cried. 'He was just drunk! He didn't mean — '

'I want him charged!'

'No! Please! He didn't mean any harm!'

'I don't care!'

'Please!' she begged.

'I want him charged!'

Then, playing the card of last resort, Olivia confessed to them my drinking problem. She told them about my struggle with depression and how I'd turned to alcohol to cope. She told them what I was doing with my life — about how I was studying commerce/law and writing a novel. She told them that while I was an alcoholic, I was not a bad person or a criminal, but rather a loving, intelligent young man who happened to have a drinking problem and a mental illness. She begged them not to press charges, promising them that it would never happen again. Out of the goodness of their hearts, they decided to give me another chance. Olivia's neighbours all returned to their homes, but said that if anything similar ever happened again, they wouldn't hesitate to press charges. The police said that even though they weren't going to charge me, they still wanted to talk to me.

Olivia led them inside, only to find me passed out on the kitchen floor with her parents – who'd been woken up by the commotion – shaking their heads furiously and trying their best to wake me up. Unable to properly do so, the cops carried me over to the couch in the living room where I slept until morning.

Of course, Olivia was irate the next day. She berated me like she usually did when I got wasted like that, but this time, she also took it a step further.

'I c-can't keep going like this, Jimmy,' she wept hoarsely. 'Everything that's been happening . . . it's breaking me. I can't take it any more. You need to sort this out. Otherwise . . . otherwise . . .'

I was stunned.

'Otherwise . . . what?'

She was crying.

'Don't . . . d-don't make me say it. *Please*, Jimmy.'

I gaped at her as tears rolled down her cheeks. I started crying too. I knew what she meant and it pummelled me with anguish.

'OK, Liv, OK. I'll change. I'll never drink ever again.'

She looked at me sternly.

'You *need* to stop drinking.'

'I will.'

'Say you'll promise.'

'I promise, Olivia.'

We both sat there crying. I felt so guilty. *Look what you've done to her, you selfish son of a bitch. She's so good to you, and this is how you treat her? You don't deserve to be with someone like Olivia. She'd be better off without you.*

Just when I thought things couldn't get any worse, the two policemen from the previous night arrived to talk to me. For the next hour they lectured me about trespass and public intoxication, and about all of the consequences that can stem from such behaviour. They inundated me with tales of youths who'd let booze ruin their lives. They chided me for being so out of control. They looked down on me, treated me like a criminal who had no future.

'If you keep being a drunk, you won't be able to get a job. You'll have to steal to get your grog. You'll be in and out of jail for the rest of your life.'

'That's how plenty of criminals start their lives of crime.'

'Prison's no joke. Some bad, bad things happen in prison – especially to young people.'

'What'll your parents think of you if you go to jail? What about your girlfriend? Pretty thing like her – do you really think she's going to stay with you if you're behind bars?'

Look at what's happened to you, I ruminated in disgust. *Two years ago, you'd just been accepted into commerce/law and you had the world at your feet. Now, you've deferred your degree, your novel isn't published, you're an alcoholic, Olivia's always stressed over you, and you're getting berated by the cops and being treated like a criminal. You're such a loser. Could you have failed any more in the last two years? Fuck you. I fucking hate you, you worthless piece of shit.*

Then, the policemen took me to each of the houses I'd disrupted the previous night and made me apologise to the residents.

'One thing most criminals have in common is that they never take responsibility for their actions. If you can admit to your victims that you made a mistake, then there's a chance that you can turn yourself around and avoid a life of crime.'

Each of the neighbours were similarly condescending, saying that they'd *"spared me, but that next time, I wouldn't be so lucky;"* or that they'd *"given me another chance to choose between the 'right' life and the 'wrong' life, and that I'd better make the correct decision."* One of them even said that *"you don't expect to see criminals come out of good homes in good areas."* It was humiliating. Finally, the police let me go, saying that they hoped to never see me again. The assault on my psyche then continued – this time my own.

You're such a fuck up. I hate you. I fucking hate you. You don't deserve to live. You should just kill yourself. The world would be better off without you.

By then, my depression was choking me with more force than ever before. Although this episode was triggered by the aftermath of my drinking, it was greatly exacerbated by the additional fact that I'd previously tricked myself into thinking I was healthy again. It scared the shit out of me, how wrong I'd been.

How the hell could I feel so good, feel so certain that I'd conquered my depression, only to feel like this seven days later? It's been a whole year now – how can I still be depressed after all these months?

And then came the most terrifying thought that a person with depression can possibly have.

Will I always feel this way? Is this just the way I am? Will I forever be condemned to a life of misery and despair?

If at the end of the day, all people want is to be happy, then isn't this feeling — *will I forever be condemned to a life of misery and despair?* — the most terrifying feeling we can possibly experience?

The fact that it haunts everyone in the throes of a prolonged depression — not to mention that by definition, sufferers are, to say the least, unhappy — is what makes clinical depression such a horrific illness.

TO BE OR NOT TO BE

I went to bed feeling dreadful that night, and found myself desperately yearning for death. I remember lying on my back and staring up at the ceiling, hoping it would come crashing down on my face and kill me instantly. And then I thought about what it would be like after death, how surreal it must be to have no connection between mind and body. I fantasised about the soothing warmth of a coffin. The apathy I'd feel. Lid bolted shut. Everything blocked out. Just blackness. Gentle, peaceful blackness. No other thought gave me any form of relief.

And for the next month, that was all I felt. I couldn't escape it – it was there when I woke up and it was there when I went to bed. I was so lost in the fog of my misery that I had no idea how to navigate my way out. I felt shockingly unstable, like a spinning top that was slowing down. And I felt so high-strung. I was sober as a judge, for fuck's sake. I'd been reading to try to relax, but when you're craving booze, reading to relax is like hugging when you're horny. I found myself feeling so miserable, so frustrated, so overwhelmed with self-hatred over the most trivial of issues: missing the ferry, getting yelled at by Dad for forgetting to clean up after dinner, getting a parking ticket. Small shit like that. My lone highlight during those few weeks was when a modelling agent gave me her card while I was at Dymocks buying books. But I was too disturbed to remember to call her.

And then there was Olivia. I'd thought that once I stopped drinking our relationship would automatically stabilise, but as I got sucked deeper and deeper into the vortex of my illness, to my horror, it not only didn't stabilise, but continued to deteriorate. Something was changing before my very eyes. Her compassion was cooling. Her warmth was evaporating. I remember one night in particular when it was as evident as ever. After a day of writer's block, I was feeling hideously suicidal. I tried to sleep it off, but I couldn't drift away. By three o'clock I was drenched with sweat. I found myself shivering, shaking violently. I held Olivia tightly, pressing my torso against her back.

'I just want to die . . . I just want to die,' I kept repeating.

190

'Just hang in there. Everything's going to be OK,' she replied.

I kept sweating, shaking, repeating the same wish: 'I just want to die . . . I just want to die.'

'Just hang in there. Everything's going to be OK,' Liv kept saying. She sounded exhausted, drained, lacking in spirit.

'I don't know what I'd do without you,' I started babbling, still clutching her tightly. 'If it wasn't for you today, I would've drunk nonstop. Cut myself over and over. God knows what else. I don't know what I'd do without you. I don't know what I'd do without you.'

She didn't say anything. I thought she may've fallen asleep.

'You awake, baby?'

'Yes.'

'Did you hear what I said?'

'Yes.'

I kept going.

'You're my saviour, Olivia. My heroine. My life would be nothing without you. You hold me together. You make life worth living. I don't know what I'd do without you.'

Once again she just lay there silently. Fresh sweat drenched my body. My shaking continued. I felt ghastly.

'I have to go to the bathroom,' Liv finally said. She slipped out from under my arms, disappeared out the door.

Sweating, shaking, fantasising about death. So passed another hour. Finally, Olivia returned.

'You were gone for ages. Where did you go?'

'Jimmy,' she sighed. 'You're still awake . . .'

She crawled back onto her side of the bed. I shuffled across, engulfed her again.

'This is so fucked up baby, this is so fucked up. My whole life is such a fucking disaster. You're the only good thing I have left. I love you so fucking much . . .'

And then she did something she'd never done. She tried to break free from my grasp.

'What is it, Liv?'

'Let go of me, Jimmy.'

She paused.

'It's . . . it's late. I need to sleep. Get up early tomorrow.'

I released her, shocked as hell.

'Liv? Are you OK?'

'I'm fine. I just need some sleep.'

She then turned away, slept by herself like I wasn't even there.

Something was definitely off. She wasn't calling me as often as usual, took forever to reply to texts, and made up excuses for why she couldn't spend the night. Whenever I asked her what was wrong, she'd say 'nothing,' that she was 'just a little busier than usual,' and to 'stop asking her all the time.' Her coldness sickened me, vastly deepened my depression. And it was around this time that the "Writers' Centre incident" happened. In hindsight, what brought everything to a boil. Meeting with death, number one.

It was a Friday morning. I had a writing course – "How To Develop Romantic Relationships Between Characters" – at the NSW Writers' Centre in Rozelle at 10:00 a.m. It was only a 45 minute drive from Manly, but my car was being serviced that day so I had to take public transport. I'd never been to the Writers' Centre before, and I wasn't familiar with Rozelle, so I knew I'd need to allow plenty of time to get there and find the place. I figured if I took the 8:00 a.m. bus from Manly I'd get to Queen Victoria Building in the city by nine, and that from there I could catch another bus to Rozelle and be at the Writers' Centre with plenty of time to spare.

As per my plan, I boarded the eight o'clock bus from Manly that would take me to the city. It chugged along slowly, its progress obstructed by the heavy peak hour traffic and having to constantly stop to drop off passengers and pick them up. I tried to read *American Psycho* by Brett Eastern Ellis on the way, but as the time kept flying by, I found myself too stressed out to be able to really get absorbed in it. At 9:10, the bus finally arrived at QVB. I crossed George Street and checked the schedule at the stop opposite Town Hall. The next bus left at 9:25. My anxiety escalated. I knew I'd be pressed for time. I waited nervously, biting my nails the entire time. The bus came a touch after 9:25, and by the time we'd gotten to Rozelle, it was 9:45. A couple of minutes later, I saw the sign that read "NSW Writers' Centre," so I got off the bus. I stood in front of the sign, but all I could see was a big grassy area and a large complex of buildings. I was panic-stricken. *Where the fuck is this place?* I ran through the field past the buildings, but I couldn't find any signs pointing to the Writers' Centre.

Fucking hell! I swore. *You fucking idiot! Why didn't you look up exactly where this place is on a fucking map?*

I looked at my watch: it was three minutes to ten. I let out a loud, desperate groan and ran back through the field to the main road. Cars passed in both directions. *Where the fuck am I?* I ran down the street, saw one perpendicular to the road I was on. Alberto Street. It meant nothing to me. I ran back to the field and the buildings and frantically searched for the Writers' Centre once again but to no avail. I checked my watch: 10:15.

Fuck you! I yelled in my head. *You stupid fucking cunt! You can't even get to a fucking course on time! What the fuck is wrong with you? You're so fucking stupid! So fucking worthless! You fucking piece of shit!*

I was so overwhelmed with self-loathing that I suddenly felt exhausted. I trudged to a nearby tree, slumped beneath it, cried into my hands.

You're a stupid, pathetic fuck, I kept telling myself. *You're such a worthless cunt. You're such a fucking loser.*

I started crying even louder.

Everyone was right about you! I bawled. *You're nothing but a washed up surfer! You deserved to have been ridiculed by everyone! You deserved to have been laughed at by the whole year at the University Seminar!*

When I'd finally stopped crying, I found myself craving a drink. Or 30. I knew I'd promised Olivia that I'd never drink again, but I just needed it so fucking badly. *She'll understand,* I told myself. *Anyone would, if they knew how shit you felt.* Eyes still lacquered with tears, I picked myself up and staggered to the main road. I quickly found a bar, but when I got to the door I thought of Olivia, and I just couldn't break my promise. But I wanted to drink so fucking much. I felt even worse than I did that night when I was clutching her in bed. *If it wasn't for you, Olivia,* I thought, *I'd drink until I passed out. Hell, hopefully I'd never wake up. With a bit of luck, I'd choke on my own vomit and die.* I was shaking, trembling at the bar's entrance. I stumbled a few steps away and threw up in a bin on the side of the street. Plenty of it missed and splattered all over my shirt. My legs shook violently. I fell to my knees before somehow regaining my balance and stumbling further down the street.

You must *cut yourself,* I thought. *You are a fucking moron. Who the fuck can't get to a fucking course on time? You stupid cunt. You deserve to be slashed up. You deserve to have blood spurting out of your body and be screaming in agony like the pathetic loser you are. You deserve to have the whole world laugh at your suffering, piss themselves at you flailing wildly in pain and begging for mercy. You worthless cunt. You deserve to have the whole world take a big fat fucking shit on your grave.*

I stumbled into a convenience store and bought a glass bottle of lemon iced tea. The lady behind the counter gasped when she saw me – at the puke down my shirt, at the tears in my eyes, and at the most miserable face she'd probably ever seen. But I had what I wanted and I didn't give a fuck.

I turned into a deserted street and smashed the bottle on the ground. I picked up the largest, sharpest piece of glass I could find and held up my shirt, tucked it under my neck.

You deserve this pain, I said for what seemed like the thousandth time. *You sure as fuck deserve this pain.*

I plunged the glass into my chest and slowly, sadistically, dragged it from one side of my torso to the other, screaming through gritted teeth as I did so. Finally, I pulled the glass out of my flesh and let it fall to the ground. I panted furiously, pressed my hands tightly against my chest. Blood seeped down my stomach, dripped down my jeans. I stared at the gigantic cut across my torso and at all the scars along my arm before I thought about something I'd read on the Internet a couple of days earlier when I did a Google search on "depression."

What are you going to do in ten, 15 or 20 years when you have a wife and a couple of kids and your little five year old asks you, 'Daddy, why do you have those scars all over your arm and on your chest?' What the fuck will you tell your child? That you hated yourself so fucking much that you used to punish yourself by slowly pulling a knife through your skin and watching the blood ooze out and dribble all over the place? You can't tell them that. You can't tell them the truth about yourself and let them know how consummately fucked up you are. You'd be the worst role model ever. A shocking father. You should never have kids. Just let all that's fucked up die along with you.

I fell to the ground and started crying again, weeping uncontrollably at the heart wrenching sadness of the picture. It was years into the future, but it pained me horridly as if it was happening right then. I was so distraught. And all I could think was, *my life is so fucked up, my life is so fucked up.* And then my anger and frustration and self-hatred seemed to gradually be replaced by a desperate lust for death. The thought of it all being over, of lying stiffly in that bolted coffin was the only thought that eased my pain.

I wiped my eyes, staggered to my feet, drifted through the streets. I thought of nothing else but death. How soothing it would be. The answer to all my problems. And then I saw a bridge, a hundred or so metres away. I felt a surge of energy and ran towards it.

My anguish seemed to fade the closer I got. In that moment, the bridge was a salvation, perhaps like what land is to those lost at sea. All of a sudden, I felt I had control over my destiny. In a strange way I felt empowered.

It's nearly over, I kept repeating. *The pain is nearly over.*

Moments later I stood at the top of the bridge. I looked down. Below was a train track, with bushy greenery on either side. The first thought that came to mind was that it wasn't high enough, and that instead of dying, I'd get screwed by luck and just break all my bones. *But not if you fall headfirst!* I finally thought. *You could fall headfirst and crack your skull open! Die instantly!*

My hands were poised over the brick retaining wall.

It can all be over, I thought to myself. *You can jump over the wall and dive into your grave!*

My whole body was slippery with sweat. My legs shook. Apprehensive chills raced up and down my spine. I bent my knees, bobbed shakily on the balls of my feet. I'd once been told that the suicide rate in Australia was one in every four hours. *This time, it will be me,* I thought. Being a Christian, I believed that suicide was a sin, and knew that it would dig me a grave in hell – but in that moment, I didn't give a fuck. All I could think about was death.

This is it, I told myself. *The solution to all your problems. No more feeling overwhelmed. No more feeling distraught, pathetic and worthless. No more needing to drink or take drugs. No more cutting yourself. No more yearning for death, wanting it so badly you feel you're about to burst. No more pain. No more agony. This is it! This is your chance to be free! Death, death, death, death, death! Finally! An escape at last!*

My trembling legs bent further and further, low enough to jump.

This is it, I said for one last time.

Then, just before I was about to hurl myself over, I thought about my life in the same way you reflect on a book after you've read the very last page.

James Gregory Wharton:
You died a month before your twentieth birthday.
You never became the rich investment banker you wanted to be.
You never got your novel published.
You never married Olivia and had a beautiful family.

The incompleteness of my obituary crashed around my head as I breathed hoarsely, pulled anxiously at my hair, bellowed in distress. It didn't feel right. I wanted so badly just to end everything and be rid of all the pain, but as I stood there looking down at the train track, seriously on the brink of death, I felt my legs gradually straighten and my hands slip off the wall. I knew I couldn't do it. I burst into tears, cried loudly as all my emotions erupted inside of me and poured right out, and it may've been because I knew I'd have to keep living in this crazy unpredictable world, but regardless, I knew I couldn't do it.

I stepped away from the bridge, called up Olivia. I remember hoping she'd answer. Phones didn't seem to get answered as often then either.

'Hey,' she said. I remember feeling relieved that she'd picked up, but I couldn't put a sentence together.

'Jimmy?'

'L-Liv . . .' I finally whispered.

'Huh?'

I was still crying, couldn't say anything.

'Jimmy what happened? Where are you?' she stressed.

'Feel so fucked . . .'

'Why? What happened?'

I continued crying, muttered something inaudible.

'Jimmy talk to me! What happened?'

'W-wanted to jump . . . couldn't . . . f-feel so fucked . . .'

'What do you mean you wanted to jump? From what?'

'The bridge . . .'

Olivia gasped.

'Jimmy what . . . ? What . . . ? Where are you?'

'I don't know . . . somewhere in Rozelle.'

Olivia was speechless. All I could hear was her shocked, heavy breathing.

'Liv can you . . . can you come and get me?'

Still silence.

'Liv?'

'Yes . . .' she finally murmured. 'Yes of course.' She cleared her throat. 'Wh-where . . . where are you, exactly?'

I noticed a street sign across the road.

'Corner of City West Link and Balmain Road.'

'OK I'm leaving now. I'll be there in 45 minutes. Don't move. Don't do anything. Just stay there and wait for me. OK?'

'OK.'

'*Please*, Jimmy.' She started sobbing. '*Please* don't do anything stupid. Just wait there for me, OK?'

'OK.'

'Promise me, Jimmy.'

'I promise.'

When she saw me – eyes red from continuously crying, my shirt splattered with puke and stained with blood – she stopped the car in the middle of the street and jumped out and threw her arms around me. She held me tightly, wailing into my neck.

'Oh my God, oh my God, oh my God!' she cried.

Despite my anguish, I still found myself cherishing being treated so warmly and lovingly. It seemed like such a long time since we'd shared such intimacy.

Olivia drove me home. When we arrived, I threw my clothes in the wash, put a bandage over the gash on my chest and collapsed on the bed. I was so exhausted I fell asleep.

Sometime later, I woke feeling slightly less dreadful. I climbed out of bed and walked hazily into the kitchen, where I found Olivia and my parents drinking tea around the table.

'How . . . how are you, Jimmy?' Mum asked.

I shook my head. I couldn't put into words how I felt.

'Liv called us at work,' Dad began. 'She told us what happened. We came home straight away.'

I looked at Olivia. She stared down at the table, completely exhausted. She had the look in her eyes of someone who's spent. Someone who's broken. I guess having your boyfriend nearly kill himself will do that to you.

'We think you should see the doctor immediately,' Mum continued. 'We've made you an appointment for tomorrow.'

I nodded.

We hardly talked through dinner. Shortly afterwards Olivia went home, saying that she'd call me the next day. An hour later I went to bed, hoping a good night's sleep would soothe my soul.

The next morning, I saw Dr King and told him what had happened. His response was just what I'd expected.

'Given the way you felt yesterday and the fact that you've been experiencing increasing levels of depression for a number of months now, I think it's essential that you start taking medication. In the past, I know you haven't wanted to because of the possibility that it might interfere with your sex life, but after what happened yesterday, it would be dangerous for you to continue without medication. You may experience side effects, but I'm afraid that's just a risk we'll have to take.'

I nodded. After coming so close to killing myself, it was almost impossible to disagree with him.

He filled out a prescription and handed it to me.

'I'm going to place you on an antidepressant medication,' he continued. 'Like I've told you before, depression is caused by a chemical imbalance in the brain, and this antidepressant will work to increase the serotonin in your system, and thereby improve this chemical imbalance. But while taking medication is likely to ease your depressive thoughts, it will not address the issues underlying your depression – the *reasons* you feel depressed in the first place. For that, a psychologist is needed, first to identify these issues and then to treat them.' He wrote me another referral for a Dr Kendall, just like he'd done the first time I saw him.

'Make sure you see him this time, Jimmy,' he said firmly. 'There's no other way for you to beat your depression. I mean it.'

I nodded. Hell, maybe he was right.

I stopped into the chemist to pick up the antidepressants, and when I got home, I took my first pill. It knocked me out for the rest of the day, the better part of which I spent in bed. The following day was fairly similar, but the day after that I was feeling much better. I spent most of it writing, and found myself in a positive, energetic mood. *This is great!* I remember telling myself. *You're well again!* Like it once used to, life again seemed to be coated with brightness: *you're doing what you most enjoy and you're in a relationship with the love of your life! How incredible is that?* I'd completely forgotten about all the tension between Olivia and me – all I focused on was how loving she'd been when she held me on the bridge. *What a sweetheart!* I thought. *What an angel!* Without depression fogging my mind, the world seemed luminous again. I was filled with a rediscovered zest for life. And as I reflected on the previous few days, I realised that I'd learned something about myself. How I'd felt in Rozelle was the worst I thought I could possibly feel. In that dispirited moment, when my legs were bent and my hands were poised on the wall ready to hoist myself over into death's waiting arms, I caught a clear glimpse into the core of my heart, and learned who I really was. And what I learned was that I was not a quitter. Fighting back was in my blood.

Killing myself when I still have so many things in the world that I want to do? So many challenges that I still want to conquer? No fucking way.

And that wasn't the medication talking.

That was me.

IT'S ALL TOO MUCH

But the reality was that things weren't right with Olivia, and as soon as I was reminded of it, my mood plummeted once again. In the week following the Writers' Centre incident, we didn't see each other at all; in fact, we only spoke for a few minutes each day – the time it would take Liv to do her routine check-up.

'How are you feeling?'

'Not great.'

'Are you feeling suicidal?'

'No.'

'Are you feeling depressed?'

'Yes.'

'Are the antidepressants helping?'

'Yes. I don't feel as depressed as before.'

'Are you experiencing any side effects?'

'Can't get a boner.'

'What about nausea or headaches?'

'No.'

'Restlessness or aggressiveness?'

'No.'

'Any unusual changes in behaviour?'

'No.'

'Mania or delusions?'

'No.'

'Have you made an appointment to see the psychologist yet?'

'No, not yet.'

'You really need to, Jimmy. How many times have we talked about this before?'

'I know. I'll get to it.'

There'd then be a few minutes of awkward conversation before it would peter out and she'd make up an excuse to hang up the phone. That was it. That was the extent of our communication. *What the fuck is going on?* I'd fret. I kept thinking back to how she'd helped me through the alcoholism, self-harm and depression that the previous 12 months had brought, and was forced to admit that she wasn't the same. That something had changed. It was such a distressing thought to consider that I tried to block it out, I tried my hardest to forget about it over the next couple of days and pretend that everything was fine. But inevitably, I snapped. The next time she called, as soon as she'd asked her list of questions I demanded an answer.

'Olivia . . . you've been acting strange for the last few weeks now. Can you please just tell me what's wrong?'

'Jimmy how many times do I have to tell you? There's nothing wrong.'

'Yes there is!'

'No there isn't!'

'For fuck's sake, Liv!' I exploded. 'Of course there fucking is! This is pretty much the whole reason why I'm depressed right now! We haven't seen each other in a week! We hardly talk any more!'

I paused, shaking my head exasperatedly.

'Something about you just seems so . . . so distant. So foreign. It's like I don't even know you any more.'

All of a sudden, I heard Olivia sobbing on the other end of the phone. It wasn't the reaction I was expecting.

'Liv?'

But she kept on crying.

'Liv what's the matter? What's going on?' I stressed.

'I d-don't want to talk about it!'

'What do you mean you don't want to talk about it?'

'Jimmy just leave it alone. *Please.*'

'Liv you have to tell me. This is driving me crazy!'

'Jimmy now's not a good time!' she cried. 'You nearly killed yourself last week!'

'Liv I don't care about what happened last week. I don't care about anything right now except what's going on between us. Just please tell me what's wrong. I can't take not knowing any more. I'm telling you I can't!'

Olivia was crying heavily now, and for close to a minute we didn't speak. I was so anxious. So nervous. I thought I was going to be sick.

'OK . . . OK,' she finally relented, trying to pull herself together. 'We'll talk. But not over the phone. You need to come to my house.'

I was there within five minutes. Olivia let me in, and we went to her room and sat down on her bed.

'What is it, Liv?' I asked straight away.

She wore that exhausted, spiritless, defeated look and sighed a long, drawn-out sigh.

'It's . . . it's us, Jimmy.'

She sighed again.

'I can't do this any more . . . it's all too much . . .' Tears filled her eyes. 'We need a break.'

'No, Liv!' I immediately panicked.

'Jimmy – '

'We don't need a break! Why – '

'Jimmy we need – '

'We don't need a break! We'll never need a break! We'll be together forever! We're going to get married and have kids and then – '

'Jimmy look at me!' she shrieked. 'Can't you see what's happening to me? Can't you see what it's doing?' She stared at me wild-eyed. Crazed. It shocked me into silence.

'It's broken me, Jimmy. The drinking, the depression – everything. I've tried my best to be there for you . . . I've tried my best to help you get through it but it's all too much. I'm worn out. I can't take it any more. I need some space. You need some space. We need a break.'

We talked for hours. I cried. She cried. I tried my damnedest to talk her out of it, but her mind was made up.

'This can't be it, baby,' I wept. 'This c-can't be it . . .'

She was sobbing too.

'You n-need to get better, Jimmy. We c-can't be together until you get better . . .'

'I'll g-get better, baby. I pr-promise.'

'You need to *really* get better, Jimmy. You n-need to see a psychologist, work through your issues. *Properly.*'

'I'll d-do it, baby. I'll do it for you. I'll do it for us.'

By the early hours of the morning, there was nothing left to say. We stood in the doorway and gazed at each other, broke down in tears once again. We hugged each other, clutched each other tightly before finally letting go. I stared into her deep blue eyes for one last time before I turned around and started walking away.

COPING SANS LIV

I felt suicidal all the way home, but I was able to resist temptation and make it into bed. I buried my head in the pillow, cried into it long and hard. I knew things had been off with Liv, but I hadn't seen that coming. I don't know if I'd ever been so shattered. That sense of bereavement was suffocating, boxing me in, crushing me every which way. *You've lost her . . . Olivia . . . your one and only constant throughout this ghastly nightmare. Your one true love.* I clutched the sheets with anguish, sweated all over the mattress. I spent the whole night wanting to die.

But by the time the sun rose the next morning, I was finally able to take stock of my situation and feel resolved.

Look, I told myself, *you and Olivia are not together any more. Right now, you need to accept that you can't be with her. And all of the pain you feel right now, all of the emotion from not being with her — you need to channel it all into getting better so that you can win her back. You can do this. It's going to be tough but you can do this. It was tough to stand on a surfboard, but you did it. You fell off a thousand times but you got there in the end. It was tough to be the Under 15 World Champion, but you did it. It was tough to overcome your spinal injury and everyone's doubt in you and get a UAI of 99.60 and get into commerce/law at the University of Sydney, but you did it. You've overcome a whole heap of shit before, and you're going to overcome this too. You just need to work hard on your novel and get it published so that you can stop hating yourself. If you do this, you will get better, and then you'll be able to win Liv back.*

I picked up the photo of her that sat on my bedside table. Brushed to one side, her thin brown hair blew slightly in the wind. Her warm blue eyes stared straight into mine. She was smiling at me. With the utmost care, I took the picture out of the frame and slid it into the transparent photo section of my wallet.

I'm going to get better, baby. We're going to get back together. And then, we're going to get married and have a big bunch of beautiful kids. Just like we always planned.

I closed my wallet and finally fell asleep, feeling fortified and ready for the fight ahead.

Over the next few weeks I stayed strong, and I did work hard at getting better. I wrote tirelessly, hour after hour after hour until my novel was ready to submit to Pierce. I also finally set up an appointment to see the psychologist Dr Kendall, because . . . well, I guess just because everyone had told me to. I felt that I was doing the right things to recover from my depression, felt that I was doing my best to keep it all together. But without Olivia, everything just seemed so . . . empty. There were nights when I cried myself to sleep. When I craved the bottle to blast me into numb oblivion. When I just wanted to die. Some of those nights were the most gut-wrenching of my life – and you know I've had some awful ones. Sometimes in my sleep, I'd roll over and expect her to be there. I'd feel for her beside me and wake up confused, before remembering that I was all alone. I could never fall back to sleep after that. The longing to hear her voice, to feel her touch, to taste her lips would be too overwhelming. And the days could be just as dreadful. I did my best to distract myself, but at times, I couldn't help but grow horribly nostalgic for the afternoons where we'd walk down The Corso arm in arm, lie as one on the beach, and then kiss in the cool ocean water, Liv straddling me as I'd hold her up amidst the undulating waves, just like they do in the movies. My heart ached for her. I felt sick with loneliness.

Nevertheless, I did my best to fill the void. With Liv out of the picture there was a lot more time to spend with the guys, so we chilled out by the beach, played rounds at Manly Golf Club and hung out at each other's houses. They were really good to me, saying that Liv and I were meant to be together, and that sooner or later we'd be back as one. When we broke up, they naturally asked me what had happened. And naturally, like many mental health sufferers, I kept the truth to myself out of fear of being judged.

'There wasn't any real reason why we broke up,' I told them. 'Liv just said she needed some time to herself.'

At no point had I ever told them about my depression. The only clues they had to go off was my excessive drinking in the past – which they'd just chalked up to me being a bit of a party animal – and my scars that they'd seen at the beach – which I'd glossed over by saying that I'd gotten in a hard-core bike accident around the time of the Writers' Centre incident. Only Liv, my parents and Dr King knew what had really been happening.

I'd intended to keep it that way, but then one night, it all came out. We were over at Brent's house for a barbeque, sitting around the TV drinking beers (me just Coke) while we waited for the meat to cook. Steve had the remote and was flicking through the channels before he stumbled across a documentary about Kurt Cobain. He left it on.

It showed Cobain singing "Smells Like Teen Spirit" and a few of Nirvana's other hits. Then it went more into his personal life – his drug abuse and how he killed himself. The topic of suicide was hitting close to home. I fidgeted uncomfortably, hoping the documentary would end shortly and that we wouldn't start talking about it. No such luck.

'I know it was ages ago, but I still can't believe he killed himself,' Corey lamented.

'He was obviously depressed,' said Steve.

'What did he have to be depressed about? The dude was a rock star. King of the world.'

'Who knows?'

'What is depression anyway?' asked Brent.

'I don't know,' Corey replied. 'Something you have when you feel depressed.'

'What do you mean "something you have when you feel depressed?" ' retorted Sean. 'Everyone feels depressed sometimes. For fuck's sake, I felt depressed tonight when we had to get Crown instead of Heineken. It's not like I have depression or anything.'

'That's why there's no such thing as depression – the so-called "mental illness" I mean,' Chris added. 'It's just something that some pussy psychologist came up with, and something that a whole lot of other pussies claim to have.'

'They're not pussies,' Steve said. 'Depression's an illness. A bona fide fucking illness.'

'Didn't Evan have it, back when we were in school?'

'Evan's gay, though.'

'What does that have to do with anything?'

'He's soft. Sensitive, you know? You've got to be to think you have depression.'

'It's got nothing to do with being gay,' Steve kept arguing. 'Plenty of straight people have it too.'

'What, like 16 year old girls?'

'No. Anyone can have it.'

'It's bullshit,' Chris continued. 'It's just a label we stick on people who are really negative or melodramatic. Instead of whining like little bitches and wasting doctors' time, they should just toughen up and get on with their lives. Leave seeing the doctor to people who are actually sick.'

'I fucking hate those people,' Sean said. 'It's like, just harden the fuck up, be grateful for what you've got, you know?'

'It's got nothing to do with not being grateful or not being positive or whatever,' Steve insisted. 'People that have depression are sick. They can't help the way they feel.'

'I still hate them. Anyone who claims to have depression is a hypochondriac.'

'Yeah, it does all sound like a bit of a joke,' said Corey.

'Do you guys know that as many as 15% of adults experience depression in their lifetime?' Steve stressed. 'You shouldn't talk so badly about it. It could be you one day.'

'It will never be me,' said Chris.

'How do you know that?'

'Because I'm not a pussy or a faggot. I'm not melodramatic, negative or obsessed with death.'

'Guess I'm safe too, then,' laughed Brent.

'And like I said before,' Chris kept going, 'it doesn't even exist. It's made up to generate money for pseudoscientists like psychologists and psychiatrists.'

'Are you guys *fucking* serious?' I finally exploded.

'Jimmy what the – '

'Don't ever fucking say that depression isn't a real illness, you fucking – '

'Jimmy – '

'I have depression! Yes – me – Jimmy Wharton! Your friend of the last 15 years! I have depression! That's why I used to drink so much! That's why I have those scars up and down my arm and on my chest! I'd feel so fucking fucked that I'd get a knife and slice my fucking skin open! What do you think of that, huh? Do you know what it feels like to wish you were dead? Wanting to get that knife and slit your own wrists? Does that sound fucking healthy to you? Does that sound like a joke? Does that sound like something made up by psychologists or psychiatrists to make a bit of money?'

Their mouths were hanging wide open in complete and utter shock. There was total silence as I glared at them with fury. No one moved. No one said a word.

'*That's* why Olivia dumped me,' I spat. 'I nearly killed myself and she finally snapped.'

I stormed out of the house, got in my car and sped right home. I just couldn't believe it. I knew mental illnesses carried a stigma, but I'd never thought anyone could be so ignorant.

What the fuck is wrong with them? I seethed. *How can they be so fucking stupid?*

I clenched my fist and punched my bedroom door as hard as I could. I paced the room frothing with rage. I was as furious as I'd ever been.

But after a while, my wrath gradually gave way to a potent sadness. I sat on the edge of the bed and buried my head in my hands. I felt so misunderstood. So alone in the world. I'd already lost Olivia, and now I felt like I was losing my mates too.

Now that they know I have depression, they must think I'm a pussy or a faggot or a freak. They'll no longer want to be friends with me any more. And if that's what they want, then I no longer want to be friends with them.

I felt so lonely. So abandoned. I burst into tears, cried into my palms – just like I did a lot of nights.

When it was time for my psychologist's appointment a couple of days later, I surprisingly found myself feeling glad as hell. Despite my best efforts, I was not coping well and needed some help.

Maybe everyone's right, I remember thinking. *Maybe a psychologist is just what I need.*

So I arrived at Dr Kendall's office feeling hopeful, and this hope multiplied as soon as I met him. He was middle-aged, with brown hair, an unassuming posture and soft, gentle features. His handshake was prolonged, full of the warm familiarity of a mate, and his smile was broad and friendly, inducing me to genuinely reciprocate even though I felt like shit. My immediate impression of him was that he was an amiable, down-to-earth bloke who wouldn't judge me no matter what I told him.

He led me from the waiting room into his office where we sat down in comfortable armchairs that faced each other. I told him that I was suffering from depression.

'How long for?' he asked.

'About a year.'

He raised his eyebrows.

'That's a long time to be depressed without seeking any professional help,' he said. 'Depression can be a very serious illness, Jimmy, and it has to be treated like one. Not seeing a psychologist when you're severely depressed is as problematic as not seeing a doctor when you have a serious physical illness.'

He paused for a moment, looking me carefully in the eye.

'So even though it's late,' he continued, 'I'm very pleased that you've come to see me.'

I nodded, not really sure what I was supposed to say. Dr Kendall went on:

'In these therapy sessions, we'll work to pinpoint what triggers your depression, and then I'll teach you techniques for how to manage those triggers. That's what these sessions are all about – learning how to manage your triggers so that they no longer trigger you. Now, do you have any questions before we begin?'

I shook my head. 'No.'

'OK. Then tell me everything.'

I started from the beginning, telling him about how I'd been the Under 15 World Champion Surfer before injuring my spine and then studying my ass off to prove all my doubters wrong. I told him all about Olivia. I told him about my book and how much I'd struggled trying to juggle it with full-time uni. I told him about the abortion, about my drinking, and about all the cocaine. I told him about how Olivia and I had recently split, and about how I'd stopped talking to all my mates. I described to him every detail of my depression: the thoughts of self-hatred and worthlessness, the cutting, feeling suicidal and damn-near attempting it. I remember feeling nervous, feeling scared as I opened up my soul and shared my darkest, innermost thoughts. But I thought of Olivia and knew I had to do it. *You need to do whatever it takes to get better,* I told myself, *no matter how scared you are.* That's what I was always told courage was – having the strength to overcome your fears.

Filling Dr Kendall in on my life consumed most of the two hour session, and afterwards, I felt a whole lot better. There's always something cathartic about letting it all out.

'We're running out of time, Jimmy,' Dr Kendall said towards the end of the session. 'You've raised a number of issues today, and there's a lot of stuff we've got to work through which will be crucial to your recovery. But before you leave today, I'd like to offer you some advice that I think will help you. First, I'd like to stress the importance of leading a healthy lifestyle – getting good, regular sleep; eating well; and exercising frequently – as studies indicate that doing all these things assists in the treatment of depression.'

He spoke a bit about possible lifestyle changes for a few minutes before he offered me another piece of advice that really caught me off guard.

'I also think you should reach out to your friends, Jimmy.'

'Are you serious?' I exclaimed. 'After everything they said?'

'That was before they knew you had depression.'

'So? What difference does that make?'

'Listen Jimmy,' he said gently. 'I know it must've been hard for you to hear them say all that stuff. I agree that they made some very ignorant comments, and I agree that they were out of line. But unfortunately, Jimmy, that's just the reality of depression in the early 21st century. Because it's still minimally spoken about, a lot of people just don't know much about it.'

He paused.

'So if you want your friends to understand what you're going through and to abandon their misconceptions, then *you* need to be the one to educate them. You need to take the time to explain to them that depression is an illness, and tell them exactly why their prejudices are misplaced. If they don't listen and continue to stigmatise you, then it might be time to consider distancing yourself from them. But I really don't think that's going to happen, Jimmy. In my experience, if a patient takes the time to do this – and does so in a calm and confident way – then the person listening is usually open-minded enough to be receptive. They usually come around.'

He paused again.

'And what's more, Jimmy, when you take responsibility for your illness and you commit yourself to fighting your demons – like you have done – then not only are you unlikely to be stigmatised, but you will command people's respect. After all, almost everybody loves a fighter. They root for them. They want them to succeed. You can be as depressed as can be, but if you're able to look another human being in the eye and say, "yeah, I know I'm struggling right now, but I'm going to do everything in my power to beat this, and one day, I will," then far more people than not will look back at you and say, "wow . . . I admire your resolve. And I really hope you do it." '

There was silence while I considered what he'd said.

'Do you really think they'll listen to me if I talk to them?' I finally asked.

He nodded.

'Yes, Jimmy. I think they will.'

I shook my head uncertainly.

'I don't know . . .'

'Jimmy . . . they're your best friends. You've known them for 15 years. Don't you think you should give them another chance?'

That afternoon was a particularly pensive one. I thought long and hard about what Dr Kendall had said about the boys.

"Unfortunately Jimmy, that's just the reality of depression in the early 21ˢᵗ century. Because it's still minimally spoken about, a lot of people just don't know much about it. So if you want your friends to understand what you're going through and to abandon their misconceptions, then you *need to be the one to educate them."*

I tried to remember what my views towards depression were before I'd ever fallen victim myself. *Did I know what it was?* I wondered. *Did I understand it? Did I think it was a load of shit?* I was forced to admit that I wasn't sure. I really couldn't remember. *Maybe I would've been just as clueless as the boys,* I speculated. *Maybe the only reason I'm not any more is because I've been through it myself.* And with that, I finally concluded that Dr Kendall was right. They deserved to be given a second chance.

So later that day, I sent them a Facebook message:

Hey guys,

I just wanted to message you all to clear the air after what happened last week. I was really pissed off with you boys – except you, Steve – for the things you said about depression. None of it was true, and I found your comments really offensive. But my psychologist helped me realise that the reason so many people have misconceptions about depression is because it's so rarely spoken about – and that if I want you guys to understand more about what I'm going through and to not be so judgmental, then I need to take the time to be open about what's happened to me and to explain the illness to you. So here goes . . .

I started by talking about how depression is an illness that's caused by a chemical imbalance in the brain – a deficiency of either serotonin, dopamine, adrenaline or noradrenalin. I explained to them the difference between "sadness" – a fleeting emotion that everyone feels from time to time – and "clinical depression," which is a horrid, ever-present despair that lasts for weeks and sometimes months or even years on end; one that can make you feel completely worthless; one that can make you feel physically, emotionally and spiritually exhausted; one that can make you hate yourself; one that can make you self-harm; and worst of all, one that can make you feel suicidal, so much so that it can drive you to kill yourself. I explained to them that because depression is an illness, a sufferer can't just "be happy" or "get over it," in the same way someone with cancer can't just snap their fingers and be well again. I explained that people who suffer from depression are rarely "attention seekers" or "drama queens," as evidenced by the fact that approximately 10% of people are afflicted by depression – yet very, very few people can name one person out of every ten they know who suffers from it. I explained to them that depression doesn't discriminate – that no matter how much money you make or what age, gender, sexuality, colour or creed you are, you're at risk of falling victim, just by virtue of being human; to prove my point, I then named a tiny fraction of the famous people who've suffered from depression who all come from different walks of life including Halle Berry, Sir Winston Churchill, Gwyneth Paltrow, Stephen Fry, Kylie Minogue, J.K. Rowling, Angelina Jolie, Mark Twain, Demi Lovato, Abraham Lincoln, Sir Isaac Newton, and of course Kurt Cobain. Lastly, I explained to them that just

212

because somebody suffers from depression it doesn't mean that they're "negative," "ungrateful," or "obsessed with death."

You guys have known me for 15 years, I said in my message. *You know I'm not a negative person — I proved that when I hurt my spine and my dream to become a professional surfer was shattered; instead of whinging and complaining, I accepted what happened to me and focused on making the best of my life. And you know I'm grateful for everything I have — I thank The Lord for all my blessings in my prayers every night. And, you know I'm not obsessed with death; again, we've been friends for 15 years — when have you ever gotten the impression that I am?*

Nevertheless, fellas, I do have depression. And like I said, it's just an illness — anyone can suffer from it — including people who are positive and grateful for all they have. It's just something I have to seek help for. And I am. And in time, I'm going to beat it. I'm going to be happy again. So how about we put all this behind us, and you guys come and chill out at my house tonight just like old times?

Cheers,

Jimmy.

As I was writing the message, I was crippled with nerves. But after I hit "send," I actually found myself feeling relatively relaxed.

I have nothing to be ashamed of, I thought. *I have an illness, and I'm getting help for it — what's the big deal? If they have a problem with that, then they're the jerks — not me.*

But low and behold, the boys reacted just like Dr Kendall had predicted they would. Within an hour, they'd all read my message and apologised for being so judgmental, and said that my taking the time to enlighten them about depression really opened their eyes. When they came over to my house that night, they asked me questions about my own experiences with the illness, and I was honest with them, telling them more about what I'd been through and assuring them that although I was still going through a rough patch, that I felt determined and fortified and was not a suicide risk. I was really happy to see that they'd all come around since the Kurt Cobain night, saying that they were there for me if I ever needed to talk. It felt great to have their support, and looking back, I wish I'd told them a whole lot earlier. True friends will stick by you – there's really no need to suffer in silence.

~~~

I followed the rest of Dr Kendall's advice, too. I cut all fast food and soft drink out of my diet, and replaced it with lean meats, fruit, vegetables and water. I also began running three times a week, starting from my wharf-side house and running up The Corso and along the beach before doubling back, which was about seven kilometres in total. As for my sleep, I worked hard at establishing a regular routine – going to bed and waking up at the same time every day, and getting at least seven-and-a-half hours' sleep each night. All in all I think it helped – by the fifth week without Liv I was starting to turn the corner, and was beginning to feel a whole lot better. *Just keep this up!* I told myself. *Just keep working hard and soon you'll be well enough to win her back!*

Speaking of Olivia, I still saw her after we broke up. Twenty-first season was just beginning, so every couple of weeks there'd be a party. Having gone to the same school and knowing the same people, Liv and I would run into each other on a regular basis. The first time I saw her was at a Disney themed party, a couple of weeks after our break-up. At first it was a little uncomfortable, but it wasn't long before we broke the ice, and pretty soon we were talking freely.

'I can't believe you dressed up as *Tarzan*,' Liv teased.

'What's wrong with Tarzan?'

'Nothing, except that like half the guys here are dressed as Tarzan.'

'So?'

'Well . . . it's just a little bit boring, Jimmy.'

'Are you dissing my loin-cloth outfit?'

She smiled playfully.

'Yep. Boring, boring, boring.'

'You take that back, Liv,' I smiled.

'Nup.'

'Take it back.'

'Nup.'

'I'll tickle you.'

'No you won't.'

'Oh yes I will!'

'Oh no you won't!'

I went to tickle her but she jerked away, and then reached out and started tickling my tummy. I doubled over with laughter.

'OK, OK! Truce!'

She relented with a smile.

'Don't mess with me, Jimmy,' she winked.

I laughed.

'OK, so if you think my costume's not original enough, then how do you explain dressing up as Donald Duck?'

'I have a very good reason for coming as Donald Duck, thank-you very much.'

'And what might that be?'

'Because . . . I can do very good Donald Duck impressions.'

'Since when?'

'Since always.'

'I never knew about this.'

'The opportunity to tell you never came up.'

'In four years?'

'How often did we talk about Donald Duck in those four years?'

'Surely at least once.'

'Nup. Never happened.'

'All right, do your Donald Duck impersonation now, then.'

She took a deep breath, and adjusted the position of her jaw a little. When her voice came out it was high and squeaky, kind of like how it would've sounded if she'd just inhaled helium.

'Hiya, Jimmy! Why are you wearing a Tarzan costume like everybody else, Jimmy? Oh boy, oh boy, oh boy!'

I burst out laughing.

'That's great, Liv. That's awesome.'

'You're meant to be an author, Jimmy!' she continued. 'You're meant to have all these original ideas, but you come dressed the same as everyone else? Aww phooey!'

'That's awesome, Liv,' I kept laughing. 'That's fantastic.'

That's how it was whenever we'd see each other. We'd catch up on one another's week, share a few laughs, and usually even flirt a bit. Sometimes we'd even revisit the past.

'I still care about you a lot, Jimmy,' she said one night, 'and I want nothing more than for you to get better. Not a night goes by where I don't pray for you.'

I only saw snippets of it, but her warmth, her compassion, seemed to have returned. She was her old self again – effervescent, caring and vivacious. I guess our separation had given her a chance to recharge her batteries.

But it was all so bittersweet. As always, I loved seeing her, and sometimes when we were talking it seemed just like old times. But it wasn't. I couldn't hold her hand. Couldn't kiss her lips. I wouldn't be going home with her at the end of the night. She was untouchable. The reality tortured me. Placing me in a platonic relationship with the girl I loved was one of depression's most sadistic acts. I'm not lying when I say that it actually crossed my mind to cut her off entirely. But I knew that if I did that, I'd never get the chance to win her back. I had to keep her close. It was my only option.

That was how things were for the first six weeks of our break-up – just talking at parties. No texts, no phone calls, no meeting up outside of that. But then one day, she rang me. My heart started pounding as I saw her name light up my phone. My torso started tingling as soon as I answered it.

'H-hey,' I stammered.

'Hey, Jimmy. How's it going?'

'Not too bad. How about you?'

'Yeah, pretty good.'

There was a pause. In my nervousness sweat dripped down my sides.

'I just felt like giving you a call and . . . seeing if you'd like to catch up for coffee tomorrow?'

I nearly burst with excitement.

'Yeah! Definitely!'

'Great. Want to meet at Max Brenner? You know how much I love chocolate.'

I laughed. 'Yeah, sure Liv.'

'What time? Like three o'clock?'

'Sounds good.'

We chatted for a quarter of an hour longer before hanging up. I was thrilled to bits. I rang Corey to tell him.

'So are you going to tell her tomorrow?' he asked.

I was caught off guard.

'Tell her what?'

'What do you mean "tell her what?" Tell her that you love her and that you want to get back with her.'

I was shocked.

'Huh?'

'Well, you said you've been feeling better lately. And you said you've been getting along great with Liv when you've been talking to her – you said it hasn't felt awkward at all and that she's been back to her old self. Now, she's asked you out for coffee. It all looks pretty good, man. I reckon you should go for it.'

We talked about it for a while before we hung up the phone and I retreated to my thoughts.

Ask her to rekindle things now? Now? *Am I really ready?* I tried to objectively think things through:

At the moment, I don't feel depressed. In fact, I feel great, because I'm meeting Olivia for coffee tomorrow. And, if we get back together, I'll be over the moon. In such an event, since I'd no longer have our relationship to be depressed about, then that just leaves my novel and my degree. Now, I submitted my novel to Pierce a couple of weeks ago, and I'm really happy with the draft. I think I've addressed all of his concerns, so all I should have to do is make a few minor corrections, after which I'll be able to get it published. So on that front, I should be fine. Then there's my degree: well, if everything with my book goes according to plan, then I'll have it all done and dusted before uni starts next year. Without my novel to worry about, I'll finally be able to focus on uni, and if I can do that, then I'll have no problem getting straight High Distinctions.

I went through the analysis one more time, and reached the conclusion that since I wouldn't be depressed about my book or my degree ever again, that I could kick my depression for good by reuniting with Olivia. My decision was then made: *I'll ask her to get back together tomorrow!*

As planned, we met at Max Brenner by the wharf the following day. Liv looked stunning in her white summer dress, her lips glistening, eyes bright, hair cascading down her shoulders. We kissed cheeks on arrival, fell into lovely conversation as we talked and laughed as if no time had passed. I just felt so comfortable around her. Everything felt so right. I got caught up in the moment, caught up in the future I was sure we could have together as I imagined us getting married at a beautiful ceremony, buying a big house down by the beach, and starting a family together. Any remnant of doubt I might've had was banished, and before I could stop myself, I'd blurted everything out.

'Olivia, let's get back together. Us being apart is stupid. Look how well we get along. Don't you think we're just perfect for each other? It should be the two of us, baby, like it used to be.'

Olivia stared at me in shock, initially too stunned to speak. Her brows were at the peak of their jump. Her mouth was hanging wide open. Then to my horror, her head began shaking from side to side.

'Jimmy . . . no.'

'Why?' I panicked.

She gathered herself, looked at me seriously.

'Jimmy it's . . . it's too soon. We've only been apart for a month-and-a-half. You've only had a couple of sessions with your psychologist. It's too soon.'

'But what does that matter? We get along *so* well. We're *so* good together. What does anything else matter?'

'It matters because until you get better, us being in a relationship will just get us back into the same mess we were in before.'

'But I *am* better! I've submitted my book to Pierce and – '

'You've only had two psych appointments!'

'But I've submitted my book to Pierce and – '

'You've only had two psych appointments!'

Without even realising it, we'd both been nearly shouting. Everyone was staring at us, but all I gave two fucks about was what was happening with Olivia. I swallowed hard, gathered myself, stared intensely into her eyes.

'Do you love me . . . or not?'

Once again she'd been blindsided.

'Jimmy I – '

'Yes or no, Liv. Do you love me, or not?'

Her face tensed with thought. Seconds passed where she wrestled with the answer.

'I don't . . . I don't know,' she finally said.

My heart fell. My whole body felt laden with anguish.

So that's it, I lamented. *It's actually come to this. She doesn't even know if she loves me any more . . .*

Consumed with devastation, I stood up to leave.

'Goodbye, Olivia.'

'Jimmy!'

She ran after me as I walked quickly out the door. She caught up to me, grabbed my arm to stop me but I knocked her hand away.

'Leave me alone.'

'Jimmy!'

I stopped walking at the foot of The Corso, turned around to look at her.

'Olivia – just go away. I don't want to talk to you any more.'

'Why? Why are you being like this?'

'Olivia just go away!'

'No! I want to talk about this!'

'What is there to talk about?'

'Us, Jimmy! Us!'

'There is no "us!" You don't even know if you love me any more!' I started walking away again.

'Jimmy!' she screamed. *'Please!'*

I turned back around.

'Why did you even want to meet up today?'

'What do you mean *why?* Because I still want you to be a part of my life. Because I still really care about you.'

'You don't care about me. You abandoned me. You bailed as soon as things got hard.'

Olivia gasped.

'Jimmy how can you say that!' she shrieked. 'I went through everything with you! The drinking! The cutting! The cocaine! The depression! Everything! *Everything!* But I finally cracked, OK? I had nothing left to give!'

'You don't care,' I said again.

Tears filled her eyes. She looked so wounded. She held out a shaking finger, pointed it directly at me. Her tone was so serious it was almost threatening.

'Jimmy don't . . . don't say that. Don't you dare say that. You know how much I care about you . . . don't you dare say that I don't care . . .' Her whole body was trembling, particularly her warning finger. It screamed exactly what she was saying: *don't you dare.* A line was being crossed here. There was probably nothing I could've said that would have cut her deeper.

But I looked her in the eye and said it again.

'You don't care.'

She slapped me as hard as she could. I recoiled in shock. She'd never, ever hit me before. My cheek throbbed. Olivia seethed with rage, with cremated feelings.

'Fuck you, Jimmy.'

'Fuck you, Olivia.'

She ran away in tears. I just stood there, feeling dreadful, trying to fight back tears of my own. Lord knows that I didn't mean what I'd said. I knew she cared about me, and I'd never harboured the feeling that she'd abandoned me. It was just something that came out of the heat of the moment, just something to get a rise out of her. I knew as soon as I'd said it that it was brutal, that I deserved to be slapped. But I was just so crushed. *I love her more than life itself, and she doesn't even know if she loves me?* My heart was being broken all over again. *There's no hope of me getting her back! She doesn't even know if she loves me!* I felt so rejected. And just like a lot of people do when they feel that way, I wanted to bury all the hurt with a quick rebound fuck.

I went home and changed into my going-out clothes before heading to the Steyne. As soon as I walked in, I noticed a blonde girl about my age sitting by herself at a table. I approached her.

'Hi,' I said, sitting down.

'Oh, um . . . hi?' she replied, clearly taken aback.

'My name's Jimmy. Can I buy you a drink?'

She looked at me like I was an idiot.

'You know I'm waiting for my boyfriend, right?'

I sighed.

'I used to have a girlfriend,' I said gloomily. 'We went out for four years, but then she dumped me. And today I saw her and then – '

'Hey, babe,' a tall, well-built bloke said, walking up to the girl I was talking to and giving her a kiss.

'Hey, Dave.'

They both looked at me.

'Who's this guy?' he asked.

'He was just leaving,' the girl ordered.

Strike one. I walked to the outside area of the bar and found another girl sitting alone.

'Hey,' I said.

'Hey.'

'Mind if I sit here?'

'Sure.'

'My name's Jimmy.'

'I'm Sally. How are you?'

'Fucking shit, Sally. I had a massive fight with my ex today. We were just yelling at each other on the edge of The Corso. She even slapped me. It was crazy. So like, fuck that, right? I figured I'd just come here and meet a new girl. I'm really glad I ran into you!'

'I, um . . . I have to go to the bathroom,' she said, quickly getting up and disappearing.

Onto the next one.

'Hey.'

'Hi.'

'I'm Jimmy, what's your name?'

'I'm Amanda. How's it going?'

'Fucking terrible, eh. I had this huge fight with my ex today. We were yelling and screaming at each other on the other side of The Corso. So yeah, that relationship's totally fucked up now. But hey, maybe that's a good thing. Otherwise, I never would've met you.'

She shook her head and walked away.

That was how the night went – me hitting on girls and getting constantly rejected. When I ran out of chicks, I cracked onto the bartender.

'You look good tonight,' I said. 'What are you doing after work?'

'Are you fucking kidding me?' she scowled.

'What?'

'I've watched you spend the whole night hitting on every girl here. You are the most desperate, pathetic twat I've ever met in my life!'

She pulled a walkie-talkie out of her pocket.

'Tony it's Steph – can you get rid of the loser standing at the bar?'

Five seconds later a bouncer grabbed me by the arm and threw me out into The Corso.

Filled with despair, I started trudging home. I thought about what I'd just done and felt disgusted, felt ashamed of myself as I tried not to cry. *It shouldn't be this way,* I lamented. *It should be you and me, Olivia, like it used to be.* And then the tears started rolling down my cheeks as I heard all the chatter and laughter of the couples who filled The Corso, strolling hand-in-hand to restaurants and bars with smiles across their faces and love in their eyes. I ran home to try to block it all out, collapsed in a heap on my bed. I was so distraught. So devastated.

It's all over, I wept. *I'll never, ever get her back . . .*

I needed to talk to someone, needed to unburden myself. I decided to call up Corey. Boy was I grateful that he was now aware of my illness and was willing to help if I ever needed him.

'How you doing, bro?' he answered.

'Corey . . . I need to talk to you, man. I'm really fucked up at the moment. I'm not in a good place.'

'Why? What is it?'

I told him about my fight with Olivia and about what had taken place at the Steyne.

'I c-can't believe it's all over,' I sobbed. 'I can't b-believe it's ended this way . . .'

'Jimmy . . . don't give up on Liv, man. She's your girl. You've got to hold on to her . . . do whatever it takes to make it work with her.'

'But she's over it!' I cried. 'She doesn't even know if she loves me any more!'

'She's just confused at the moment,' he said. 'Listen to me, bro. I know you. And I know Olivia. And I really mean it when I say that I have never met two people better suited for each other.'

He paused momentously.

'But right now, Jimmy, you're unstable. You're a mess. You're not well at all. *That's* why Olivia left you – because you're not healthy enough to be in a relationship right now. And if you're ever going to get back with her, then you *need* to get better.'

We talked for a while longer before hanging up the phone. I felt awful, but as the night wore on, I was able to think clearly and take assessment of my life.

Corey's right, I thought. *You* are *a mess right now. You* are *unstable. You're not well enough to win Liv back.*

And then I thought about everything I'd done in the past year-and-a-quarter to try and overcome my depression: trying to drink my way out of it. Working myself to exhaustion, and when that failed, cutting myself as punishment. Snorting coke. Rushing things with Olivia. Hitting on girls at the Steyne like a desperate, pathetic loser.

And where has it gotten me? I thought. *In a battle with alcoholism, scarred up and down my arm, on the brink of suicide, and split from the love of my life.*

I kept replaying it all, tossing and turning the past over in my mind before reality set in.

Nothing I have tried has worked. Every one of my attempts has failed.

I released an exhausted sigh before reality landed me another punch square in the face.

I don't know how to fix my depression. Admit it: I've got no idea how to fix my depression.

In an act of surrender, I fingered the cross around my neck, looked up towards Heaven.

Lord, I whispered. *Please guide me, please show me the way. How do I beat this? What do I have to do?*

Sometime later that night, the answer came to me: Dr Kendall. Dr Kendall, my psychologist of two sessions. The man I was meant to see at the start of my demise. Dr Kendall. How many times had I been told to see a psychologist? How many times had I been told that seeing a psychologist would give me the best chance of recovery? It finally clicked.

I don't know how to fix my depression, but he *does. I need to surrender myself to him — do whatever he says — and then hopefully I'll recover and be OK.*

And with that decision, I finally felt unburdened. I felt liberated.

There's still plenty of reason to be hopeful, I thought. *My best recourse has barely been explored.*

Fortified with newfound optimism, I pulled Olivia's picture out of my wallet, gazed into her deep blue eyes. I imagined a future where I was healthy, a future of infinite possibilities.

'I'm going to get better, baby,' I whispered. 'I know things are a mess right now, but I'm going to get better. And when I do, we're going to get back together, we're going to get married, and we're going to have a big bunch of beautiful kids. Just like we always planned.'

THE MAN WHO SAVED MY LIFE

The next day, I rang up Dr Kendall's office and booked an appointment for that afternoon. When I saw him, I told him all about what had happened with Olivia and about my vow to commit myself to therapy.

'I'm sorry things are on the rocks with Olivia,' he said genuinely. 'But if it's motivated you to give therapy a proper go, then I think it's really a blessing in disguise.'

He paused.

'I'm not going to lie to you, Jimmy – you'll have to work very hard. Getting healthy again will involve a lot of self-analysis on your part, and a lot of hard work to implement the things you learn in therapy into your day-to-day life. Do you understand?'

I nodded affirmatively.

'Yes.'

'OK,' he smiled. 'Now whenever you're ready, let's keep talking about Olivia.'

So I went on to explain in more detail what had happened with her, and about the events that had occurred before our break-up.

'So if I can surmise,' Dr Kendall said, 'it appears that since the Writers' Centre incident, the main cause of your depression has been your tumultuous relationship with Olivia. Is that fair to say?'

'Yes,' I nodded.

'But your depression was rife before that, wasn't it? You were depressed for an entire year for reasons unrelated to Olivia, am I right?'

'Yes,' I nodded again. 'Up until recently, my relationship with Olivia has always been great. I was depressed all last year, but she was never the cause of it. Really the complete opposite – she was the best thing in my life. The only thing that was going "right." '

'That's what I thought,' Dr Kendall said. 'The reason I'm mentioning this is because it's good to think of things in terms of "triggers" that we need to treat. And judging by what you've told me, there appear to be two clear drivers of your depression. Your relationship with Olivia is obviously one, and the other one is whatever caused you to get depressed in the first place – whatever fuelled your depression in the months before your relationship with Olivia started to turn sour. Would you agree with that?'

'Yes. I think that's spot on.'

'OK,' he said. 'Now I want to treat the "Olivia trigger" first, as that's obviously what's causing you the most distress at the moment. However in saying that, I don't believe it's the underlying cause of your depression. The underlying cause of your depression is the "other trigger" I just mentioned – whatever caused you to feel so depressed in the first place; whatever caused you to drown yourself in alcohol, to cut yourself, to snort all that coke and nearly jump off that bridge. That's the main culprit of your depression. The "Olivia trigger" follows on from that, in the sense that Olivia only left you because you were already depressed and she no longer felt able to be in a relationship with you. For this reason, this "underlying trigger" is what we need to address after we've dealt with your relationship with Olivia. Only once that has been resolved will you be healthy again. Only once that has been resolved will you be able to win Liv back.'

So over the next couple of sessions – now twice a week instead of only once a fortnight, in line with my new commitment to therapy – we discussed how best to handle everything with Olivia.

'I think you had it right on the night of your break-up when you told yourself that the best thing you can do right now is to accept that you can't be with her. Because that's the truth. Right now, you're just not ready. Liv's told you, Corey's told you, and now I'm telling you – you're just not ready. Accept it. I think part of the reason why this is getting you down so much is because you're holding on to the fantasy that just because you still get along great with her, that it means you should still be together. But it's not that simple. It's reason to have hope that you might be able to get back together in the future, but right now, there's no chance of that happening until you get your depression under control. If you can accept this, and turn your attention to trying to deal with the underlying causes of your illness, then I think it will be a huge weight off your shoulders. I think you'll be able to find some peace with your relationship.'

This was much easier said than done, of course, but over time, I managed to let go, and allowed myself to breathe with a little more ease.

Dr Kendall's right, I kept saying to myself. *You're not ready to win Liv back yet, and the only way to get ready is to work through the issues triggering your depression and to eventually overcome them. This needs to be your focus. If you're thinking about trying to get back with Olivia before you've conquered all your demons, then you're kidding yourself. Only afterwards will you be healthy enough to be in a relationship.*

It took three intense months to understand the issue that formed the crux of my depression – the "underlying trigger" as Dr Kendall chose to call it. Over this time we were able to dig deep into my psyche, and after analysing my behaviour and the way I thought, Dr Kendall concluded that the origin of my depression was a very unhealthy level of perfectionism.

'You relentlessly seek excellence, and you always set extremely challenging goals and then throw yourself into achieving them. Being perfectionistically goal-driven like this is fine in and of itself, but the problem with you, Jimmy, is that you measure your self-worth entirely in terms of whether or not you achieve these goals. If you don't achieve a goal that you set out to achieve – like getting a High Distinction average at uni or getting your novel published by a particular point in time – then you hate yourself. You feel worthless. You want to kill yourself.

'You're human, Jimmy. And humans, by our very composition, are not perfect. Humans encounter obstacles. Humans make mistakes. Humans don't always achieve their goals. You need to accept this, and not be so hard on yourself. You need to accept this, and be able to love yourself regardless. You need to be able to love yourself no matter how you go in your uni exams and no matter what happens with your novel. Even if you fail every exam for the rest of your degree and your novel never gets published, you should still be able to love yourself. You should be able to find things about yourself that you love that will be there no matter what. That will let you love yourself no matter what.'

He paused.

'If you can do that, then I think you'll go a long way towards conquering your depression.'

I didn't sleep the night of that session. I just sat up in bed, trying to find things about myself that I liked. The fact that it took me an entire night to do so may seem downright absurd to you, because if you don't suffer from depression, then you can probably list half a dozen things you like about yourself right off the top of your head. But me? I sure as hell couldn't do it. It wasn't something I'd ever thought about before. All that mattered to me was whether or not I was achieving my goals. If I had, or was on track to, I loved myself. If I hadn't, or was not on track to, I hated myself. The concept of loving myself regardless of whether or not I succeeded was completely foreign to me.

But after hours of pondering, I finally had a list written.

1. *I like it that I'm a kind person – someone who always tries to treat other people with respect.*
2. *I like it that I'm an honest person who acts with integrity.*
3. *I like it that I have the determination and the work ethic to pursue my dreams through to completion.*
4. *I like it that I have the courage to face my problems and deal with them, instead of denying that they exist.*
5. *I like it that I'm mentally strong – that I had the mental strength not to kill myself and to keep fighting no matter what.*
6. *I like the fact that I'm a positive person. I like the fact that even after everything I've been through, I still feel tremendously blessed, still feel immensely fortunate to have everything the Lord has bestowed upon me. I like the fact that instead of thinking of myself as unlucky for having suffered such a severe depression, I think of myself as lucky for having all the support I'm getting to help me beat it.*

I read through the list several times before feeling a strange surge of power as a profound epiphany crystallised in my mind.

'Wow,' I said out loud. 'There really is a lot to love about me. I really am a good person. And this really is true, regardless of what my marks are at uni or whether or not my novel ever gets published. These are the reasons why I can love myself, and whether I succeed or fail has nothing to do with it.'

I marinated in those thoughts for the next few days, mulling them over and over in my mind. Their strength, their conviction, only seemed to grow with time. At our next session, I talked them over with Dr Kendall.

'That's excellent, Jimmy,' he said. 'Measuring your self-worth entirely in terms of accomplishment is not healthy, but this – what you've just told me – *is*. And combined with you taking your medication, I think it will be the key to you overcoming your depression.'

Hearing that made me feel so empowered, so unburdened. But I also felt a pang of unease.

'But Dr Kendall . . . I like being a perfectionist. I like setting challenging goals for myself and then working hard to achieve them. Are you saying it's not healthy to do that?'

He shook his head.

'Of course not, Jimmy. It's perfectly healthy to have goals and to pursue them passionately. It's good, even, and you should continue to do it. But it's critical that you love yourself, regardless of whether or not you achieve those goals.'

He paused.

'There are many good aspects of perfectionism, Jimmy. Like we've said, it obviously pushes people to strive for excellence and reach their true potential. And in your case, I suspect it was the underlying reason why you never killed yourself. To you, suicide would've been quitting – the ultimate failure. And there is nothing, *nothing* a perfectionist hates more than failing.'

He paused again.

'It's a double-edged sword, perfectionism. The challenge for you, Jimmy, is going to be to retain the positives of it while banishing the negatives. And if you can remember and apply what we've talked about today, then I think you'll be able to do it. I *know* you'll be able to do it.'

That list became my pseudo-Bible. I'd make a point of reading it every hour, and then another ten times before I went to bed. Sometimes I'd read it many more times. Once, I read it 146 times in a row. Another day I read it 83 straight times. Twenty or 30 consecutive times wasn't out of the norm either. I knew it was the answer to my depression, and I was determined to make it stick.

'Altering the way you think is like learning a new skill,' Dr Kendall said. 'You've got to keep training your mind to think healthily. You've got to keep practising and practising until after a while it becomes automatic.'

I felt I was getting there, slowly but surely, and then God set me a test to assess my progress.

One morning in August – about four months after I'd broken up with Olivia – I got out of bed and sat down at my computer to log on to Facebook and check my emails. Straight away I saw Pierce's critique waiting in my inbox. I instantly became racked with nervousness. I'd been waiting weeks for his review, and now the moment of truth had finally arrived. Goose bumps raced across my body as I read it intently:

> *Dear Jimmy,*
>
> *First off, I'd like to say that this draft is much, much better than your first one. You really brought the time period to life, and a lot of the silly schoolboy symbolism you used beforehand was eliminated. The ending was far less contrived. Good job.*
>
> *However, I still feel you have a significant amount of work to do before you submit your novel for publication.*

Just like last time, Pierce then went on to detail the problems with the draft. Firstly, he said that although my writing style had improved, the novel still wasn't as well written as it needed to be. Secondly, the hardships that befell the protagonist occurred too close together, making large chunks of the novel too dark to be enjoyable. With regards to Nicola, Pierce said that I still hadn't portrayed the "racial issue" anywhere near well enough, and for that reason, should just make her white. He also reiterated that their love still wasn't convincing, and that the poetry still wasn't anywhere near up to scratch.

My heart fell when I read it. I was so disappointed. So deeply and utterly disappointed. *You still have so much work to do,* I lamented. *Your book's still nowhere near where it needs to be. Your dream is still so far away.* I sat hunched at my desk in dismay for a long, long time, just processing and processing what Pierce had said. *You still need to fix the plot – have a few chinks of light shining through the darkness. You still need to improve your writing style. You still need to fix things with Nicola. You still need to rewrite the poetry. Fucking hell. This will take a long time. A very long time. Fuck-ing hell.* I was crushed. I spent the whole morning stewing in disappointment before at some point checking the time on my computer: quarter-past-eleven. Fifteen minutes late for my morning run, I decided to try and push the review from my mind, get laced up and hit the pavement.

At some point while I was running, I came to realise what had just happened. It stopped me still in my tracks, bringing a look of wonder to my face.

'Oh my God!' I actually exclaimed out loud.

And then in my head: *oh my God! You just got a very disappointing review and you didn't go to pieces! You didn't abuse yourself! You don't hate yourself! You don't feel worthless! You just feel disappointed! Not depressed! Only disappointed!*

I sat down on a bench to continue roaming through my thoughts.

Before you saw Dr Kendall, this review would've destroyed you. It probably would've led you to get piss-blind drunk and plunged you into a debilitating depression. But now, you only feel disappointed – a perfectly healthy emotion. Over time, this disappointment will pass. You'll address Pierce's concerns and work hard to improve your novel, and then sooner or later it'll be finished and then you'll be able to get it published. This is just a temporary setback. You'll overcome it and still achieve your dreams.

And believe it or not, once I'd made that realisation, I actually felt great.

You've finally conquered your demons! I thought. *God set you a huge test, and you passed it with flying colours!*

My disappointment was replaced by an overwhelming satisfaction, and on that day, regardless of what Pierce had said about my book, I truly had succeeded.

I told Dr Kendall about it at my appointment later that week.

'That's fantastic, Jimmy,' he beamed. 'Absolutely fantastic.'

I was beaming too. The high hadn't worn off yet.

'I feel really good,' I said. 'I feel like I've actually conquered the issues underlying my depression.'

Dr Kendall nodded.

'You've done exceptionally well in these last few months, Jimmy. You came to me an emotional wreck, and you've transformed yourself into a brand new man. You've worked so hard to change the way you've been thinking, and it's allowed you to overcome the issues at the heart of your depression. You ought to be congratulated, Jimmy. I know it hasn't been easy, but you've done a great job.'

I smiled at him gratefully.

'Thank-you for all your help, Dr Kendall. Like you said I was such a mess when I first came to see you, but now, I really do feel well again.'

I paused for a moment, looking him earnestly, emotionally in the eye.

'You've saved my life.'

He smiled at me, and a few seconds passed where we shared a warm moment together. But then in a complete change of direction, I asked him the one question that I'd been dying to ask as soon as I'd started therapy.

'Dr Kendall .. . . I really do feel healthy and stable right now. I feel how I used to feel – back in the days before I got depressed.'

My heart was thumping like crazy. I paused for a moment, gathering myself.

'Do you think I'm ready to be with Olivia again?' I asked. 'Do you think I'm healthy enough to be able to make it work this time?'

Dr Kendall considered my question for one, two, three, four seconds before finally nodding his head slowly.

'Yes, Jimmy, I think you're ready to be in a relationship with Olivia.'

He paused again.

'But you can't right now, of course – because she has another boyfriend.'

GAVIN

I've jumped too far ahead with this story – let me take you back to the night Olivia and I had our fight outside Max Brenner a few months earlier at the end of May.

The next day – although optimistic as I was that I thought I'd found the solution to my depression in Dr Kendall – I also woke to a sickening guilt. *How could I have possibly said what I'd said to Olivia? How could I have uttered such cruel, malicious words?* I was racked with shame. Imbued with regret. I called her but there was no answer. I admitted with dismay that there probably wouldn't be one for quite some time.

I rang Corey to ask for his advice.

'I think you should just give her some space, man. Give her some time to cool off a little. Maybe send her a text saying you're sorry, but aside from that, I'd wait for her to call you.'

I took it a little further, sending her a dozen roses with a note saying that I didn't mean any of the horrible things I'd said; that I was deeply, deeply sorry; and for her to please call me when she felt ready to talk. But aside from that I didn't contact her. Every day I waited for her to call. Whenever my phone started ringing my heart would skip a beat, and for a split second of bliss I'd think it might be her. But it'd always be Corey or Brent or one of the other boys. Her absence hurt so much. I was choked with sorrow. I talked it over with Dr Kendall repeatedly. His advice was the same as it was the first time I'd raised it.

'Tell me something, Jimmy,' he began. 'Do you think you and Olivia are meant for each other?'

'Yes,' I replied. 'I think we're destined to spend the rest of our lives together.'

'Well if that's what you believe, then it implies that you also believe that it's only a matter of time before she calls you. Right?'

'Well . . . yes. I guess so.'

'And it also implies that you believe that once she calls you, that it's only a matter of time before you get back together – once you're healthy enough, of course. Isn't this so?'

'I suppose so, yes.'

'Then do you really need to be stressing out wondering when she's going to call? She's going to call eventually, right? So just try to relax. Give her some time to get her thoughts together. Spend this time focusing on trying to get healthy, and whenever she calls, she calls.'

Dr Kendall's advice was helpful, and it usually calmed my nerves and prevented me from becoming a nauseous wreck. But I was still only human, and logic to a man in love can only go so far. Not to mention that after two weeks of not hearing from her, I actually started to have serious doubts.

Maybe I'm wrong, I grieved. *I mean fuck! It's been two weeks! We've never gone that long without talking before!* I started panicking. *Should I send her more flowers? Should I try to call her again? What if she doesn't pick up? Should I just turn up on her doorstep and not leave until I've talked to her?*

I called Corey again for more advice, but once again he just said to leave it.

'Just give her some time, man. You'll hear from her eventually. I guarantee it.'

And then, after another anxious week, I finally heard from her – 22 days after our fight. She called me in the morning. I answered with overwhelming relief.

'H-hey, Liv.'

'Hey, Jimmy.' I breathed a blissful sigh at the sound of her voice.

'How are you?'

'I'm doing OK. And you?'

'Yeah . . . not too bad.'

There was a pause for a few seconds before Olivia finally sighed.

'So . . . you want to meet up? Have a chat?'

'Yeah, for sure.'

'Bacino Bar in The Corso? 11:00 a.m.?'

'Sounds good.'

We said our goodbyes and hung up. It was already 10:30, so I giddily had a shower, got dressed and walked to Bacino Bar.

I met Olivia as planned. It was kind of awkward at first – flaky small talk and fussing over the menu: *"should we get something each or something to share?"* *"Garlic bread or herb bread?"* *"Spaghetti bolognaise or creamy carbonara?"* Stupid stuff like that. But once we'd finally ordered, we settled into the conversation that we needed to have.

'I was so upset with you, Jimmy,' she began. 'I was so angry. For a while there, I actually questioned whether I'd ever be able to speak to you again. But after a week or two, my anger began to fade. I know you didn't mean it. I know how sorry you are.'

She paused for a moment.

'I still think you're a great guy, Jimmy, and I'm not going to change my opinion of you just because of a few things you said in the heat of a moment – no matter how hurtful they were.'

Once again I apologised profusely, and reiterated how much I didn't mean what I'd said. Olivia said 'let's just forget about it,' and we agreed to put the incident behind us and never speak of it again.

Our food soon arrived, and we chatted freely while we ate. I told her that I'd been seeing Dr Kendall twice a week, and that I'd also been spending a good chunk of my days reading self-help books about happiness and how to beat depression (which I had been).

'That's great, Jimmy!' she said gladly. 'You have no idea how happy it makes me to hear you say that!'

We talked some more with the same comfort and ease that there had always been. I was feeling great. *Dr Kendall was right!* I thought. *It was only a matter of time before she called! And once I get healthy, it'll only be a matter of time before we get back together!*

But then Olivia dropped her bombshell.

'I've been seeing someone, Jimmy.'

I was so shocked, so horrified that I actually asked her to repeat it.

'Wh-what . . . ? What did you say?'

'I've been seeing someone, Jimmy.'

I was so dismayed. So gutted. Crushed beyond belief. *Olivia with another guy? No . . . no it can't be!* I actually felt sick. Physically sick. But I tried to stay composed.

'That's ah . . . that's good for you, Liv.'

She nodded.

'Yeah, it is.'

She said it so casually, so carefree – like I was just her friend instead of her very recent ex of four years. The cold hard reality kicked me straight in the balls: *right now, that's all we are.*

'H-how did . . . how did the two of you meet?' I managed to ask.

'Gavin's a builder who came to put up a new fence at my house a few weeks ago. He was constantly hitting on me, but I always resisted, because of . . . well, you know. But then we had our fight and . . . I don't know . . . I said I'd have a drink with him – I guess because I was angry with you. I didn't really have any intention of seeing him again, but to my surprise, we actually hit it off. And, yeah . . . we've been together ever since.'

I plummeted to a whole new low. *Oh my God,* I lamented. *I'm the reason they're together. I pushed her into his arms. Oh my God. Oh. My. God . . .*

'I was hoping to bring him to Brent's 21st next week,' Liv continued. 'But if you think it'll be too weird . . . I'll tell him not to come.'

The thought of Olivia being lovey-dovey with another guy at a party was too overwhelming to comprehend. But at the same time, I had an undeniable urge to meet this Gavin. I had to know who he was. Who I was up against.

'That's, ah . . . that's fine, Liv. If you want to bring him, then bring him.'

We parted ways at around two o'clock. In a whirlwind of hurt I called up Dr Kendall and scheduled an emergency appointment for later that afternoon.

'What's the problem, Jimmy?' he asked.

I told him all about how I'd practically set Olivia up with another guy.

'I'm so sorry to hear that,' Dr Kendall said gently. 'I'm really, truly sorry.'

'What am I . . . what am I supposed to do?' I pleaded desperately.

He considered my question.

'Well . . . you know you can't be with her now anyway – because you're not healthy enough. Right?'

'Yeah but – '

'So it doesn't really make a big difference that she has a boyfriend now, does it? It's not the right time for you to be with her anyway.'

'Yeah but what about when I'm better? How am I supposed to get back with her then if she's going out with another guy?'

Dr Kendall then asked me the same question he usually did when my relationship with Olivia was ripping me to shreds.

'Jimmy, do you think you and Olivia are meant to be together?'

I answered like I always did.

'Yes. I truly believe we're meant for each other. I think we're destined to spend the rest of our lives together.'

'Well then you don't need to be worried about this guy, do you? If you and Olivia are meant to be together, then this Gavin guy is just a bump in the road. They'll break up at some point, and then you'll have your chance. Now I know that not worrying about it is much, much easier said than done, but just keep reiterating this same thing over and over again in your mind. Sooner or later, it will hopefully begin to stick.'

There was truth in what Dr Kendall said, because I genuinely did believe that Olivia and I were meant for each other. In the week leading up to Brent's 21st, sometimes that belief was so strong that I could sit with the knowledge that Olivia had a boyfriend and not feel too bad about it. But more often than not, it hurt like hell. More often than not, all I could think about was Olivia being with that other guy – laughing at his jokes; flirting with him; kissing, kissing, kissing him and then straddling him naked, falling on the bed, letting him inside her and then . . . fucking hell. I did my best to block it out, but the image was so vivid that it would torment me like a nightmare. During those times, I felt like taking Olivia's picture out of my wallet, tearing it to pieces and throwing it in the bin. But I loved her way too much to ever seriously consider it. I thought she was "the one," for Heaven's sake. There was no way I was going to let her go.

On the day of Brent's party, I had woodpeckers in my stomach. *Today's the day,* I told myself. *By the end of the night, you'll know what you're up against.* I was so nervous. So anxious. I had no idea how I was going to handle seeing Olivia with another guy, but at the same time, I was dying to meet him. *"Keep your enemies close,"* as the old adage goes.

The fellas and I headed over to Brent's in the afternoon to help get everything ready, and the rest of the guests started coming in dribs and drabs after eight o'clock. By then I was choked with apprehension. Sweating through my shirt, feeling sick in the gut, I staggered into the bathroom and started gulping water from the tap. A minute or so later I heard a knock on the door.

'Oi Jimmy, it's Corey.'

'What is it, man?'

'Just letting you know, dude – Liv's here. And she's with her guy.'

I spat out my mouthful of water and took a few deep breaths to compose myself. Then I opened the bathroom door and pulled Corey in.

'Dude,' I whispered, closing the door again. 'When you see me with them, come and distract Olivia so that I can talk to him alone. I just want to size him up while she's not around.'

'Yeah, all right. When do you want me to do that?'

'I'll give you a sign – I'll scratch my head.'

'Cool. You done with the bathroom yet? I need to piss.'

'Two secs.'

He went back outside. I took a few more deep breaths, splashed some water on my face to try and relax.

This is it, I whispered to myself.

I re-joined the party, sitting down with Chris, Sean and Brent, listening to them talk about how they thought the Sea Eagles would fair that year before I spotted Olivia and her boyfriend on the other side of the room. I profiled him like a cop profiles a suspect: tall – around 185 centimetres; well built – probably 90-95 kilos; early-mid 20s; fair skin; blue eyes; shaved head; swarthy beard; wearing a tight white Cotton On t-shirt, faded blue jeans and Vans canvas shoes. I suppose it would've been unfair of me to deny that he was good looking in a coarse, I-don't-give-two-fucks-about-what-anyone-thinks-of-me sort of way. I took note of his mannerisms – the way his mouth was closed when he wasn't speaking, the way his jaw protruded from the side of his face, the way he stood with his hands on his hips and his head cocked upwards in a proud, almost arrogant kind of way. In particular, I paid attention to the way he behaved towards Olivia. If his hands weren't on his waist then he was drinking a beer – at no point in my watching of him did he hold her hand, put his arm around her or even flirt with her – and neither she, him. That at least came as somewhat of a relief.

It wasn't until about halfway into the party that I finally got to meet him. Liv and I hugged and kissed cheeks before she introduced us.

'Jimmy, this is Gavin. Gavin – Jimmy.'

We shook hands – a tight, strangled shake of two fighters before a bout. Judging from that handshake, he knew exactly who I was.

'How are you guys enjoying the party?' I asked, trying to appear casual.

'Oh, you know,' Gavin drawled, wrapping his arms around Olivia's waist from behind. 'It's great to finally meet all of Olivia's friends.'

When he said "friends," he winked at me. He smiled at me smugly as if to say, 'look who's got his arms around her *now*.' I was taken aback. I guess I always give people I first meet the benefit of the doubt, assuming them to be good blokes until they prove to be otherwise. But it only took me a minute to realise that Gavin was a Grade A cunt. *That fucking asshole!* I seethed. *He's only holding her like that to rub it in! He hasn't touched her all night except for now!* I was frothing with rage, barely able to control my anger. I scanned the room, quickly caught Corey's eye and started scratching my head. He was there in an instant, and within a few seconds had managed to take off with Olivia on the pretence of signing a communal birthday card for Brent. Alone now with Gavin, I sized him up again. On closer inspection, I noticed he had freckles scattered across the bridge of his nose, and to my dismay, the faint outline of a hickey on the side of his neck. I tried my best to calm myself, to speak civilly, despite already hating the prick.

'So,' I began. 'Liv said you guys met when you were working at her place.'

'That's right. I had my eye on her from the start. Soon as I saw her I thought, "now there goes a fine piece of ass." '

I was speechless. On he went.

'She's a little skittish, Olivia. It took me a good month to crack her but when I did – fuck *me* dead! What an amazing lay!'

He laughed.

'Man you must be spewing that you lost her! I've never met a bitch that's so good in bed!'

I pushed him.

'What the fuck's your problem?' he snarled.

'Quit fucking talking about her like that!'

I was in his face and we were staring each other down. We were moments away from fighting before Corey came back with Olivia.

'Is e-everything . . . ah . . . OK?' she asked nervously.

Gavin smiled slimily.

'Sure,' he drawled. 'Jimmy and I were just getting to know each other. Weren't we, Jimmy?'

I reluctantly took a step back.

'Yeah,' I muttered, playing along with the act that nothing was wrong.

He laughed out loud and then walked away. Liv smiled weakly at me and followed him to the bar, leaving me standing there alone with Corey.

'What the fuck was all that about?' he asked.

I was so angry I couldn't even reply. I just kept replaying what Gavin had said in my mind.

'Jimmy?'

I shook my head furiously before pulling him into a spare room and telling him exactly what had happened.

'How the fuck can Olivia be going out with someone like that? He's the biggest cunt I've ever met in my life.'

'He sounds like it.'

'If he ever says anything like that ever again I'm going to punch him in the fucking head. I'm going to beat the fucking shit out of him. Then I'm going to tell Olivia what he said. I can't let her keep seeing a dickhead like that.'

'No, Jimmy!' Corey exclaimed. 'That's the worst thing you could possibly do!'

'What else am I supposed to do?' I fretted. 'I can't let her keep seeing that guy. He's a fucking asshole. He doesn't care about her. He's only with her because he wants to fuck her!'

'You're probably right, but you still can't fight him. Think about it – do you really think that's going to help your chances of winning her back?'

'But – '

'It's just going to cause problems. And you can't tell her about it either. How do you think *that's* going to look? You – her ex-boyfriend – bitching to her about her new boyfriend. Do you really think she's going to believe you? It's just going to push her away, man. Then how are you going to win her back?'

I wasn't convinced. Corey then brought the fellas into the room, and after they'd been caught up to speed they all echoed what Corey had said – that the best thing to do was just to leave it alone. That sooner or later

Olivia would realise that Gavin's an asshole and that I shouldn't get involved. After a while, they were finally able to convince me.

'Just try not to think about it,' Brent said. 'Now, come back outside and pour some drinks down my throat. It's my 21st, for fuck's sake.'

We re-joined the party and got Brent wasted. Not long after, the boys and I all made speeches and rehashed a few of our favourite "Brent stories." I didn't speak to either Olivia or Gavin until we said our goodbyes at the end of the night.

'Pity we didn't get a chance to talk at all tonight,' Liv said. 'Maybe we could meet up for coffee sometime this week?'

'Yeah, sure, Liv.'

I then turned to Gavin.

'Good meeting you, mate,' I forced myself to say, sticking out my hand. He clasped it tightly.

'Very good,' he drawled smugly.

'Have a good night.'

'We will,' he mouthed with a wink. Olivia – who'd missed it – smiled warmly. I smiled back at her before she gave me a hug and both of them left. I loathingly figured that that's just how it would have to be. I'd just have to grin and bear it.

DIARY ENTRY: AUGUST 1, 2009

I am so full of hatred. Sometimes I write lines to try and get it all out:

I fucking hate Gavin.
I fucking hate Gavin.
I fucking hate Gavin.
I fucking hate Gavin.

But it doesn't help. My rage doesn't quell, my blood keeps boiling. Fucking Gavin. He's a fucking dickhead, a fucking asshole whose sole purpose in talking to me is to rile me up, to fuel his ego by constantly reiterating that he's the one "banging" Olivia instead of me. I don't know if he's narcissistic or just has a fat-ass inferiority complex, but the guy's a fucking wanker.

"Olivia's cunt smells so nice." "She gives head like a porn star. Makes me blow all over her face." "I'm going to pound her in the ass one of these days. She keeps saying no, but I'm going to break her." *Fuck I hate him. I want to beat the fucking shit out of him. I love Olivia with all my heart, and to hear her get talked about so crudely . . . it takes every ounce of mental strength I have not to fuck him up. All the discipline it took to become the best 15 year old surfer in the world, all the discipline it took to get 99.60 at the end of school – it takes all of that to restrain myself and not lay into his face. I know I can't do it. Fighting Olivia's boyfriend – no matter what the reason – wouldn't endear me to her. It would only add another messy chapter to our recent past.*

How the fuck do I release this rage? For fuck's sake, I can't even tell Olivia what's been going on. What if she doesn't believe me? Just like Corey said, it would fuck our whole relationship. Then I'll have no chance of winning her back.

So I'm boxed in. I'm trapped. Gavin has me right where he wants me. This is a war and he keeps bombing my psyche.

I feel so lonely. Every day I yearn to be with her. I write this parked down the end of her street. It's night time. I drove past to see if Gavin's truck was parked outside her house. It was. I can still see it in my rear-view mirror. It's 10:30. I hope to God he leaves soon.

I'm writing now to try and work through the rage, so let's get back to that, back to Gavin. Maybe if I can break my wrath down into its components it would be a good start. Here goes: how much of this anger is jealously felt for Olivia's boyfriend, and how much is white-hot hatred for Gavin himself? How much would I hate him if he was a good bloke who treated Olivia with respect, who didn't rub the fact that I was no longer with her in my face? Would I hate him as much as I hate Gavin? Definitely not. Would I still hate him? Fucking hypotheticals. I don't know. All I know is that Olivia's dating the biggest cunt on the planet and I'm sitting in my fucking car writing about how much I hate it.

Anyway, who cares where the rage comes from? All that matters is that I feel it. Fucking oath do I feel it. All of a sudden, some of those criminal law cases I studied back in second year are starting to make a lot more sense. Lately, I've been thinking a lot about the defence of provocation. Back when I studied crim, I always thought the defence was bullshit. "Having what would otherwise be a conviction of murder reduced to manslaughter because, among other things, the deceased's conduct caused the accused to lose self-control and kill is, as stated by Lord Hoffman in *Smith*, a 'concession to human frailty,'" *I remember saying in class.* "It condones barbaric and inhumane behaviour, and gives rise to a society that blames the victim. New South Wales would do good to follow Victoria and abolish this defence in its entirety." *But lately, I've been able to empathise with the defendants who've been pushed so far that they've snapped and killed. I can understand why they did it, just as they would understand if I picked up a baseball bat and smashed in Gavin's face.*

Fucking hell. I just spent the last five minutes fantasising about how good that would feel. This writing isn't working.

Ten minutes later – home in bed. I don't know if my heart's ever beaten this quickly. What the fuck did I just do?

I was just so fucking angry. And I fucking needed to release it. It was one o'clock in the morning. Gavin's truck was still outside Olivia's house. Her lights were out. That son of a bitch was staying the night. He was probably trying to pressure her into having anal sex. How dare he! How fucking dare he! I looked around the street. Everyone's lights were out. There was little chance of getting caught. I picked up a brick on the side of the road, drove up beside Gavin's car and hurled it through the window. Glass shattered all over the seats. I quickly reached in and grabbed his GPS to make it look like a robbery before jumping back in my car and flooring it home.

LYDIA

From the day Olivia and I split, a vast emptiness rooted itself in my heart, a titanic longing to once again be able to hold her in my arms, taste her lips, exchange 'I love yous' and melt into each other's bodies. For a while my yearning was mollified by the knowledge that I wasn't healthy enough to be in a relationship yet, but after I'd conquered my perfectionism, that was no longer the case. I experienced full throttle the pain of not being with her, and the maddening jealousy that she was still with that dickhead Gavin. During one of our weekly coffee catch-ups, I told her about my progress with Dr Kendall and how well I'd handled the disappointment of my book review, desperately hoping it would lead her to realise that I was well again and that she should forget about Gavin and come back to me. I remember her reaching across the table, giving my hand a little squeeze.

'I'm so happy for you, Jimmy,' she said. 'I really, really am'

The look in her eyes was so sincere, so emotional. I know mine was too as we gazed at each other, temporarily transported back to the time of us. It was a beautiful moment, but to my grave devastation nothing came of it. Every week it was always the same. We'd fall into lovely conversation, talking and laughing as if no time had passed – but it was just as friends.

'How's Gavin going?' I'd ask.

'Gavin's OK.'

And so my heart would continue bleeding. I kept on waiting, trying to convince myself that their break-up was inevitable, that it was only around the corner, but the weeks kept passing and pretty soon it was January of 2010 – nine months after we'd broken up – and Olivia and Gavin were still going strong. I sat on the end of my bed in the pits of despair, filled with sorrow and that ever-present longing. Even though I'd beaten my perfectionism and had come a long way in the time I'd been seeing Dr Kendall, there were still times like this where I'd yearn for Olivia so much that I'd feel bitterly depressed. I wouldn't be able to eat, wouldn't be able to sleep, wouldn't be able to function. I'd miss her so much that I'd be paralysed with anguish.

What had set me off that particular night was going to Olivia's 21st birthday party. It was the first time I'd been to her place since we'd split up, and as soon as I arrived I instantly regretted going. It was too hard talking to her parents again, having them say that they hadn't seen me in months – ramming home how much I'd fallen out of their daughter's life. It was too hard seeing her little Jack Russell, having him jump all over me and lick my legs, just like he used to do every time I'd come over. It was too hard just being in her house, reliving all the memories of our four years together. It was too hard giving a speech as Olivia's friend, and not being able to express the love that filled my heart. It was too hard hugging Olivia goodbye, and knowing she was about to go to bed with Gavin.

I was so depressed by the time I'd returned home. I didn't move from my bed for a long, long time as I wept into my hands. Then at three in the morning, I finally snapped.

What the fuck are you doing? I thought. *You're just yearning, yearning, yearning. You've spent the last 270 days just waiting in pain.*

I sighed.

Something has to give. Something has to change.

The next day I rang up Corey.

'I've got to do something, dude,' I said.

'About what?'

I sighed.

'You know . . .'

'But what can you do?'

'I don't know. But I've got to do something. I can't take waiting any more. It's not going anywhere. It's just hurting and that's it.'

'You know what I reckon you need?' Corey said.

'What?'

'Another chick, man.'

I was shocked. In the past nine months, apart from that night at the Steyne, I'd hardly even looked at another girl.

'Are you serious?' I asked.

'Damn straight, man. Liv's just making you miserable. I know you love her bro, but you can't wait forever.'

'I know I can't wait forever, but – '

'If I was you, I'd start dating other girls. Nothing serious — just dating. Do that for a bit, see where it goes. Maybe you'll find another chick you want to be with. Maybe you won't. Either way, you'll still have a bit of fun, right? You'll snap out of this funk you're in.'

I pondered it for a moment.

'What about Olivia?'

'What about her? Dude, she's with another guy right now. You can have your shot when they break up, but in the meantime, try and have some fun. Play the field a bit, see where it takes you. You've got to stop putting your life on hold for her, man. It's not like she did for you when you were trying to get healthy.'

His last line cut deep, but I knew it was true. As was everything else he'd said. Pining over Olivia was getting me nowhere.

'Yeah, you're right,' I said. 'I should try and date a bit.'

'There you go.'

We talked about it for a bit longer. I tried to picture myself with another girl, but Olivia kept coming to mind.

'Anyway,' I eventually sighed, looking for a change of subject. 'Are we still heading out with the boys for a feed tonight?'

'Yep. Seven-thirty at BenBry Burgers.'

'Cool, man, I'll see you there.'

'Yeah, mate, see you there.'

That night at BenBry, Corey announced my decision to the fellas.

'Hey boys, did you hear? Jimmy's going to start playing the field!'

They all hooted and hollered.

'Glad you've finally decided to move on from Liv, mate!' Chris said.

'About fucking time!' Sean added. They all laughed. I tried to laugh along with them but it was fake, forced laughter.

'You got anyone in mind?' Steve asked.

I shook my head.

'Nah.'

'Man you should hook up with my friend Lydia,' Chris said. 'She's always been into you, bro.'

'Who's Lydia?' Sean asked. 'That blonde chick?'

'Yeah. Tanned, big tits. She's hot, man.'

'Yeah, I remember her from your 21st. She's a good sort, Jimmy.'

'Want her number?' Chris asked.

I shrugged.

'Ah . . . all right.'

He pulled out his phone and gave it to me.

'Give her a call now,' Brent said.

'Now? I'll do it later.'

'Fuck that, I don't trust you,' he laughed. 'Call her now.'

'Dude . . . I'll call her later. Don't worry about it.'

'Nah do it now,' Sean said.

'Yeah,' agreed Chris.

'Do it,' pressured Steve.

'Do *it!* Do *it!* Do *it!* Do *it!*' they all started chanting, banging their fists on the table.

'All right! All right!' I said, trying to calm them down. 'I'll call her now.'

I dialled her number as they all listened in. My heart was pounding. I was imbued with nervousness. I hadn't called a girl besides Olivia for a date in . . . forever.

'Hello?' she answered.

'Oh, um . . . hi. Is that Lydia?'

'Yeah. Who's this?'

'Hey, Lydia . . . ah, my name's Jimmy. I'm friends with Chris Webke.'

'Tall, brown-haired, brown-eyed Jimmy?'

'Ah, yeah. That's the one.'

'Oh hi, Jimmy! How's it going?'

'Yeah, not too bad. And you?'

'I'm well, thanks.'

'Cool.'

There was a pause. The words 'feel like getting a drink sometime?' got lodged in my throat. After a couple of seconds, Corey punched my arm.

'Ask her!' he mouthed.

'Hello? Jimmy, are you still there?' she asked.

'Yeah . . . um . . . hey Lydia . . . do you want to maybe . . . ah . . . go for a drink sometime?'

'Yeah, sure! When's good for you?'

'Um . . . I don't know. Maybe Tuesday night?'

'Sure. How about we go to Shark Bar? 7:30?'

'Yeah, OK.'

'Great! I'll see you then!'

'Yeah, see you then.'

We hung up.

'Yeah, Jimmy!' the boys cheered, slapping me on the back and giving me nooggies. 'You got yourself a date!'

I laughed along weakly.

'Yeah, I guess I do.'

I spent every day between then and Tuesday trying to brainwash myself into believing that what I was doing was right: *you've got a date with a hot girl. This is awesome, this is good for you. It's about time you stopped dwelling on Olivia and started seeing other chicks.*

Tuesday night came. *This is good for you,* I kept telling myself. *You're finally getting back into dating. About fucking time! No more obsessing over Olivia. She's with somebody else and you should be too.*

I met Lydia at Shark Bar a touch after 7:30. I'd seen her a few times before, but this was the first time I'd really taken notice. She looked kind of like a Barbie Doll with her wavy blonde hair, blue eyes and long, tanned legs. She wore a white crop top that showed off her breasts, and a short black skirt that was tight enough for me to tell that she had a great ass. There was no doubt about it – she was definitely a babe.

I ordered a Coke and she got a vodka, soda and lime and we sat down on the balcony overlooking The Corso. We went through what I suppose is the regular first date routine, all the questions and the getting to know each other, the 'what do you do's' and what not. I found out that Lydia was from Wales, and that after doing a gap year working and travelling around Europe, she'd come to Australia to study graphic design at Sydney Uni's College of the Arts. She worked as a tattoo artist in her spare time, was a keen surfer, and had dreams of one day becoming a children's book illustrator. *If you really want to get back into dating,* I remember thinking, *Lydia's a pretty good option. You have a lot in common and she's hot as hell.*

After a couple of drinks, the topic of exes somehow came up. She asked me about Olivia, and I told her that we broke up a while ago and that this was my first date since. She then told me that she'd recently gotten out of a two-and-a-half year relationship herself with a bloke called Dave, her first year graphics design tutor.

'He dumped me for another student,' she lamented. 'That fucking bastard. I loved him.

'Sorry,' she said quickly. 'That's way too heavy for a first date. Forget I said anything.'

'No, it's fine,' I said. 'I'm still on the rebound too.'

I opened up a bit more about Olivia, and told her how much it'd hurt to see her with Gavin.

'But I want to get back into dating,' I said. 'Forget about Olivia for a while.'

Lydia smiled.

'I want to get back into dating too. Forget that Dave ever existed.'

Ten minutes later we were back at her apartment, making out on the living room pool table. Pretty soon I started fingering her, and she had her hand down my pants and was rubbing my cock. But I wasn't getting hard.

Antidepressants! Fucking antidepressants! The side effects included erectile dysfunction.

After five minutes, Lydia stopped and looked at me questioningly.

'I'm-I'm really tired, Lydia,' I bullshitted. 'I got on a roll with my writing late last night so I hardly slept. And I jacked off just before we met up.'

It was better than the truth but still a pathetic excuse. Lydia's eyebrows were raised in a you've-got-to-be-kidding-me sort of way. The mood had been killed. It was time for damage control.

I quickly started kissing her again before descending slowly down her chest as I slipped off her panties. I worked my way down to her honeysuckle, rubbing her thighs as I tongued her lips in a slow, circular motion. She moaned loudly, breathed short, harsh breaths as I moved to her vagina, licking it softly before pushing my tongue inside and thrusting in and out. When she was close to coming, I went for her clit with quick fast licks before her moaning heightened and her muscles tensed and she ejaculated all over my mouth. Then I did it all over again and she came for a second time. After washing my face and pashing her goodnight, I walked back to my house with a pang of sorrow. All I could think about was the first time I went down on Olivia on the cream leather couch at her place.

Nonetheless, Lydia and I started seeing a lot of each other. We'd watch old surfing flicks, listen to live music at the Steyne, head to the beach and swim in the summer waves, or have dinner in The Corso and then go to the movies. Once we even worked side by side at her place, Lydia drawing, me writing.

'We should do a children's book together one day,' she said.

'Yeah, we could do that.'

I did what was expected of me, calling her and seeing her. I'd like to say 'sleeping with her' too, but due to the antidepressants that would be a lie, so I'll leave it as 'eating her out.' I tried my damnedest to use the mystery of the unknown to distract me from all things Olivia, from the engulfing emptiness that tugged at my heart. I knew it would help if we could actually have sex, if we could lose ourselves in sweet carnal bliss. Not to mention, it was awkward as fuck having your dick sucked and not being able to get a boner. So after my third failed attempt, I went to see Dr King. We had the inevitable embarrassing discussion and then he prescribed me some Viagra.

Now, let me tell you a bit about this particular drug. Viagra is not quite the quick fix for impotency that everyone believes it to be – at least it wasn't in my experience. It's a peculiar sort of pill that has a temperament of its own. The first night I took it, we were at Lydia's place. I popped it and started hooking up with her, knowing from the accompanying guidelines that it took about 30 minutes to kick in. I found myself anxiously watching the clock. When half an hour had passed and I was still flaccid, I really started to freak out. *What the fuck's happening? Why isn't it working?* After another ten minutes of kissing her, I could feel myself slightly stiffen. Lydia felt me and crawled down my chest, took me in her mouth. I felt myself growing harder. *It's working!* I told myself. *It's finally working!* When I thought I was ready, I withdrew and fumbled around the bedside table for a condom. But by the time I found one and was about to apply it, I was soft again.

'For fuck's sake,' I swore.

Lydia sighed before going down on me again. We repeated the same process a handful of times, but I could never get the condom on in time to have sex.

This was getting really embarrassing.

'I'm-I'm sorry, Lydia,' I stammered. 'I don't know what it is. I guess I'm just psyched out from the first time when I . . .' I winced. 'When I couldn't get it up. I can't stop thinking about it. It's freaking me out.'

I still hadn't told her the truth yet. I felt it was too early, too soon to disclose something so personal.

Lydia sighed. She wasn't very impressed.

'Can't you just try to relax?' she said.

'I *am* trying. It's not working.'

An awkward silence settled in. It was beyond uncomfortable. I would've rather been anywhere else than there.

'Do you want me to . . . eat you out?' I asked hesitantly.

'No,' she said. 'I'm not in the mood any more.'

I ended up leaving ten minutes later. Then on the way home, I suddenly got a massive boner – I'm talking a full blown erection bulging out of my pants. I tucked it under my belt and walked uncomfortably to my house before taking a huge wank in my room and coming all over the sheets. Didn't I tell you it was a strange sort of drug?

The next couple of times I saw her, we didn't try to have sex – we went to the beach once and out for coffee the second time. It was decent. But in between both dates I caught up with Olivia, and I'd be lying if I said that it wasn't by far the highlight of my week.

It was a beautiful sunny day, and on a fun-loving whim we decided to get in touch with our inner seven year old selves and go racing down the slides at Waterworks near the wharf.

'I bet I can get to the bottom before you can,' Liv teased.

'I bet you can't,' I smiled.

'I bet I can!'

'I bet you can't!'

So when we got to the top of the line we chose different slides.

'Ready?' Liv smiled.

'Of course.'

'OK! Go!'

We both jumped in and flew through the winding tunnel, twisting and turning and picking up speed before we shot out into the shallow pool at the bottom. As I wiped the water from my eyes I could hear Liv giggling.

'I told you I'd get to the bottom before you did!' she exclaimed.

I laughed.

'You just got lucky.'

'So tell me, Jimmy . . . how does it feel losing to a girl?'

'Let's have a rematch, Miss Lucky.'

'Jimmy stop embarrassing yourself. We both know you're going to lose again.'

'No I won't, Miss Lucky.'

'Stop calling me that!'

'Whatever you say, Miss Lucky.'

She looked at me with a smile and then playfully flicked some water in my face. I splashed her back and she got me again and it turned into a mini water fight before she reached out and held my hands.

'OK, OK!' she laughed. 'Truce!'

Talking and laughing like all the other kids, we ran back up the top before barrelling down the slides with huge smiles on our faces, landing with a splash in the water, and then jumping back up to do it all again.

'Jimmy come down the slide with me!' Liv exclaimed one time when we were at the top.

'Huh? They'll kick us out if we do that.'

'The guy's head's turned. Come on!'

So we slid down together, holding one another tightly, our nearly naked bodies pressed up against each other as we skated through the tunnel, laughing all the way before tumbling out the other side. It was pure bliss being so close to her, and it sure would've been worth getting kicked out just to be able to experience it again.

It was early evening by the time our session at Waterworks had finished. We were still on a high as we towelled ourselves off and put on some clothes.

'That was the most fun I've had in ages!' Liv said. 'We've got to do that again sometime!'

'Me too, Liv. We'll definitely do it again!'

We stood there smiling at each other. I never wanted the day to end, and evidently, neither did Olivia.

'So do you want to, ah . . . have dinner or something?' she asked.

My smile grew even wider.

'Yeah! Sure!'

So we ate fish and chips on the beach as we watched the sunset together. It was the perfect ending to the perfect day.

After it was dark, I walked Liv home. We hugged each other when we reached the door.

'I really did have an amazing time today,' she said.

'I did too, Liv.'

'Kind of like old times, huh?'

I nodded.

'Yeah, it was.'

We were gazing at each other affectionately. I wanted so badly to be able to pick her up, carry her into her bedroom and then make love to her all night long. And as I stared back into her deep blue eyes, I could've almost sworn I sensed a twinge of disappointment, a flicker of regret that I couldn't sweep her off her feet and do just that.

'Well, I'll see ya, Jimmy,' she finally said.

I sighed.

'Yeah. See ya, Liv.'

The weekend came. Since our Waterworks day, I hadn't been able to get Olivia out of my mind, so I was glad that I was spending Saturday night at Lydia's. Sex was definitely on the cards, and I felt more relaxed about it this time, having had a week to experiment with Viagra. I'd tried taking it a few times, altering the doses and gauging responses in front of lesbian porn. It seemed that one-and-a-half tablets was the ideal amount, which took me in the vicinity of 35 minutes to get completely hard. So with a fresh pack of pills I went to Lydia's place, convinced that if I could just have sex with her, that it would go a long way towards helping me forget about Olivia for a while.

After sharing a pizza and watching *Click* on Foxtel's movie channel, we chatted for a bit before getting into bed. I popped a pill-and-a-half as planned and we started making out. Half an hour later I was hard, and when Lydia began fondling my balls I got rock solid. With great relief I reached for a condom on the bedside table. But I couldn't find one.

'Shit! Don't I have any dommies?' Lydia asked.

'No biggie,' I said. 'I've got one in my wallet.'

'Where's that?'

'In my pants pocket.'

Lydia was on top, so she reached down to get it. She fumbled around for a few seconds before she pulled out a package and gasped.

'Jimmy . . . you're taking *Viagra*?'

I was frozen with horror. I was so happy I'd gotten a proper erection that I'd completely forgotten about the pills in my pocket.

'I ah . . . um . . .'

'Are you impotent?' she demanded.

I tried to think of a lie, but in the moment I couldn't come up with anything. I'd been caught out. There was nothing I could do except tell her the truth.

So I told her about the antidepressants, and that I was taking them because I was suffering from depression. Even while I was telling her, I could feel her attitude towards me changing. She was disturbed. Freaked out. She looked at me like I was a contagious disease.

'We need to stop seeing each other,' she said bluntly.

I was a little shocked, but at the same time I didn't fight it.

'Oh, um . . . really?'

'Jimmy I can't be with someone like you. You're too . . . you're too *fucked up*.'

I was out the door a few minutes later.

Well, that's the mental health stigma for you, I thought to myself as I walked home. I knew I could've tried to explain depression to her so that she'd realise it was just an illness like any other and thus not stigmatise me, but I didn't care enough to put in the effort required to do so. At the end of the day, I'd never really been that invested in the relationship. There'd only ever been room for one girl in my heart.

I got home and kept thinking and thinking, mulling over everything that had happened since Liv and I had broken up. I reached the same conclusion that I'd arrived at a month ago: *something has to be done. Something has to change.*

The next day I rang up Corey and told him what had happened.

'What a bitch!' he said. 'I can't believe she did that, bro.'

'Yeah,' I said.

'That sucks, man, but you wouldn't want to be with a chick like that anyway. The ones like that can go fuck themselves. You want to be with a girl who understands you – someone who gets what you're going through and who won't judge you for it.'

'I know,' I said. 'That's why I'm going to go for it with Olivia.'

'What?' he exclaimed. 'Dude, she's got a boyfriend!'

'I don't care. I've tried waiting for her to break up with him, and I've tried to forget about her by dating other girls. Nothing's worked. I'm still as in love with her as ever, and I won't be able to move on from her until I tell her. If she rejects me she rejects me, but I can't give up on her until I tell her.'

We talked about it for a while.

'Are you sure?' Corey asked. 'This is a big, big step, bro.'

'I know. But I can't take being in limbo any more. I've got to give it a shot.'

We kept talking.

'So when are you going to tell her?' he asked.

I thought about it. My 21st birthday party was the following weekend, and no matter what happened I wanted her to be there. And if our talk went badly, she probably wouldn't come.

'Sunday,' I answered. 'The day after my 21st.'

YOU COULD SAY, I SUPPOSE, THAT THINGS DON'T ALWAYS HAPPEN THE WAY WE PLAN

I spent the following week working on my novel as usual, prepping for my 21st, and writing my speech to try and win Liv back. I spent hours writing it, rewriting it and polishing it profusely until I felt it was ready. I'd arranged to have lunch with her on Sunday, so all that was left to do was wait for the big day. But until then, I had my 21st to distract me.

I was having it at my house. My parents were being really cool about the whole thing, paying for a DJ and forking out for booze. The theme was "three pieces of clothing or less" (shoes only counting as one). I was wearing boxer shorts and overalls.

People started coming after seven-thirty. There were a lot of stupid clothing combinations – Corey wore boxers and a Yankees baseball cap, Brent wore a dress with pearls, and Steve wore a one piece female bathing suit. The night started off well, everyone drinking and having a bit of a dance. A little after eight o'clock, Olivia and Gavin arrived. Liv wore a white nightie with "matching" heels, and Gavin wore shorts and a toga. I didn't want to invite the cocksucker but obviously I had to.

'I'm not sure how much I care for this theme, Jimmy,' Olivia laughed, kissing me on the cheek and handing me a present.

'Thanks. Glad you got in the spirit of things,' I laughed back. Gavin and I clenched hands but didn't say anything.

Everyone was having a good time, getting drunk and letting loose. Even I was drinking this time. Hell, it was my 21st – it seemed fine to drink as a once off. But my tolerance for alcohol was not what it used to be, so by the time the fellas started making speeches at around half-past-ten, I was well on my way. They retold a few of my more interesting stories – the World Bar and Star City incidents, to name a couple. Olivia also said a few words, saying how loyal and caring I'd been over the years and how much I meant to her. It was sweet, and once again I felt flushed with love.

After the speeches, the boys made me scull a disgusting alcoholic concoction through a funnel, and then I was wasted. Sometime later, I found myself talking to Gavin.

'Olivia's speech was nice,' he drawled.

'Yeah, it was.'

'Pity you won't be getting any birthday sex tonight,' he smirked.

I restrained myself, didn't say anything.

'Don't worry,' he laughed, smacking me on the shoulder. 'When I'm smashing her in the pisser tonight, I'll be thinking of you.'

Normally, I wouldn't have said anything. Normally, I would've just gritted my teeth and kept my cool. But unlike all the other times I'd been drinking heavily, so my self-control wasn't what it had been. Consequently, some of my anger, my hatred, finally shot through.

'Don't fucking talk about her like that!' I seethed, staring him straight in the eye.

He was shocked.

'What did you just say?'

'You heard me. Don't fucking talk about her like that.'

He gathered himself, his lips curling into a cruel smile.

'Yeah? What're you going to do about it?'

We were staring each other down.

'Say something about her again and I'll beat the fucking shit out of you,' I said.

I leaned in a little closer.

'Just give me a reason, *bitch*. Just give me a fucking reason.'

He leaned in even closer, so close that our noses were only inches from touching. His lips formed that cruel smile again as he drawled, calm as anything:

'When we go home tonight, I'm going to ass-fuck Olivia so hard that she craps blood tomorrow.'

I punched him in the face and he buckled to the ground. I jumped on top of him, unleashing months of hatred as I kept on hitting him.

'Don't *ever! Fucking! Say* that about her!' I yelled.

But being bigger than me he was able to roll me over and start laying into me.

'I'll say whatever the fuck I want, *cunt!*'

He nailed me a few times before the boys managed to restrain him. Others jumped in to hold me back too. Blood dripped down our faces, covered our knuckles. We were the centre of attention as we kept on yelling.

'Don't fucking talk about her like that!'

'I'll say whatever I want, you fucking pussy!'

All of a sudden, Olivia stood before us. We both stopped yelling.

'Oh my God!' she shrieked. 'What the hell happened?'

'He was talking shit about you, Liv! He was saying all sorts of shit!'

'No I wasn't. He's just trying to break us up.'

'He's lying! He said that when you go home he's going to ass-fuck you so hard that you crap blood tomorrow!'

Olivia gasped. Her usually soft eyes grew sharp with rage. Her brows narrowed. She was furious.

'Gavin . . . did you say that?'

'No. Of course not.'

'Yeah you did, you fucking liar!'

'Fuck off!'

Olivia stared at us both, infuriated, embarrassed, thinking about God knows what before someone piped up:

'Jimmy's telling the truth, Liv. Gavin did say that.'

Everyone turned to the source. It was a girl called Natalie, one of Olivia's best friends.

'Gavin said that. I heard him,' she repeated.

Olivia shot him a look of pure disgust before storming out of the house. Gavin ran after her. I went to follow them but the guys stopped me.

'Leave it, mate.'

'All right, party's over,' Dad called out from behind the crowd. 'Time to go home.'

All the guests silently filed out except for the fellas. I immediately went to the bathroom to check out my face. Both my top and bottom lips were split, my forehead was throbbing and bleeding, and my cheeks ached and were sure to bruise.

My parents came in with some towels, the bucket of ice that kept the drinks cold, and a few medical supplies.

'Oh my God, Jimmy!' Mum exclaimed. 'Are you all right? Do you need to go to hospital?'

'Nah, I'll be OK. Don't worry about it.'

I told them what happened as I cleaned the blood off my face before icing myself down. After I'd assured them that I'd be fine and that I didn't need to go to hospital, my parents left and the fellas came in.

'Man you fucking nailed that guy!' Corey said.

'You serious? Look what he did to my face.'

'You got him just as bad though, bro. He was bleeding like anything!'

We all laughed.

'Do you guys reckon he and Liv broke up?' I asked seriously.

'I reckon they would've,' Brent said. 'I can't imagine her staying with him after the shit he said.'

'How much did Natalie hear?' I asked. 'Have any of you guys talked to her?'

'Yeah, I have,' Steve said. 'She heard something about you saying you'll hit him if he says anything bad about her. And then what he said after that – the whole ass-fuck thing.'

'Yeah, dude,' Chris said. 'Particularly with Natalie backing up your story, there's no way she's going to stay with him.'

Suddenly there was a knock at the bathroom door. Everyone looked around.

It was Olivia.

'Mind if I, ah . . . talk to Jimmy?' she asked.

The boys left amid a flurry of 'see yous' and 'I'll call you tomorrows.' I was sitting on the bathroom floor propped up against the shower door, icing my face. Olivia knelt in front of me. I was desperate to know what had happened to Gavin, so I tried to casually bring him into conversation.

'Your boyfriend really did a number on me,' I chuckled.

Olivia took the ice from my hand and began rubbing it gently over my forehead.

'He's not my boyfriend any more, Jimmy. Not after what he said about me. And the fact that he said that to *you*, of all people. And on your 21st birthday! No. I never want to see him ever again.'

I was flooded with relief. With mirthful, euphoric happiness. I was speechless. Almost a little breathless.

'That's . . . that's great, Liv,' I finally said. 'You deserve . . . so much better than him.'

She nodded, didn't say anything.

'How do you . . . how do you feel?' I asked.

She shrugged.

'Not great. But not heartbroken, either. It's not like we were in love or anything.'

I felt another rush of joy to the heart.

'You weren't in love with him?'

She shook her head.

'It was never . . . you know . . . how it was with us.'

This was quickly turning into the best birthday ever.

'God! He's just such an *asshole!*' Liv stressed.

'Yeah,' I nodded. 'Yeah, he is.'

We were silent for a while.

'I can't believe I stayed with him for eight months,' she lamented.

'Why did you?'

She shrugged her shoulders, shook her head.

'I don't know. I mean looking back, it wasn't even that good. We weren't in love. And we fought a lot.'

'What did you guys fight about?'

Olivia laughed.

'You, for most of the time.'

I laughed too.

'Really?'

She nodded, smiling slightly.

'I kind of have a habit of talking about you a lot, which I guess always annoyed him. And whenever I'd see you I'd always be so happy afterwards, and if I saw him that day he'd always realise and get really jealous.'

That explains a lot, I thought.

We talked for ages. I comforted her about Gavin for a while, but she really didn't seem too torn up about it. Sooner rather than later he dropped out of conversation, and we found ourselves reminiscing about the past.

'Remember the first time I took care of you like this?' Liv smiled, gently sponging my cheeks.

'Yeah,' I laughed. 'The Star City night.'

'You've come such a long way since then, Jimmy. I mean you beat your alcoholism. And your depression.'

She stopped wiping the sponge over my bruises, gazed deeply into my eyes.

'That was so strong of you – to face your demons, to work so hard with your psychologist and read all those self-help books. To rewire the way you think and overcome your depression. And the way you handled that book review . . . I mean *wow!* I was so happy for you that day. I really, really was. I kept thanking God, over and over and over again.'

She paused for a moment.

'I admire you so much, Jimmy – for going through all you went through and being strong enough to beat it.'

Our eyes were locked. I gazed adoringly right back at her, the way I'd done all those times at her picture in my wallet. My heart was pounding. I was so caught up in the moment. All I felt was love.

'Well,' I said breathlessly. 'I couldn't have had a better reason to get healthy, could I?'

Liv tilted her head.

'What do you mean?'

I'd said too much. I hadn't meant to let on so quickly. I tried to backtrack.

'Oh – nothing,' I said, looking away.

'What? Jimmy tell me.'

'No it's nothing. Really.'

'Jimmy . . .' She reached out and squeezed my hand. I looked back into her eyes.

'Just tell me . . .'

Did she know the reason? Did she just want to hear me say it? It seemed like the worst time to tell her – she'd only broken up with Gavin a few hours ago. But there was something about the moment that just brought it out of me. Hell, she was finally more than just a picture. I couldn't wait any longer.

'Olivia . . . I mean . . . I wanted to get better for myself, obviously. But at the front of my mind . . . at the front of my mind it was always you. I thought that if I could just get healthy again that we could . . . that we could get back together. That things could be like they used to be.'

I paused, swallowed, took a deep breath.

'I did it all for you, Olivia. Because I love you.'

Her eyes narrowed. She smiled at me warmly, beautifully. She made the softest, most mellifluous sound, 'Mmmm,' and her smile widened as she made it. Without breaking her gaze, she picked up a cotton ball out of the medicine pack, tipped on a little Betadine, and started dabbing it ever so gently over my face, smiling all the while.

'Mmmmm.'

Part III

WARNING SIGNS, PART 2

Over the next few weeks we waltzed back into a relationship. It happened slowly but surely, coffees turning into lunches turning into dinners. Then one night we went ice-skating at Macquarie Shops. We held hands as we glided around the rink, partly for balance, mostly because we wanted to. On the way home, we listened to Mix's Love Song Dedications in romantic silence. Then back at Liv's place, sitting together on her bed, we had the heart-pounding talk.

'Jimmy these . . . these last few weeks . . . I've fallen in love with you all over again. Well, maybe that's not saying it right – I don't think I ever *wasn't* in love with you. Gavin . . . I was hurt. I was on the rebound. I think I was lying to myself about how I felt about you. Because I was scared, Jimmy. I was confused after . . . after you know . . . everything that happened with us.'

'But you know how healthy I am now, right baby?' I stressed, clutching her hands. 'You know how hard I worked to fix myself, to become the sort of guy who's ready to be in a relationship with you. The sort of guy that can give you everything you deserve.'

Olivia nodded fervently.

'I know, baby. I know.'

Her eyes grew teary. She was squeezing my hands now.

'And I know that I want to be with you,' she said ardently. 'My God, Jimmy . . . I've missed you so much and I just want to be with you.'

We fell into each other's arms. We held each other tightly, immersed in passion.

'I love you, Olivia,' I whispered in her ear. 'I love you so damn much.'

'I love you too, Jimmy. I love you too.'

And then gradually, our heads leaned backwards. We beamed at each other, smiled in rejoice before our lips moved closer together. We kissed slowly, fervidly. Such a beautiful, enchanted kiss. My eyes grew teary. I was suffused with joy.

'You've made me so happy, Liv.'

Olivia was crying.

'You've made me so happy too, baby. I love you so, so much.'

And from then on, we were fused together as if no time had passed. Love once again became the oxygen that we breathed each day. It was like we were 16 again, getting struck by Cupid for the very first time. All we wanted to do was be together, get into each other's body, leap into each other's soul. We danced in our own beautiful, ethereal universe. It was kind of like a fairy tale, our own Cinderella story.

But having sex on my medication was challenging. Like I said, the Viagra was temperamental, and in any sense, a packet of four costs about 75 bucks, so it was hardly a long-term solution. Consequently, I decided to see Dr King about it.

'I've been working hard with my psychologist for close to a year now,' I said. 'I feel that I'm now able to tolerate imperfection in my life without letting it depress me, and I'm also back in a relationship with Olivia. I feel stable, and for the first time in a long time, I actually feel happy. I don't think I need to be on antidepressants any more.'

'I'm afraid I'm going to have to disagree, Jimmy,' Dr King said. 'It's generally not wise to stop taking antidepressants until at least six months after your last depressive episode. This is standard procedure, just to be on the safe side and to help prevent any sort of relapse. So with that in mind, I wouldn't advise you to wean off your medication for at least another few months.'

We talked about it for a while, and I eventually came to agree with him – the last thing I wanted was a relapse, especially now that I was back with Olivia. But I was still concerned about the impotency factor.

'Can I maybe change medications then?' I asked. 'Try and find one that I can have sex on?'

Dr King shrugged his shoulders.

'Yeah, OK. We can try that.'

So over the next week I weaned off my meds and began taking a new one. I'd have a 50 milligram tablet every night before going to bed.

I wasn't impotent on the new pills. On my second day of taking them Liv's parents were away, so I went over to her place to have dinner and watch a movie. We hugged at the door, kissed for a few seconds . . . which became a few more seconds . . . and then a few more seconds after that. My cock came to life beneath my shorts, rubbed up against Olivia's hip. When we pulled away, we were breathing deeply. Our hearts were pounding. It'd been almost a year. We were starving for it.

'I want to be inside you,' I murmured.

'Baby . . . I'm on my period.'

'Who cares?' I said quickly. 'We'll fuck in the shower.'

Olivia gazed at me adoringly. After a few emotive seconds she started nodding.

We ran to the bathroom and closed the door. I threw off my clothes, turned on the shower, felt to make sure the water wasn't too hot. Liv's legs were already spread on the floor as it glided over the tiles, mixed with her blood, washed down the drain at my feet. Overcome with desire I fell to my knees, lunged towards her, entered her honeysuckle. We started thrusting in the hot, flowing water; quick, hard, loud thrusts; almost with urgency; with a wanting so powerful that it contained desperation. I rubbed my hands all over her body, recalling all the curves of her figure, the smoothness of her skin, the roundness of her tight, menstrual breasts as Olivia dug her nails into my back, screamed with passion. We tried to kiss between gasps for air as we grinded even harder, slid beneath the shower nozzle. Water pelted the back of my neck and plumes of spray soaked Olivia's face as she bit my ear, nibbled it eagerly before wrapping her arms around me and just pushing, pushing. We were one, a ball of lust rocking back and forth, both on the brink of coming before I withdrew myself and fell back off her, onto my bottom and the palms of my hands. I gazed at her. Her eyes were narrow, mouth open as she panted in rhythm with her heaving breasts. She tried to say something but no sound came out. I think it was 'come back to me.' I stood up, helped her to her feet, pressed her up against the wall. Our faces were inches from touching. Our bodies were quivering with anticipation.

'I just wanted to make it last . . .' I said breathlessly, 'for a little bit longer . . .'

And then I entered her again, directly beneath the shower nozzle. I held her up around the waist as she wrapped her legs around me, rested her chin on the curve of my shoulder. It was slower this time, a few hard, elongated thrusts before I came inside her. It wouldn't have lasted longer than ten seconds but it felt like a few minutes as I pushed her up against the wall and released a long, ardent sigh, and in those ten seconds, I couldn't really hear anything, wasn't really aware of anything but how she felt on my prick. It was such a self-contained moment, isolated from the rest of the world. It was only a few full seconds after I'd relieved myself that I could hear the water slamming down on the hard tiled floors and I remembered we were in the shower. We didn't bother to turn it off. We just stared at each other, and for some reason I can't quite pinpoint, I kissed her nose.

'That was . . . amazing,' Olivia murmured. 'How did we . . . how did we wait this long?'

And then we just seeped to the floor, lay there in the steamy mist, melted into one. And I remember holding her naked body in my arms, promising myself that I'd never let her go again.

'This is it this time, baby,' I whispered in her ear. 'No more drinking, no more depression, no more drama. It's just you and me, baby. Just you and me forever.'

For the first couple of weeks on my new medication, I felt stable. I felt good. And why wouldn't I? I was back at uni and on top of my subjects, I'd recently sent the newest (and what I hoped would be close to the final) draft of my novel to Pierce, and I was back together with my one true love. Life was great, and I lived very happily.

But a couple of weeks after I started taking my new meds, everything began to change. I gradually went from being "happy" to "permanently euphoric." Life went from being "great" to "sublimely rapturous." For seven spectacular days, the first thing that would pop into my head after I'd jump out of bed would be: *what a beautiful day! I'm so lucky to be alive! I'm so blessed to be able to live and breathe in this wonderful world!* I'd then pray out loud (standing up – I'd be too excited to kneel):

> *Dear God,*
>
> *Thank-you for the gift of life – for giving me the senses to be able to see, smell, hear, taste and touch this beautiful planet that you've graced us with!*
>
> *Thank-you for blessing me with everything anyone could possibly want!*
>
> *I pray for everyone who's less fortunate than me – everyone who didn't wake up this morning feeling that today is a glorious gift from above!*
>
> *I love you, God!*
>
> *Amen!*

I'd then joyously indulge in a breathtakingly hot shower, eat the crunchiest corn flakes with the most deliciously fresh milk for breakfast before walking out into the golden sun and starting up my car with a big fat grin spread across my face, giddily about to embark on a fabulous new day.

Maybe you've felt this way before. Maybe you don't think this is strange at all, and you're wondering why I'm bothering to bring it up. So far, you might have a point. But let me continue.

During this weeklong period I felt high on life. Literally. I was brimming with energy, teeming with enthusiasm. I was so motivated that I did two-and-a-half weeks of uni work in that seven day span. I'd study long into the night and never get tired. I'd constantly have only five hours of sleep and wake up in the morning feeling like gold. I was horny as a jackrabbit. That week, Olivia and I had sex 15 times, and I masturbated another 25 times. I thought nothing of money, handing out $20 notes to beggars along George Street and buying Olivia a $500 dress for absolutely no reason. All I felt was a deep, celestial bliss, a perfect love for the world and everything in it. One afternoon, instead of going to class I just strolled around Victoria Park, marvelling at the gorgeous green grass, smiling broadly at the ducks, picking flowers off the jacaranda trees and twirling them hypnotically between my fingers, convinced that it was the most beguiling phenomenon I'd ever laid eyes on.

Life is so beautiful! How can anyone be unhappy when life is this beautiful?

When I was in hospital, four weeks later, I was told that this period of euphoria, this surreal, sensational ecstasy, is actually what's characterised by the psychiatric profession as an episode of hypomania. But I had no idea what hypomania was back then. All I knew was that the world was an oasis, a magnificent confluence of beauty, and that I was so happy. So deliriously, utterly happy.

WILL YOU MARRY ME?

And then I crashed. After seven days my highs started to wear off, and I was thrown into a horrific depression, as bad if not worse than ever before. I felt like a starving journeyman lost deep in a forest, blindly wandering in the hope of making it out alive. The journeyman has no food. He goes for four or five days, sometimes even a week without eating. Eventually he'll find something, wolf it down, but it's only a quick fix. Not long after he'll be famished again. Replace hunger with depression and that was me. Food was my equivalent to all forms of escape: TV, reading and masturbation. They were temporary as fuck. Depression always prevailed.

During those days, I'd think of suicide as much as the starving journeyman would think of food. We had the same goal, too: get through today. Live til tomorrow. Sometimes that seemed too overwhelming, so I'd have to break it down into more manageable sub-goals: *just survive the next eight hours. The next six hours. Hold off killing yourself until then* (at which point, I'd tell myself the same thing over again). I avidly yearned for death, but I was not a quitter. *Just keep going. Try to hold on. Things can get better.* I prayed every day: *Lord . . . I am struggling . . . I'm in agony . . . please help me . . . please have mercy on my soul.* Every day I fingered the cross around my neck. *Stay strong,* I kept telling myself. *Trust the Lord, He knows what's best.* I felt so fucking dreadful but I had not abandoned hope. That's the one thing I had going for me. Hope and depression are bitter rivals until one inevitably defeats the other. As long as I had hope I was in with a shot.

But depression had all the momentum and was going in for the kill. Mercilessly amplifying my pain was the shock of it all, my complete and utter bewilderment at the fact that I was feeling depressed again.

I've done everything, everything *to beat my illness: work hours on end with my psychologist, pour over self-help books, diligently take my medication, exercise, sleep- and eat well. What more can I possibly do? How the fuck can I still be feeling this way?* Adding to my confusion was the seemingly inexplicable reality that, unlike before, my depression didn't seem at all related to perfectionism. When I was depressed in the past, it was because I felt like I'd failed at something. I could always point to a "cause" – like a bad book review or a mediocre exam mark. But this time, there was no such cause, and as a result, I couldn't use any of the techniques Dr Kendall had previously taught me to try and work my way out of my despair. For fuck's sake, I had no idea *why* I was so depressed. Reminding myself of all the reasons why I ought to love myself didn't work this time.

Rubbing additional barrels of salt into my wounds was what I thought being depressed again might do to my relationship with Olivia. It had broken us up the first time, and I was terrified it was going to destroy us again. The very thought made me nauseous, vastly deepened my depression. I was so scared of the potential ramifications that I didn't want to tell her. And on the first day, I didn't. I ignored her calls. *Hopefully it'll pass and she'll never have to know,* I wished. But the second day was just as ghastly. Once again I didn't answer the phone, but I did send her a text: *Hey baby, swamped with uni work at the moment. Call you tomorrow. Love you.* I desperately hoped I'd be better the next day, but once again depression choked me ruthlessly. By then I knew I was flailing in quicksand. I couldn't delay the inevitable much longer. Olivia called me a couple more times throughout the day, and when I didn't pick up, she sent me a text:

Jimmy, why aren't you answering your phone? Is everything OK? I haven't talked to you in 3 days. Please call me xx

I was trapped. I could either call her and risk her finding out, or not call her and cause a rift. I weighed my options imbued with fear. Realistically, not calling her was out of the question. So I concluded that I'd have to ring her up, put on a cheerful front and hope for the best. I spent the next half hour composing myself before dialling her number.

'Jimmy!' she answered.

I tried my best to act like nothing was wrong.

'Hey, baby!' I exclaimed. 'How's it going?'

'Where have you been the last few days?'

'I told you, baby. I've been busy with uni work.'

'What do you mean you've been busy with uni work? You're miles ahead in all your subjects.'

'Yeah, well . . . I've got to stay on top of it all, don't I?'

'Were you so busy that you couldn't even answer my calls?'

She was hurt. I could hear it in her voice.

'I'm-I'm sorry, Liv. I was just really busy,' I mumbled, the chirpiness having long faded from my voice. I heard Olivia sigh. It was a pathetic excuse and we both knew it.

'Jimmy . . . is something wrong?'

'What? No. Nothing's wrong.'

'Something is.'

'Why would you say that?'

'Because you're not acting yourself. You're acting cold and standoffish and it feels like you're avoiding me. I know *something's* wrong. Just tell me what it is.'

I sighed a long, drawn-out sigh. We'd gone out for four years – of course she'd be able to see through my vapid little act. I sighed again through gritted teeth, felt my heartbeat accelerate to a sprint, became aware of the sweat that was saturating my body.

'M-maybe,' I stammered. 'M-maybe I've been a little bit . . . a little bit . . . a little bit *sick* lately.'

Olivia seemed surprised.

'You've been sick? What, with the flu?'

I sighed again.

'No,' I whispered.

'Well what with, then?'

I couldn't say the word. I just couldn't say the word.

'Jimmy?'

I cleared my throat.

'Liv . . . you know what I'm talking about . . .'

She was silent for a few seconds. But then it came to her.

'Jimmy you mean . . . you mean you've been feeling . . . *depressed?*'

I felt like I was going to puke. I tried to say something but nothing came out.

'Is that it, Jimmy? Have you been feeling depressed?'

Another sigh. My eyes were clenched shut.

'Yes,' I croaked.

'OK, Jimmy – I'm going to come over, and then we're going to talk about it, OK?'

'No I'm fine!' I panicked. 'There's no need to come over!'

'Jimmy I'm coming over. I'll be at your house in five minutes.'

I protested, but she wouldn't hear of it. Five minutes later we were sitting together on the edge of my bed, and she was urging me to tell her everything. I didn't want to. I really didn't want to. But I knew she wouldn't let it go.

So I told her. At first I tried to downplay it, but she saw through that facade as well. Pretty soon she knew the whole story.

'You've got to use those techniques that Dr Kendall taught you,' Liv said soothingly. 'You've got to read through the list you made for yourself – remind yourself of all the reasons you have to love yourself. That's how you need to handle anything that you perceive to be a failure – that's how to make sure your disappointments don't lead to depression.'

I shook my head frantically.

'You don't get it, Liv,' I stressed. 'This isn't anything like before. This has nothing to do with perfectionism. I don't hate myself because I think I've failed at something. I don't feel worthless. I *do* love myself – unconditionally. But I still wake up every morning wanting to die. That's it. That's the only thing I feel. I don't know where it comes from and I don't know how to get rid of it.' If Olivia was going to know about it, I wanted her to understand that it was different from the first time around – that I was doing all I could to beat it and that I was depressed regardless. It was an important distinction to make.

We talked about it a bit more before falling silent. Olivia was holding my hands, running her thumbs over the backs of my fingers as I sat slumped on the end of the bed, staring down at the carpet. After a while, she lifted up my hands and gently kissed them, one after the other.

'You'll be OK, baby,' she said tenderly. 'Just hang in there – we'll work it out. And I'll be here with you, every step of the way.'

For the first time in the conversation, I looked up at her. My eyes were desperate. Bloodshot, teary and desperate.

'Will you really?' I asked.

She squeezed my hands with all her might.

'Yes,' she whispered.

The next day I felt suicidal again, and I found myself thinking about the best way to do it. There are numerous methods, each of which vary in terms of their success rate and how painful they are. Bleeding out is a fairly common way, usually achieved by slashing your throat or slitting your wrists. But while getting hold of a knife is easy, bleeding out takes time, so often the bleeder is found and their death attempt is stifled by the paramedics. Another problem is that the cuts are often too shallow to cause the amount of blood loss required to render the suicide attempt successful. Jumping off a bridge or throwing yourself in front of a speeding train is easy enough, but the last thing you want to have happen is to survive and then become a paraplegic, which makes it all the more difficult to finish the job. Overdosing is actually rather tricky in the sense that you have to take the right combination of drugs for you to successfully die, which is something that people often screw up, and just like with bleeding out, you've also got the problem of someone finding you unconscious and calling an ambulance, and then having what would otherwise have been a successful attempt thwarted by those fucking paramedics. Electrocuting, poisoning or hanging yourself hurts like hell, and drowning yourself is hardly pleasant either. Shooting yourself in the side of the head is a pretty good option, but gun laws are relatively tight here in Australia so not everyone has access to one. For me personally, I always thought gassing myself was the best option, as it's simple to do, arguably the most successful, and apparently absolutely painless. These are the things you think of when you're that consummately depressed. But for me, it was just thinking – I still clung to the hope that life could get better like it was the only thing I had left in the world.

Throughout the day, Liv called to check up on me. We talked disjointedly for a bit. I'd booked an appointment to see Dr Kendall the next day, and she insisted on driving me to and from.

'I don't want you driving when you're depressed, Jimmy. It's not safe.'

'I'll be fine. Don't worry about it.'

'No, Jimmy. I'll drive you.'

'Liv – I've driven depressed heaps of times. How do you think I got everywhere when we weren't together?'

'Well we are together now, and I don't like the idea of you driving when you're this suicidal.'

So the next day – day five of my cycle – she took me to see Dr Kendall.

'I'm afraid I'm not really sure what to think of this, Jimmy,' he said. 'This has never happened to you before – feeling this depressed for no apparent reason. I agree that it doesn't appear perfectionism-related, and since there doesn't seem to be any other contributing factor, I'm left thinking that it may have something to do with your new medication. You just changed antidepressants, and now you're having an episode – I doubt that's a coincidence. But I'm not a medical doctor – psychologists provide therapy, they don't prescribe medication – so I'm not the best person to judge. My advice would be to go back to Dr King – tell him what's been happening and see what he has to say.'

Olivia picked me up at the end of the session.

'What did he say?' she asked.

I sighed.

'He said it might have something to do with my medication. He said I should talk to Dr King about it.'

Olivia nodded slowly. She waited before starting the car.

'What do you want to do now?' she asked.

I shrugged apathetically. Everything I could think of seemed equally dreadful. And 'die' wasn't a valid answer.

'Do you want to maybe watch a movie?' Liv suggested. 'Something at your house?'

I shrugged again before eventually nodding.

We watched *The Pursuit of Happyness* back at my place. Olivia and I didn't speak much, just held hands and watched the film. After it was finished, Liv tried to talk to me about how I was feeling, but I wasn't receptive. We then went to The Corso to get some food, and it was the same story there too. Later on in the afternoon when we were back at my place, she called me out on it.

'Jimmy . . . what's the matter with you?'

'What?'

'What do you mean *what*? Why aren't you talking to me?'

'I feel like dying, Liv. I don't feel like talking.'

'That's not what I mean.'

'Well what do you mean?'

'I mean you used to talk to me about how you felt. You used to open up to me, give me a chance to help if I could. But now you're shutting me out. You've barely said a word to me in the past five days.'

I shrugged my shoulders. I didn't know what to say.

'Well?' Liv asked. 'Why are you doing this? Why are you keeping me at such a distance?'

I never thought I'd admit the reason to her, but in the moment, I found myself wanting to get it off my chest.

'Because last time you were too involved. You were so involved that it all got too much for you and then you left me. And I'm scared that if I let you in this time, that the same thing's going to happen and you'll end up leaving me again.'

'Oh sweetie, sweetie,' Liv said urgently, reaching for my hands and holding them gently. 'Please don't say that. Please don't ever say that.'

'But it's true, it's true,' I stressed, pulling my hands away.

'Baby how can you say that?' she exclaimed, reaching for them again. 'This time is completely different from last time!'

'How?'

'Because last time you were depressed for months, and you weren't doing any of the right things to get better. You weren't taking medication. You weren't seeing a psychologist or reading self-help books. You weren't making sure you were living healthily. You were just depending solely on me. And eventually I couldn't take it any more. But you've come such a long way since then. You're taking medication, and you've been seeing a psychologist for over a year.'

She paused.

'This is just a temporary setback. You'll work it out, just like you worked it out the first time. And I'll be here with you, every step of the way.'

'You keep saying that, but how am I supposed to believe you after what happened last time?'

'Because the circumstances are entirely different from last time!'

'But how do I know you won't leave me again?'

'I'm telling you I won't!'

'But how do I know that?'

She spent the next two hours trying to persuade me, but the scars ran too deep. I couldn't be convinced.

'So what are we going to do?' she eventually asked. 'Just not talk about it? Pretend that it doesn't exist?'

I nodded.

'Yes.'

'Jimmy that's ridiculous.'

'Why is it ridiculous?'

'Because we're a couple. Couple's talk about the major things going on in their lives. If you don't feel comfortable talking to me, then – '

'Liv it's only this issue that I don't want to talk about. Just this issue. *Please*. Can we just drop it?'

We argued for a while longer but made no headway. Eventually, Olivia went home, feeling devastated. I felt so drained after our discussion. So exhausted. So horribly, utterly depressed. I didn't think it was possible, but I felt even worse than I did when I'd woken up that morning. Everything with Olivia was messed up once again. *But what else am I supposed to do?* I fretted. *What fucking choice do I have?* I tried to cling to whatever scrap of hope I could muster: *maybe seeing Dr King tomorrow will help,* I thought. *Maybe it's a medicinal issue like Dr Kendall said and I can get it resolved tomorrow.* That's all I could do: hope with everything in me that things would get better.

I opened my eyes the next morning feeling just as awful, and wishing I'd died instead of ever waking up. But I tried to push on, heaving myself out of bed and sitting down at my desk like I did every morning to check Facebook and my emails. Straight away I noticed one from Pierce. I opened it anxiously.

> *Dear Jimmy,*
>
> *This draft is very solid – still a little rough around the edges, but on the whole it's a good piece of writing. Most of the problems I'd identified in the past have been dealt with, and the novel reads well from start to finish.*

Pierce went on to say that I still had to work on my writing style and tidy up a few things, but that in a nutshell it was *"pretty close to finished,"* and *"nearly ready to submit for publication."* And just like that, I was alive again.

This is amazing! This is great! All my hard work has finally paid off! I've finally written a quality book, and after I've tidied up a few things I can get it published! Fuck yes! Fuck yes!

I could taste my dream coming true. I could feel it in my bones. I was just so joyous. So elated. My depression had vanished. The wandering journeyman had found a feast.

Giddy with excitement I called up Olivia.

'Baby! Guess what! I got my book review from Pierce! And he liked it! He actually liked it! He said that all I have to do is improve the writing style a little bit and fix up a few things and then I'll be done! It'll be ready to submit to agents and publishers!'

'Wow! Baby that's fantastic!'

'I know! How awesome is that!'

'It's amazing! Wow, Jimmy! I'm so proud of you!'

'Can we go to dinner tonight, baby? Celebrate?'

'Of course!'

'Great!'

'So you're feeling all right? You're not feeling depressed or anything?'

'After this news? No way!'

'Ah that's great, sweetie,' Liv sighed with relief. 'That's really, really great.'

We talked merrily for a while longer before Olivia had to go to class. I hung up the phone feeling incredible. *This is awesome! This is amazing! This is the best fucking feeling ever!* I just felt so vindicated – I'd worked so hard for three years, and now, I'd finally produced a quality novel. The rush was sensational. The thought that I could soon be a published author filled me with glee. I was thrilled. Completely over the moon.

But over the course of the day, my feelings began to change. My glee, my excitement, escalated to unabashed, unbridled euphoria. I'm not trying to split hairs or nit-pick with language here, but rather describe to you a completely different mood state – that of full-blown mania.

Mania – as distinguished from its similar but less intense blood brother, hypomania – is, at least in my experience, kind of comparable to being high on coke. Your thoughts race at a million miles an hour – and unlike with mere hypomania, far too quickly for you to be able to think productively. You're erupting with energy. You never get tired. You're a sex-crazed animal. You can get delusional, grandiose ideas and lose complete touch with reality. There are stories of patients being so manic that they've gambled their house, car and savings away. There are others of sufferers being so hypersexual that they've had multiple affairs and ruined their marriages. Then there are those catastrophic freak incidents when the mania's at its most extreme, when the victim's lost complete touch with reality and is sometimes also hallucinating: *he jumped off a bridge thinking he could fly. She thought she saw Jesus on the horizon, so she swam to meet him and drowned in the ocean.* While it would be a lie to say that being manic doesn't feel spectacular, it's extremely, extremely dangerous.

That afternoon I tried to study, but I was way too hyped. *"Private international law is the body of principles, rules and occasionally even policies that indicate . . ."* That's so fucking amazing that Pierce likes my book! It's so incredible that it's nearly finished! Soon I'm going to be a published author! This book is going to make me millions! I'm going to be fucking loaded! . . . Wait! Focus! . . . *"Private international law is the body of principles, rules and occasionally even policies that indicate how . . ."* My book's nearly finished! My book's nearly finished! Fuck yes! Fuck yes! And it's such a masterpiece! I'm such a great writer! I'm going to be famous! I'm going to be the next J. K. Rowling!" . . . *"policies that indicate how a foreign element in a legal dispute should be handled. Usually legal issues are domestic, but through international migration, trade and communication, legal disputes . . ."* Yep, I'm going to be the next J. K. Rowling! The next Stephen King! This is so unbelievably amazing! Life is so ridiculously good right now!

Far too invigorated to study, I went for a 20 kilometre run, starting at my house and racing through The Corso and down the beach, and then through Queenscliff, Harbord, Dee Why, Brookvale, Balgowlah and Fairlight before charging back home. As soon as I got back, I cancelled my appointment with Dr King (*I feel the best I've felt in my entire life – what possible need do I have for seeing a doctor?*) and then jumped in the shower. I masturbated twice before washing myself and sitting back down again to study.

"Private international law is the body of principles, rules and occasionally even policies that indicate . . ." But I was too ecstatic to focus. My mind was just buzzing. *I'm going to be a published author! I'm going to be a multimillionaire! I'm going to be the most famous author the world's ever seen!* And I was so horny – like a rowdy, unneutered dog that humps everything in sight. I jacked off three more times that afternoon, and then an hour or so before I was due to meet Olivia, I decided to get my rocks off to some lesbian porn. Girls were licking each other's clits on the screen as loud, orgasmic screams blared from the speakers. I tugged my pulsing cock, moaning at the top of my voice before the door opened behind me. I turned around.

'Oh my God, Jimmy!' Mum shrieked before slamming it shut.

I laughed out loud – *oh Mum, how funny!* – before finishing myself off, having another shower, getting dressed, kissing my extremely uncomfortable and embarrassed mother on the cheek as if nothing had happened and then skipping with a great big smile over to Liv's place.

We went to Le Kiosk for dinner, and my comedown was nowhere in sight. I was talking so loudly that on separate occasions, the manager had to come over and tell me to keep it down. I ordered the whole rainbow trout and the duck confit because I couldn't choose between seafood and poultry, and then ended up eating neither because I decided I wasn't hungry. I purchased a $145 bottle of Veuve Clicquot before knocking it to the floor while I was flapping and rambling about how stoked I was with the book review. And of course, I made all sorts of ridiculous statements about how rich and famous my novel would make me.

'Just try to get it published first,' Liv would say diplomatically. 'Then see what happens after that.'

I had a throbbing erection for the second half of the meal, so before eating four servings of vanilla and lemon cheesecake, I went to the toilet to straddle the paddle. If Olivia thought any of this was strange, she didn't let on. If I had to guess, I'd say that she just passed it off as over-excitement about finally getting a good book review. In any sense, knowing Olivia, she was probably just so relieved that I wasn't depressed any more that she didn't give my euphoria a second thought.

When you're manic, everything's brilliant. The world is beautiful. You think you're invincible, and that everything always goes exactly according to plan – that everything always works out perfectly. This is how I got to thinking that I was going to be the most famous author in the world. It's also how I got it in my head to ask Olivia to marry me.

I made my decision the night we went to Le Kiosk. We'd gone back to Liv's place, and since her parents were still away, we made love in front of the fire. The flames crackled softly, burned a passionate orange-yellow as we lay cuddled up together, watching it in silence. I was running my fingers through her thin brown hair when the thought took life in my racing mind.

Just do it! You always said you would so why not now? Olivia's beautiful and gorgeous and wonderful and being married to her would be so incredible and magnificent

and amazing so you should just do it! You should do it now! Now! Now! Now! Start
planning it right away! Ask her ASAP!

I was too excited to sleep that night. The next day, instead of going to uni with Olivia, I told her that my classes had been cancelled and went to a jeweller to look for a ring. There were so many choices, so many different combinations of band, shape, size, colour, setting, cut, carat and clarity. Apart from a sterling silver necklace with a heart-shaped pendant that her parents had bought her for her 18th birthday, Olivia didn't wear any jewellery, so I didn't have much insight into her taste. After a lot of consideration, I decided to go with a platinum band, thinking it would look nice against her clear olive skin. I spent the rest of the day considering the other aspects, going from jeweller to jeweller to jeweller. *What's Olivia most likely to love?* I thought. Being so down to earth I knew she wouldn't go in for the fancy stuff. *She'd probably just want something nice and simple, just something that says 'I'll love you forever.'* After hours of toing and froing and changing my mind, I ended up settling on a modest round solitaire in a tiffany setting. It was beautiful and traditional, and I was sure that Olivia was going to love it. I paid the $3,500 upfront, nearly maxing out my credit card in the process. But in the midst of my mania I couldn't have cared less. I was convinced that I was soon to be married and I felt high as a kite.

Later that night, I told my parents my decision and showed them the ring. They were shocked as hell.

'You're going to do *what?*'

'I'm going to propose to Olivia!'

They were both gaping at me.

'Jimmy . . .' Dad began uncomfortably. 'Don't you . . . don't you think it's a bit . . . a bit *soon?*'

'Of course not!' I exclaimed.

'But you only just got back together. You've only been going out for *four* weeks!'

'So? I love her *so* much. And I know she loves me. We're meant to be together.'

'Maybe so, but that doesn't mean you have to propose right away. Wait a while – see how things go. If you still feel the same way a few years down the line, you can propose to her then.'

'But I can't wait that long! I want to do it now!'

We discussed it for the rest of the night, everyone firmly holding their ground. Mum and Dad stressed all the warning signs: how we'd only just gotten back together. How young we were. How Olivia and I clearly had some deep-rooted issues that we hadn't yet resolved.

'When you were depressed last week, you were so worried that Olivia was going to leave you that you completely shut her out. You didn't trust her enough to be open with her. That's not the behaviour of a couple that's ready to get married. You both need more time to grow, more time to sort yourselves out. We just don't think you're ready yet, Jimmy.'

But there was no talking sense into me. In the state I was in, the sun's always shining, the birds are always chirping, and the concept of absurdity just doesn't exist.

I spent the next three mania-fuelled days getting everything ready so that I could ask Olivia to marry me that Saturday night. I chose a romantic restaurant on the beach called Whitewater, and spent hours writing my proposal speech and committing it to memory. When I was finished I was on such a high, I was so imbued with rapture that I played love songs on my computer and slowly, methodically danced around my room as I sang along to the choruses:

'You'reeee hereeee, there's noo-thing I fear!

And I knooww that my heart will . . . go ooonnnn!

Weeee'll staaay, foreeeeever this way!

You are saaafe in my heart and,

My heart will . . . go oonn and ooo-ooonnn!'

In those three days, I hardly slept. In fact, if you also take into account the night before I bought the ring, I'd slept a grand total of seven hours in four nights. I was just too overzealous. Too overhyped. And I still felt so alive with vigour. When I was finished with my speech, I fanatically started planning the wedding itself. I researched the feasibility of having it in my local church, down on Manly Beach or in Sydney's Botanical Gardens. I drafted a list of people to invite, and asked Corey to be my best man and Brent, Sean, Chris and Steve to all be groomsmen. They were as shocked as my parents were.

'Jimmy . . . are you serious?' they asked.

'For sure, fellas! Fuck, yeah!'

'Dude . . . you only just got back with her. Don't you think you're rushing things?'

'Nah no way! We're made for each other!'

'Jimmy . . .' Corey began. 'As your "best man," I have to say that I really think proposing to Olivia is a bad idea. I really think you should wait.'

'Nah, man! I want to get married now!'

Just like my parents, they couldn't talk me out of it.

'You'll see! You'll see!' I exclaimed, pointing at them and flapping my arms around before I accidently sent my glass of water flying across the room and smashing into a wall.

'Shit!' Brent yelled.

'Jimmy are you OK?' Steve asked.

'Yeah, man! Why would you ask that?'

'Because you seem really . . . really sort of . . . overexcited. Like you're about to explode or something.'

'I'm about to get married, man! Of course I'm excited!'

And so I continued with the wedding preparations. I looked into places to hold the reception, asked Corey to start writing his best man's speech, visited numerous stores to try and find the perfect tuxedo, put together shortlists of florists and photographers, and started auditioning bands and sampling the food of potential caterers.

Then came Saturday night. I was suffused with ecstasy, felt like I was flying through the clouds.

This is so spectacular! By the end of the night, Olivia will be my fiancé!

I was jumping up and down in the shower, singing loudly to the radio as I got dressed and dancing in front of the mirror as I did my hair. I felt phenomenal.

I rang Liv's doorbell blazing with energy. She answered looking beautiful as ever, wearing a red satin dress and matching heels. We hugged each other, kissed for a few seconds before I zestfully led her to Whitewater.

'You want to walk along the beach?' I asked her on the way.

'Not really. We'll get all sandy.'

'Can we? It's such a wonderful evening!'

'But we'll get all sandy.'

'Don't worry about it! Come on!'

I was eventually able to convince her. It was a breathtaking evening, the sun making love with the sparkling blue sea, the gentle wind superb, the sand soft and golden beneath our feet. I led Olivia to the spot where we'd kissed for the very first time way back in Year 11. We were relatively alone. I stopped walking, squeezed her hand. She looked at me questioningly.

'Olivia . . .' I whispered.

She was facing the sunset. I was standing in front of her.

'Olivia . . . Olivia there was a time when I carried a picture of you in my wallet . . . and every night before I went to sleep, I used to gaze into your beautiful blue eyes and hope to get you back, hope to be able to hold your hand throughout the days and go to sleep with you at night. I'd hope to marry you, Olivia, have kids with you, and spend the rest of my life with you. And now that we're together again . . .'

I trailed off with a huge rush of emotion. I released a sob from deep in my throat, tried to compose myself before emitting another and then another. A tear ran down my cheek as the rest of my speech was wiped clear from my mind. For the first time all week, I was feeling something other than crazed euphoria. There was a ferventness that was breaking through the mania. I squinted, panted loudly as I tried to compose myself. I took a deep breath, wiped my eyes. And then, as another tear ran down my cheek, I knelt in the sand, retrieved the ring from my pocket, and held it out in front of her.

'Olivia . . . will you marry me?'

I'll never forget the look on her face. Her eyes were bulging. Her jaw had dropped in consummate shock. She was staring at me incredulously, completely and utterly aghast. And her head was shaking from side to side.

'Jimmy . . . you can't be serious . . .'

'Olivia what? Why?' I panicked, quickly scrambling to my feet.

'Marriage?' she exclaimed. '*Marriage?* Jimmy . . . I love you, OK. And I want to be with you. But we've only been back together for four weeks. There's no way we're ready to get married yet.'

'But if we love each other and – '

'But we've only been back together for *four* weeks!'

'But we always talked about getting married and spending the rest of our lives together!'

'Jimmy . . . that was *before* we broke up.'

She sighed.

'Look . . . I still love you, OK. And I do think we'll end up getting married and spending the rest of our lives together. But I'm not ready to make that commitment yet, Jimmy. I need more time. A lot more time. OK?'

I couldn't believe it. In the midst of my mania, it had never occurred to me that she might actually say no.

We walked to Whitewater in silence as I fell from the sky.

She said no . . . of course she said no . . . you've only been back together for a few weeks. What the fuck did you expect? How the fuck could you be so stupid? How the fuck could you be so blind?

The rest of the night was choked with awkwardness. Conversation was reduced to the emptiest of chitchat.

'Do you like the fish?'

'Yes, I like the fish. How about you?'

'Yes, I like the fish too.'

'I think these fish were caught in the Tasman Sea.'

'I don't know about that. I think we catch most of our seafood on the Western Australia coast.'

Blah, blah, blah. So much superficial filler spaced by uncomfortable silences. But I guess a refused proposal will do that to a dinner.

I left Whitewater feeling suicidal. After walking Liv to her door and then trudging home, I muttered to my parents what happened before crawling into bed. I curled up in the foetal position, trembled under the covers. I clutched the cross around my neck, prayed for the strength not to slit my wrists.

AND SO HE DECIDED TO GIVE ME MORE PILLS

This was the worst I'd ever felt. Period. There was no relief from the ceaseless dread. I could barely function. Paying attention in class was almost impossible. Studying was too overwhelming. After being so far ahead of the syllabus, I was now starting to fall behind. I hadn't touched my novel in days. I was constantly exhausted. Drained of life. Depression sucked at my soul. My spirit withered. My goal for the day was broken down even further: *just survive the next four hours. The next two hours. Hold off killing yourself until then.*

By this time, I was void of hope. Depression had well and truly suffocated it.

You will never get better, I told myself. *This is who you are. This beast will always persecute you, choke you mercilessly for the rest of your life.*

And I was so trapped in the moment that I believed it, wholly and completely. And because I was so convinced that I'd never get better, there seemed no point in fighting my illness. Instead of willing myself to "hang in there" because I believed that my suffering was temporary and that everything would be better one day, I comforted myself with the knowledge that human beings are not immortal.

You will die, one day. One special, glorious day. Then you can spend the rest of eternity mouldering in a grave. Free from pain. Safe and serene.

You might be wondering why I didn't just kill myself if I wholeheartedly believed that my future consisted of nothing more than excruciating misery. Well, first of all, I still was not a quitter. But more importantly, I didn't want to hurt the people that loved me – mainly Olivia and my parents.

It's not fair to commit suicide and ruin their lives. You have to hold on. No matter how much it hurts you you have to hold on.

Hence why I drew comfort from the thought that one day I'd die and finally be free.

When you're that depressed, that insanely and utterly depressed that you genuinely believe you'll suffer that acutely for the rest of your days, life seems to lack all purpose. *After all,* I figured, *what's the point in working, fighting, striving for a better life if you're sentenced to one of chronic anguish and despair? There is no better life. There is no life outside of pain. So what's the point in doing anything but waiting until death finally arrives on your doorstep and whisks you away to the Promised Land?* I was still studying, and I still planned on finishing my novel and submitting it to publishers and literary agents, but it was more for the sake of it than anything else. My passion had been drained. My zest for life asphyxiated. I was like a ghost, just drifting through the ghastly days.

I cut myself off from everyone. After telling the boys that Olivia refused my proposal, I stopped answering their calls. I barely spoke to my parents, just nodding here and there and mumbling short, evasive answers to their concerned and worried questions. They were distressed as hell, but what could they do?

Of course, I still couldn't talk about my depression with Olivia, which at the time, meant that we couldn't talk about anything. My illness had engulfed me, wholly and completely. Add into the mix all the awkwardness and discomfort that bled from the rejected proposal and our relationship was a fucking disaster. After that Saturday night, I spent a few days avoiding her calls. I think she expected as much, but when it kept on happening, she grew more and more concerned. On Thursday, she sent me another one of those messages begging me to call her. When I finally did I tried to hide my depression, but once again she saw right through me. She wanted to talk about it, but I resisted. She wanted to see me, but I said no. I didn't want to see anyone, didn't want to do anything except lie in bed all day, wrapped up tightly in the covers. But I eventually agreed to see her that upcoming Saturday.

It was one of the saddest days of my life.

The sun was out, so Liv suggested that we have a picnic – pack a lunch, grab a Boost Juice and walk to the beach. When we sat down on the sand to eat, she tried one more time.

'So . . . how've you been feeling?'

I shrugged. I wanted to tell her. I wanted to tell her so badly. *Please, God, open up my soul, let Liv inside it, let everything be like it used to be.* But I just couldn't do it. I shrugged again. I could feel her stare as I studied my ham, cheese and tomato sandwich. I unwrapped it and started eating, waiting for her to say something else. Eventually I heard her sigh, noticed her shake her head from the corner of my eye.

'The weather's nice today,' she eventually said, trying to make the best of things.

'Yeah, I guess.'

'It's meant to be getting cold now, heading into winter and all that. But the weather's so beautiful today – blue sky, sun out, gentle breeze . . . so beautiful.'

'I hope it doesn't rain,' I said. 'They're predicting showers.'

'Do you think it will?'

I looked up at the sky.

'No, I don't think so.'

I paused.

'What do you think?'

'No, I don't think it will either.'

We continued eating.

'Nice sandwiches, Liv,' I said.

'Yeah, well,' she sighed. 'I know how you like them. Thick on the ham, easy on the tomato.'

I nodded.

We finished eating in silence. Then a few minutes passed where we both watched the sea. I desperately tried to think of something to say, but I couldn't for the life of me come up with anything. It was so sad. It hurt so much. I wanted to cry, sob myself to death.

'Do you want to go for a swim?' Liv eventually suggested.

I shrugged despondently.

'OK.'

We spent the next hour-and-a-half in the water. I guess doing something seemed to numb the discomfort, or at least put it on hold. But there's only so long you can swim without getting bored, so eventually, we returned to our spot on the sand.

'How beautiful was the water?' Olivia asked.

I shrugged apathetically. Depression has the ability to deaden the senses, suck the pleasure out of everything.

Liv unwrapped another sandwich.

'Go halves with me?'

'I'm fine, thanks.'

She ate half. Some seagulls flew up to us. She tossed them some bread.

'I like seagulls,' she said. 'A lot of people don't, but I do.' She threw them another piece of bread.

'I mean, I guess they're always scavenging, which isn't the best. I remember one time when I was walking through The Corso eating a wrap – a seagull swooped down and snatched it right out of my hand!'

I nodded vaguely.

'But I like it how they're always together. Kind of like a family, you know? You don't see many birds like that. I mean, think about kookaburras or something. Whenever I see them laughing and what not, they always seem to be alone. But seagulls? They're always together.'

I nodded again. At Whitewater, we'd given way to the awkward silences, letting them give birth to an unpleasant atmosphere. But this time, Olivia seemed determined to keep conversation flowing, or at least creeping along jaggedly.

'What about you, Jimmy? Do you like seagulls?'

I shrugged. 'They're OK.'

Olivia nodded.

'What about when they fly? Do you like watching them fly?'

'It's OK.'

Olivia nodded again.

'I like watching them fly. They look so together, so in unison, you know? It kind of reminds me of a dance the way they . . .'

I tuned out. It was so frustrating, the way she was so obviously talking about rubbish just for the sake of it, just so there would be no more silences. But I could hardly blame her. In truth, I still felt nothing but love for her. But I knew that something was broken between us. Maybe something we'd never get back. I felt my eyes begin to well with tears. What had become of us? I never wanted to hear about another fucking seagull for the rest of my life.

'Liv,' I interrupted.

'Yes?'

My lacquered eyes met hers for the first time that day.

'Don't,' I whispered.

I turned away as tears began to roll down my cheeks. Olivia joined me crying. We sat upright, hugging our knees, occasionally wiping our eyes as we silently watched the waves wash up upon the shore. We stayed there until dusk.

We didn't speak for the rest of the afternoon.

I knew we couldn't go on like that. I knew I was facing the prospect of losing her again. While even further deepening my depression (*just survive the next hour*), such a realisation also caused me to dig deep and muster up some fight.

You have *to figure out how to beat this. You just have to. Otherwise, you're going to lose her again, and your depression will be all you have left.*

So I booked an appointment to see Dr King. Obviously I should've seen him earlier, however earlier I was void of hope and convinced there was no getting better, so I couldn't see the point. But after the picnic I was desperate as can be, and willing to try anything.

'Dr King . . . you've got to help me,' I pleaded. 'Every minute of the day I want to die. It's controlling me. I can't function, can't do anything. And Olivia . . . we're growing apart. She's going to leave me again. I can feel it. Please Dr King, I need you to help me. *Please* . . .'

We talked a little more before he made his decision.

'Well, Jimmy,' he began, 'I think it's clear that the medication you're currently taking isn't strong enough to manage your depression. Accordingly, I'm going to double your dosage.'

He gave me a prescription.

'Tonight, start taking two pills before you go to bed instead of one. That ought to make a difference.'

THE LAST TIME I SAW HER

This is the point where my memory gets hazy. I remember doubling my medication, and I remember feeling much better afterwards. I had a couple of productive days studying, and spent an enjoyable evening playing Scrabble at Liv's house. Things were looking up, and I was hopeful that everything would settle down and that life would get back to normal. But then I went from feeling good to great. Then from great to even greater. Before I knew it I was manic again – feeling everything I'd felt previously and this time, I was also hallucinating.

I remember waves. Waves, coming and going, line upon line of them. Beautiful, crisp blue waves with fluffy white-tipped crests. That's what I remember. I remember seeing them in front of me. I remember wanting to catch them, just like I used to back in the old days. I felt so invigorated, so alive and free, so ebullient and full of bliss. And I wanted to surf. It had been so long and I just wanted to surf.

Olivia and I were meant to go to a party or something, I can't recall where. I picked her up in the car. I remember her beaming at me, full-lipped with her blue eyes sparkling. We kissed for the last time.

'Hi, sweetie! How are you?'

'I'm great, baby! I'm bloody brilliant!'

'That's good! Any particular reason?'

'Because of the waves, baby!'

Olivia laughed.

'What waves?'

'The waves, baby! The waves!'

'What waves?'

'The *waves*! Can't you see them?'

She laughed again.

'Sweetie what are you talking about?'

'Olivia look in front of you! Don't you see all the waves? Those beautiful rich blue waves!'

She thought I was joking. She kept on laughing.

'Honey it's night time! All I see are dimly lit streets!'

'No, baby! You're missing the waves right in front of us! Look at them go up and down! Up and down! They're so spectacular! They're like magic! I've been waiting to see you, baby! We can go surfing together!'

I started to speed up.

'Whoa! Jimmy take it easy! Why are you driving so fast?'

'To catch the waves, baby! We've got to speed up so we can catch the waves!'

'Jimmy slow down,' she said sternly.

'But then we won't be able to catch the waves!'

'Jimmy what the hell are you talking about? Slow down!'

'I was such a good surfer back in the day, Liv!' I went on, flooring the accelerator. 'It's a pity that you never got to watch me! I was – '

'Jimmy slow down!'

'But the waves – '

'Shut up about the fucking waves! Slow down!'

But I kept going faster and faster. We were really flying now, blasting through narrow suburban streets at 140K's. Olivia was screaming hysterically, but I was focused on those waves.

I haven't been surfing in years! I remember thinking. *This is going to be so good! Come on! Just a little faster! Just a little faster and we'll both be dancing along the crest! Flying through the sky! Come on! Come on!*

I tried to follow them around the bend but the back tires fishtailed. I lost control of the car. Liv shrieked with terror as I smashed into the side of a telegraph pole.

It all happened so quickly. The waves disappeared. My face was buried in an airbag. Olivia was crying, howling in pain. It was enough to snap me back into the moment. *What the fuck have I done?* I freaked. And then I realised that her screaming was growing fainter. That she was running away. I jumped out of the car and started chasing after her.

'Olivia! Olivia! Are you all right?'

But she wouldn't stop.

'Olivia!

I finally caught her, grabbed her shoulder to slow her down.

'Olivia I'm sorry! I'm so, so sorry!'

'Stop touching me! Stop touching me!' she shrieked.

'Olivia I – '

'I said stop touching me!'

I jumped back in alarm. And then I noticed the blood running down her face where she'd hit her head. I noticed her broken arm, split in two, cradled by the other against her chest. She was scared shitless, crying and screaming at the same time.

'Get the fuck away from me! Get the fuck away from me!'

'Olivia I – '

'I said get the fuck away from me!'

'Liv let me help – '

'Fuck off! Fuck off!'

I'll never forget the look in her eyes. There was shock. There was agony. Horror. Fear. But most of all there was the look of heartbreak. Her trust was destroyed. Our relationship was shattered. She wanted nothing more to do with me. And as I stared at her wailing there, I knew that the best thing I could do for her was to let her go.

So I did. I watched her grow smaller and smaller in the distance, listened to the sound of her cries die down before she turned the corner and was out of sight. I burst into tears, fell to my knees, started babbling hysterically.

'God, please help her! Please ease her pain! Please get her to a hospital as soon as possible! Please! *Please!*'

I bawled my eyes out. *How the fuck could I do this?* I thought. *Waves? Waves? What the fuck was I thinking? What the fuck is wrong with me? I'm crazy! I'm fucking crazy! Oh my God . . . and Olivia . . . she's . . . it should've been me. It should've been me that got hurt. No – I should've just died. The world's better off without me.*

I staggered up, stumbled back towards the car. Residents had grouped outside, staring at the accident, inspecting the damage. They swarmed when they saw me.

'Are you all right? Is everything OK? We've called an ambulance! We've called the police! They're on their way!'

I pushed past them, fell to the ground beside the car.

'Careful!' one of the neighbours warned. 'The side window's smashed. There's glass everywhere.'

I picked up the sharpest piece I could find and put it to my throat.

'No!' someone screamed, running towards me.

'Stay back!' I yelled, holding out the glass.

The man froze, raising his hands in the surrender sign.

'Pl-please . . .' he stuttered. 'Please don't do this. Whatever happened . . . it can be fixed.'

'What the fuck do you know?' I yelled. 'You didn't just crash a car because you were chasing waves! You didn't just break your girlfriend's arm! You're not fucking crazy! You don't want to kill yourself one week and chase hallucinations the next! What the fuck do you know? What the *fuck* do you know?'

'OK, OK,' he motioned, patting the air. 'I'm sorry. Just please don't do this. *Please.*'

The crowd all tried to talk me into dropping the glass, but once again I brought it to my neck. I pierced the skin, felt hot blood dripping onto my hand.

Death. I craved it, craved it – more so than ever before.

It was like a maddening hunger that I wanted to feed so badly. Everything was just so fucked up. Everything had been fucked up for so long and I was sure that this was the only way out. There was nothing I wanted to do but satisfy that craving. Nothing I wanted to do but die. Running that piece of glass over my throat made me feel better, thinking that the craving's about to be fed, thinking that the pain's about to end. So close to the apathy of death. Nothingness! The end! An escape at last!

Plunge it through your throat! Through your fucking throat! Now! Now!

My hand trembled wildly. My whole body shook.

Do it! Kill yourself! End it now!

My hand kept trembling and trembling before finally, the glass slipped through my fingers and fell to the ground. I couldn't do it. I exploded into tears, cried loudly as all my emotions ruptured inside me – in large part because I knew I'd have to keep living and fighting in this crazy fucked up world – but regardless, I knew I couldn't do it. I'm just not a quitter. When it really comes down to it I'm just not a quitter. Throughout my tale, I've stated that when you're at your lowest point, you get a clear glimpse into the core of your heart, and realise who you really are. And at that moment when I was closer to death than I'd ever been, I caught the purest glimpse I'd ever had. The purest glimpse I'll ever get. And at that moment, I learned, well and truly and beyond a shadow of a doubt, that while fighting back may be hard as hell, giving up was *impossible.*

A couple of people helped me to my feet, moved me away from the wreckage. I sat hugging my shins on the sidewalk, crying with my head buried in my knees as the crowd watched on silently.

'You're not a quitter,' I kept sobbing to myself. 'You're not a quitter.'

The cops arrived. They asked me what happened.

'You're not a quitter,' I kept repeating.

'So fix this.'

Taking a deep breath, I did my best to gather myself before looking up at the officers. And then I told them what happened.

'I'll plead guilty to whatever offense you see fit to charge me with,' I said when I had finished. 'But first, I need to be admitted to a psych ward.'

Epilogue

~ ~ ~

Dear Olivia,

I've tried to write this letter so many times. Sometimes I started before realising I wasn't ready. Sometimes I started before thinking that maybe you wouldn't be ready. Other times I just stared at the page, not even knowing where to begin. So much has happened since the accident, Olivia, and I'm not sure what you know and what you don't, what the police told you and what they didn't. But with the charges having been dismissed today, I felt it was time. There's a lot I owe you, Olivia, not the least of which is an explanation.

As I'm sure you know, I've been in a mental hospital for the last six weeks. When I first arrived on the night of the accident, I was the most depressed I've ever been. I'm not sure if you heard, but I nearly slit my throat that night — so distraught was I that I'd lost my mind, so guilty was I about what I'd done to you. I was stripped of my belt, socks and shoelaces and placed on suicide watch in a video monitored room. It was the barest room I've ever seen — void of anything you could tie a noose to if you were crafty enough to make one. There were no protrusions from the walls or the ceiling, and there wasn't even any furniture. I slept on a thick mattress on the floor, without any sheets for obvious reasons.

The next day I saw a psychiatrist called Dr Delacor. She asked me how I was feeling.

'I wish I was dead,' I murmured. 'But I'm not a suicide risk.'

She nodded softly, asked me a few preliminary questions. One of which was whether I was currently on any medication. When I told her what I'd been taking, she looked shocked.

'Are you serious?

'Yeah.'

'What dosage?'

'I was taking 50 milligrams for a month or two. Then a few days ago my doctor doubled it to 100 milligrams.'

Her eyes were bulging.

'What sort of a doctor did this? A GP?'

'Yes.'

She shook her head angrily.

'What is it?' I asked.

She sighed.

'You should've never been placed on that particular medication, Jimmy. It's a relatively new drug, and its safety and efficacy has not yet been established for children, adolescents and young adults under the age of 24 – this age being of particular significance since the average brain is still developing up until one reaches the age of 24. So since its effects on 21 year olds aren't yet known, it was dangerous for you to be taking it. Not only that, but studies have shown that if a patient is not finding 50 milligrams to be effective, then increasing the dosage to 100 milligrams will only increase the side effects. So not only should you have never been taking it in the first place, but under no circumstance should your GP have doubled the dosage.'

I was shocked, Olivia. It all came so abruptly. I was silent for a long time, processing and processing the information I'd just heard before my mind went back to what Dr Kendall had said when I saw him during my first cycle of depression while I was taking it: "it might have something to do with your new medication. Go back to your GP and see what he has to say." And then with a rush of horror, it all made sense.

'Is that . . . is that the reason I've been so sick? I asked, flabbergasted. 'Because of the new medication?'

She gave me a sympathetic look that told me the answer was probably going to be "yes."

'Tell me everything, Jimmy,' she sighed.

But I didn't want to. The way I saw it, I'd already trusted the medical profession once, and they'd fucked me over.

Why would I place my trust in them again? I thought. So they can make me even sicker? So they can fuck my life up even more? To hell with that! I'm done with them! I'll find some other way to beat my illness!

I told Dr Delacor so.

'Jimmy . . .' she said empathetically. 'I don't blame you for feeling the way you do, because you've got every right to be angry at Dr King for what's happened to you. But please, please don't let one doctor's mistake turn you against the entire medical profession.'

She paused.

'You are very, very, very sick at the moment, Jimmy, and you need a lot of help – a lot of medical *help – to get better again. Like any profession, the medical one is not perfect. Like any profession, it has its bad apples. But you still need to use it. If you don't, you'll be this sick for the rest of your life.'*

She paused again.

'You're in good hands now, Jimmy,' she said. 'I promise I'll do everything in my power to help you get better, but you need to work with me. You need to trust *me.'*

Once again I retreated to my thoughts. I mulled over everything Dr Delacor had said, weighed up all my options. Eventually, I realised she was right.

I can't get better by myself, *I concluded.* I need her to help me.

I took a long, deep breath.

'OK,' I finally said. 'I'll trust you.'

'Good, Jimmy,' she smiled. 'Now how about you tell me everything that's been happening so that I can try and make sense of it for you.'

So I did, focusing on the last couple of months after I'd switched medications. Dr Delacor then asked me a litany of questions before diagnosing me with medicine induced bipolar disorder. Let me be clearer – she diagnosed me as being bipolar, a condition that she said was triggered by me taking my new medication.

I was bewildered.

'Wh-What . . . ? What's bipolar disorder, exactly?'

'Manic depression,' she said. 'High one week, suicidal the next. It explains your depression for the past month, as well as your hyper-elation and irrational behaviour – proclaiming yourself to be the next J. K. Rowling, proposing to Olivia when you'd only been back together for a month, and chasing imaginary waves when you crashed your car. Your bipolar was developing over this time, Jimmy, and now it's an illness that we'll have to manage going forwards.'

'What do you mean "manage going forwards?" ' I asked. 'How long does bipolar disorder last for?'

'It's hard to say. Most people who have it receive some form of treatment for the majority of their life. But in saying that, Jimmy, bipolar disorder's very manageable. Through a combination of medication, therapy and maintaining an active, healthy lifestyle, many patients become stable enough that they can live a happy, healthy life that isn't impeded by their illness.'

She talked some more about the malady before we finished our session. I was so overwhelmed when I left her office, Liv. I remember being in some sort of trance, spinning in this foreign world of new illnesses and incompetent GPs as a nurse led me to my new room in the non-suicide watch section of the hospital. If they knew how depressed I was, I'm almost certain they would've sent me right back. Olivia, do you remember what thought had always depressed me more than any other? It was the notion that my suffering was permanent. That I'd be battling my depression for the rest of my life. That I'd never be happy again. Well, Dr Delacor had just told me that I now had bipolar disorder, and that I'd more or less have it for as long as I lived. I know she also said there was a good chance I'd be able to manage it, that in actual fact if I managed it well it may not disrupt my life at all – but in that moment, that wasn't a concept I could fathom. All I could comprehend was the possibility that my life would be a never ending nightmare, a ghastly rollercoaster through hell where I'd alternate between feeling suicidal or so manic that I'm a danger to myself and everyone around me. I was so scared, Liv. My parents were allowed to come over a little while later, and as soon as I saw them I burst into tears. Mum and Dad cried too. We were all terrified.

But that night, I gave up the antidepressants and instead took my first dose of a mood stabiliser, which is a medication for bipolar patients to balance out the highs and the lows. It knocked me out until morning, and my subsequent doses knocked me out for the next few days. But by my fifth day in hospital, I was feeling much, much better. For the first time in weeks I was neither manic nor depressed, but rather on a fairly even keel. I remember feeling hopeful again. Once again I could envision a future, one where I could finish my degree, publish my novel, get married and have a family. One where I could be happy, *again.*

Maybe Dr Delacor's right, *I thought.* Maybe I can get on top of this and live a normal, healthy life.

This is how I've felt for the last few weeks, Olivia: optimistic. I'm by no stretch of the imagination "there" yet – I'm still coming to terms with everything that's happened, and I'm still learning new techniques to better manage my illness – but I do feel reasonably stable, and I'm improving every day. I've even recently started to accept visitors besides my parents, and this week I had the guys come and see me. It's hard – they didn't really know what to say, so there was a lot of small talk and idle chitchat. But at least they came. Hopefully the next time they visit we'll be able to talk more like how we used to. Hell, hopefully I'll be home in a couple of weeks and we can get back to having barbeques and going to the beach like no time's passed.

But while I'm confident that the future is bright, I'm at the same time haunted by our recent past. As difficult as it's been to accept the fact that I have bipolar disorder and to get over my anger at Dr King for the part he played in inducing me to develop it in the first place, by far the hardest thing I've had to do within these walls has been to come to terms with what I did to you. Even though the police dismissed the charges because I was in the throes of a manic episode, I'm still filled with a guilt that hasn't begun to pass. My only consolation is that you weren't permanently hurt, something for which I will thank the Lord every day for the rest of my life.

I hope what I've written explains the last couple of months, Olivia. I want you to know that I am truly sorry, and I hope one day you can find it in your heart to forgive me. I guess I have nothing more to add except for this: Olivia, I said before that I could once again envision a future for myself, but I'd be lying if I said you weren't the centre of the picture. Even after everything that's happened, the truth is that I still love you as much as ever. I'm sure you can think of a dozen reasons why we should call it quits once and for all, but there is one very good reason why we owe it to ourselves to give it another chance — and that is because all the drama we've ever been through has been triggered by my illness. And if you strip it all away, I'm still the same old Jimmy. The same Jimmy who was your first love. The same Jimmy you gave your virginity to. The same Jimmy you did everything with for four whole years. The same Jimmy you wanted to marry and spend the rest of your life with. I'm still that guy, baby. I'm going to overcome this illness and live a normal life, and nothing would make me happier than to do it by your side. Because we are made for each other, Olivia. Because we're soul mates. And even after everything that's happened, I know that deep down you feel the same way.

All my love,
Jimmy.

I gave it to one of the nurses to post before lying on my bed, closing my eyes. I thought about what she might say. Several different scenarios ran through my mind, and I was forced to admit that I had no idea what would happen in the days to come. But as with everything else in my life, I chose to have hope. I pulled her picture out of my wallet, lost myself in the blueness of her eyes, in the beauty of her full-lipped, vivacious smile. A lone tear ran down my cheek as the memories flooded my mind, as I recalled all the wonderful moments spent in her presence. I found myself leaning forwards to kiss her, pressing my lips against hers before I pulled back, gazed at her again. And through my mind rippled the lone refrain: *I hope you come back to me, dear Olivia.*

I Just Want To Be Happy, Olivia

Danny Baker

I Just Want To Be Happy, Olivia

Now available: The sequel to *I Will Not Kill Myself, Olivia*

So much has been broken. So much has been lost. But against all the odds, Jimmy Wharton is determined to wipe the slate clean, put his life back together again, and find the happiness that has been eluding him. Two years, eight countries, one degree change and a brand new career later, it looks as if he's finally found it – until his world once again implodes around him, and his friends have to rush him straight back to hospital.

When he wakes up, his life appears more in ruins than ever. However, there is one person who can help him finally find the light at the end of the tunnel.

But, it's someone from his past.

Someone who he was sure he'd never speak to again.

Picking up right from where *I Will Not Kill Myself, Olivia* left off and building towards another climactic finish, the sequel *I Just Want To Be Happy, Olivia* is a tale about trying to find your way in the world, and about how much we sometimes need to fight, the sacrifices we often need to make, and the courage we often need to display in order to be happy. But above all else, it is the story of Jimmy, of Olivia, and of the love that binds them.

ACKNOWLEDGEMENTS FOR *I WILL NOT KILL MYSELF, OLIVIA*

Although writing is a solitary pursuit, producing a book is a team effort, and I am indebted to a lot of people who've helped transform *I Will Not Kill Myself, Olivia* from an idea in my head into the novel you've just read. In particular, special thanks must go to the following people:

To my psychologist and my psychiatrist, Chris and Sharon, for helping me navigate my way out of the abyss when I came to them both a wreck of a young man, and for helping me remain not only healthy and stable enough to write this book, but happier than I ever thought I could be.

To Nanna and Papou, for their continued love and support.

To my brother Mat for his blind faith in me, when almost everyone else had written me off.

To Dr Martin Seligman, whose book *Authentic Happiness* induced me to follow my dream of becoming an author.

To my mentor Nick Bleszynski, for his unwavering support; for teaching me most of what I know about writing; for editing this novel countless times; for giving me advice about everything related to its production; and for doing it all because he cared. Whatever success I achieve with this book – and every other book that I go on to write – is due in very large part to Nick.

To my parents, for their undying love; for always believing in me; for teaching me that I can do anything I set my mind to; for not flipping out when I said I wanted to drop out of commerce/law to chase my dream of becoming an author; and for supporting me emotionally – and to an extent, financially – throughout the whole process. Special thanks must also go to my mum, who always, always made time for me whenever I came to her saying, 'Ma, we need to talk about Jimmy and Olivia.'

ABOUT THE AUTHOR

Danny Baker was born and raised in Sydney, Australia. In 2007 he took a scholarship to study commerce/law at Sydney University before trading in his textbooks in 2012 to pursue his dream of becoming an author. At the time of writing, he's published four books: *I Will Not Kill Myself, Olivia;* the sequel *I Just Want To Be Happy, Olivia;* the third book in the series titled *Let Me Tell You My Stories From South America, Jimmy;* and also a memoir titled *Depression is a Liar,* which recounts his struggle and eventual triumph over depression.

To find out more about Danny's books or to get in touch, visit his website at www.dannybakerwrites.com.

Made in the USA
Middletown, DE
10 August 2018